1991 buick

CENTURY

CENTURY CUSTOM (4 Cylinder)

Mfgs. Code	Description	Base Cost	Sgstd. List
H69	4 Dr Sedan	11810	13685
H37	2 Dr Coupe	11896	13785
H35	4 Dr 2 Seat Wagon	13213	15310

CENTURY LIMITED (4 Cylinder)

Mfgs. Code	Description	Base Cost	Sgstd. List
L69	4 Dr Sedan	12768	14795
L35	4 Dr 2 Seat Wagon	14006	16230

Destination Charge: All Models . . . 480 480

STANDARD EQUIPMENT:

CENTURY: Acoustical package, air conditioner, fixed-mast antenna, Delco Freedom II Plus battery, power front disc/rear drum brakes, front and rear bumper guards, front and rear bumper protective strips, integrated body-color bumpers, load floor carpet (Wagon), carpet, front, side-window outlet defogger, front-wheel drive, electronic warning tone (seatbelt, ignition key, "headlamps on"), 2.5L Tech 1V engine with EFI, soft-ray tinted glass, composite tungsten halogen headlamps, adjustable front headrests, inside release hood lock, dual horns, rear compartment light (Wagon), lights (ashtray, instrument panel, courtesy, glove box, trunk, engine compartment, map), mirrors (deluxe black, outside, rearview (left remote, right manual); moldings (belt reveal, pillar, wheel opening, roof drip, black door, window frame), black wide body-side moldings, Plastisol protection paint, ETR AM/FM stereo radio with seek and scan and clock, dual front standard range and rear extended range speakers, split folding rear seatback (Wagon), automatic front safety system and rear seat lap/shoulder seatbelts, cloth notchback seats with armrest (Custom), power rack and pinion steering, storage compartment - lockable load area-side and floor (Wagon), DynaRide suspension, front, independent MacPherson strut suspension, compact spare tire, P185/75R14 steel-belted radial-ply all-season whitewall tires, automatic transmission, trunk floor covering (Custom), deluxe wheelcovers, 2-speed wipers. **Limited Sedan And Wagon Also Has In Addition To Standard Equipment:** front-seat storage armrest (Limited), instrument gauges (volt, temperature, trip odometer), front door courtesy and warning lights, 55/45 cloth seats with storage armrest.

ACCESSORIES

Mfgs. Code	Description	Base Cost	Sgstd. List
—	**Engines**		
LR8	2.5 litre (151 CID) EFI L4	STD	STD
LG7	3.3 litre (204 CID) MFI V6	604	710
—	**Transmissions**		
MX1	automatic (req'd w/LR8)	STD	STD
MX0	automatic with overdrive (available w/LG7 only)	170	200
BF9	**Carpet Savers Delete (from Packages) —** all except w/SA	(38)	(45)
C47	**Delete Rear Defogger (from Packages) —** all except w/SA	(136)	(160)
YF5	**California Assembly Line Emission Equipment and Testing —** (req'd in California)	85	100
AUO	**Keyless Entry, Remote —** (remote trunk release required, Coupe & Sedan)	106	125
V58	**Luggage Rack, Deck Lid —** chrome-Coupes & Sedans	(98)	(115)
—	**Radio Equipment**		
UM6	cassette player w/auto reverse - Custom with SB Pkg, Limited & SC Pkg	119	140
UN6	cassette player w/search repeat and auto reverse. (req'd with UK3 less		

Mfgs. Code	Description	Base Cost	Sgstd. List
	U1C) (included SE Limited) - Custom & SB	145	170
	- Limited & SC	145	170
	- Custom & SC/SD/SE	26	30
	- Limited & SD	26	30
U1C	compact disc player - Custom & SC/SD/SE	233	274
	- Limited & SD	233	274
	- Limited & SE	207	244
—	speakers, premium		
U62	- Coupes, Sedans	60	70
U79	- Wagons	30	35
A83	**Recliners, Power Seatback (Dual)** — Custom & SB Pkg	94	110
UK3	**Steering Wheel Mounted Radio Controls** — (included in Limited SE Pkg) (requires UN6 or U1C)	106	125
—	**Stripes — Body Side (Order By Color)** — Custom & SA/SB/SC	38	45
14A	light gray		
21A	dark blue		
34A	saddle		
40A	white		
41A	black		
55A	gold		
64A	light auburn		
66A	dark auburn		
75A	red		
79A	dark red		
87A	pewter gray		
—	**Tires** — (all are steel belted radial ply)		
QFF	P185/75R14 whitewall	STD	STD
QFE	P185/75R14 blackwall - all less SA Pkg	(58)	(68)
—	**Trim, Interior**		
	Custom		
15	cloth notchback bench - Custom	STD	STD
36	cloth 55/45 w/armrest - Custom & SB Pkg	(156)	(183)
54	empress cloth 55/45 w/storage armrest - Custom & SB	468	551
	- Custom & SC/SD/SE	313	368
	Limited		
56	cloth 55/45 w/storage armrest - Limited	STD	STD
96	leather & vinyl 55/45 - Limited Sedan	383	450
A90	**Trunk Release, Remote — (req'd w/AU0)** — Coupes & Sedans (included SE)	43	50
—	**Wheels and Wheel Covers**		
N91	locking wire wheel covers - Custom & SB/SC Pkg	183	215
PC7	styled steel wheels (4) - Custom & SB/SC Pkg	98	115
PG4	aluminum wheels (4) - less N91 Packages	230	270
	- w/N91 Packages	47	55
WDV	**Warranty Enhancement — New York State** — (req'd in New York)	55	65
C25	**Windshield Wiper, Rear Window** — (package air deflector deleted - Wagons & SA	106	125
	- Wagons & Pkg	72	85
A31	**Windows, Power** — Coupe & SB/SC Pkg	208	245
	- Sedan & SB/SC Pkg	264	310
BX3	**Woodgrain - Vinyl Applique** — (stripes are deleted) - Custom Wag & SA/B/C	276	325
	- Custom Wag & SD/SE	238	280
	- Limited Wagon	238	280
—	**SA Package** — represents individual model w/standard equipment (see listing)		
SB	**Century Custom Sedan Popular Package** — includes tilt steering column;		

Mfgs. Code	Description	Base Cost	Sgstd. List
	electric rear window defogger; windshield wipers with delay feature; carpet carpet savers, front; carpet savers, rear	336	395
SC	**Century Custom Sedan Premium Package** — includes SB Century Custom Sedan Popular Pkg equipment plus electric door locks; cruise control, electronic; cassette tape player; 55/45 seat with storage armrest; dual electric seat back recliners	1078	1268
SD	**Century Custom Sedan Luxury Package** — includes SC Century Custom Sedan Premium Pkg equipment plus locking wire wheel covers; accent stripes; power windows; dual lighted visor vanity mirrors	1641	1930
SE	**Century Custom Sedan Prestige Package** — includes SD Century Custom Sedan Luxury Pkg equipment plus electric trunk release; 6-way power driver's seat; automatic power antenna; dual electric remote mirrors; front seat reading lights	2080	2447
SB	**Century Custom Coupe Popular Package** — includes tilt steering column; electric rear window defogger; windshield wipers with delay feature; carpet savers, front; carpet savers, rear	336	395
SC	**Century Custom Coupe Premium Package** — includes SB Century Custom Coupe Popular Pkg equipment plus electric door locks; cruise control, electronic; cassette tape player; 55/45 seat with storage armrest; dual electric seat back recliners	1044	1228
SD	**Century Custom Coupe Luxury Package** — includes SC Century Custom Coupe Premium Pkg equipment plus locking wire wheel covers; accent stripes; power windows; dual lighted visor vanity mirrors	1551	1825
SE	**Century Custom Coupe Prestige Package** — includes SD Century Custom Coupe Luxury Pkg equipment plus electric trunk release; 6-way power driver's seat; automatic power antenna; dual electric remote mirrors; front seat reading lights; radio controls - steering wheel mounted	1991	2342
SB	**Century Custom Wagon Popular Package** — includes tilt steering column; electric rear window defogger; windshield wipers with delay feature; carpet savers, front; carpet savers, rear; remote tailgate lock release; luggage rack, roof mounted	489	575
SC	**Century Custom Wagon Premium Package** — includes SB Century Custom Wagon Popular Pkg equipment plus electric door locks; cruise control, electronic; cassette tape player; 55/45 seat with storage armrest; dual electric seat back recliners; third seat; air deflector, rear	1448	1703
SD	**Century Custom Wagon Luxury Package** — includes SC Century Custom Wagon Premium Pkg equipment plus locking wire wheel covers; accent stripes; power windows; dual lighted visor vanity mirrors	2010	2365
SE	**Century Custom Wagon Prestige Package** — includes SD Century Custom Wagon Luxury Pkg equipment plus 6-way power driver's seat; automatic power antenna; dual electric remote mirrors; front seat reading lights	2407	2832
SC	**Century Limited Sedan Premium Package** — includes tilt steering column; electric rear window defogger; windshield wipers with delay feature; electric door locks; electronic cruise control; dual electric seatback recliners; carpet savers, front; carpet savers, rear; locking wire wheelcovers	986	1160
SD	**Century Limited Sedan Luxury Package** — includes SC Century Limited Sedan Premium Pkg equipment plus cassette tape player with auto reverse; automatic power antenna; power windows; dual lighted visor vanity mirrors; front seat reading lights	1531	1801
SE	**Century Limited Sedan Prestige Package** — includes SD Century Limited Sedan Luxury Pkg equipment plus 6-way power driver's seat; electric remote trunk release; dual electric remote mirrors; steering wheel mounted radio controls; cassette tape player with search/repeat and auto reverse; premium speakers	2077	2444

Mfgs. Code	Description **BUICK**	Base Cost	Sgstd. List
SC	**Century Limited Wagon Premium Package** — includes tilt steering column; electric rear window defogger; windshield wipers with delay feature; carpet savers, front; carpet savers, rear; remote tailgate lock release; luggage rack, roof mounted; electric door locks; cruise control, electronic; dual electric seatback recliners; air deflector, rear . .	990	1165
SD	**Century Limited Wagon Luxury Package** — includes SC Century Limited Wagon Premium Pkg equipment plus locking wire wheel covers; power windows; dual lighted visor vanity mirrors; cassette tape player with auto reverse; automatic power antenna; front seat reading lights; third seat	1901	2236
SE	**Century Limited Wagon Prestige Package** — includes SD Century Limited Wagon Luxury Pkg equipment plus 6-way power driver's seat; dual electric remote mirrors; premium speakers; steering wheel mounted radio controls; cassette player with search/repeat and auto reverse	2375	2794

LE SABRE

LE SABRE (6 Cylinder)

P37	2 Dr Coupe	14826	17180

LE SABRE CUSTOM (6 Cylinder)

P69	4 Dr Sedan	14740	17080

LE SABRE LIMITED (6 Cylinder)

R69	4 Dr Sedan	15905	18430
R37	2 Dr Coupe	15819	18330

Destination Charge: All Models 535 525

STANDARD EQUIPMENT:
LE SABRE: Air conditioner, fixed-mast antenna, Delco Freedom II Plus battery, power front disc/rear drum brakes, bumper guards, front and rear bumper protective strips, front and rear carpeting, front, side window outlet defogger, front-wheel drive, electronic warning tone (seatbelt, ignition key, and "headlamps on"), 3800 SFI V6 engine, soft-ray tinted glass, composite tungsten-halogen headlamps, adjustable front-seat headrests, inside-release hood lock, dual horns, lights (front or rear door operated dome, instrument panel, courtesy, ashtray, glove box, trunk and engine compartment), mirrors (deluxe body-color, outside, rearview (left remote, right manual), moldings (body-side, belt reveal, roof drip and wheel opening), clearcoat Plastisol protection paint, ETR AM/FM stereo radio with seek and scan and clock, automatic front safety system seatbelts, rear-seat lap/shoulder seatbelts, cloth notchback bench seats with armrest (Le Sabre, Le Sabre Custom), dual front and rear extended range speakers, power rack and pinion steering, tilt steering column, Dyna Ride suspension, front, independent MacPherson strut suspension, rear independent suspension, compact spare tire, P205/75R14 steel-belted, radial-ply, all-season blackwall tires, 4-speed automatic transmission with overdrive, trip odometer (deleted when quartz analog cluster is ordered), full trunk trim, deluxe wheelcovers, 2-speed wipers. **Le Sabre Limited also has in addition to above standard equipment:** Bright "B" pillar applique moldings, lower Gunmetal wide body-side moldings, recliners (manual seatback - driver and passenger), 55/45 cloth seats with front storage armrests.

ACCESSORIES

LN3	**Engine** — 3.8 litre 3800 (231 CID) SFI V6	STD	STD
MX0	**Transmission** — automatic with overdrive	STD	STD
F79	**Axles** — 2:97 ratio (V08 required, included Y56)	NC	NC

Mfgs. Code	Description	Base Cost	Sgstd. List
JM4	**Brake System** — anti-lock	786	925
V08	**Cooling Heavy Duty Engine And Transmission** — (req'd w/F79) (included with Y56)	34	40
C47	**Defogger Delete (from pkg)**	(136)	(160)
AU3	**Door Locks** — electric (included SC, SD, SE) (also in all Limited Packages)		
	- Coupe	162	190
	- Custom Sedan	196	230
YF5	**California Emissions** — (req'd in California)	85	100
BF9	**Delete Carpet Savers (from package)**	(38)	(45)
U21	**Instrumentation** — gauges & tachometer (includes temperature, oil, volt gauges & tachometer)	94	110
V58	**Luggage Rack, Deck Lid** — chrome	98	115
—	**Radio Equipment**		
UM6	cassette tape, AM/FM stereo ETR radio with seek/scan, auto reverse, clock (included Custom SC, SD, SE and Limited SB, SC, SD Pkgs) - Custom & SA or SB	119	140
UX1	graphic equalizer, cassette tape and ETR AM stereo-FM stereo radio with seek and scan, automatic reverse with search/repeat, clock, & concert sound (included Limited SE pkg) (*requires power windows - A31) - all SA*, Custom SB*	319	375
	- Custom & SC* or SD	200	235
	- Limited & SB, SC, SD	200	235
	- Custom & SE	128	150
U75	**Automatic Power Antenna**	64	75
—	**Stripes, Body Side** — (order by color)	38	45
18A	slate		
21A	dark blue		
40A	white		
41A	black		
55A	gold		
66A	dark auburn		
72A	claret red		
75A	red		
85A	dark gray		
G67	**Suspension, Automatic Level Control** — included in Y56	149	175
C09	**Top, Full Vinyl** — Sedans	170	200
WDV	**Warranty Enhancement — New York State** — (req'd in New York)	55	65
—	**Trims**		
	Le Sabre Coupe, Custom		
15	cloth notchback - Le Sabre, Custom	STD	STD
36	cloth 55/45 seat & storage armrest - Le Sabre, Custom	156	183
	Limited		
56	cloth 55/45 seat & storage armrest - Limited	STD	STD
96	leather/vinyl 55/45 seat - Limited	383	450
—	**Wheels & Wheel Covers**		
N78	styled aluminum wheels (4) (14") - all & SA or SB	230	270
	- all & SC/SD/SE	47	55
N91	locking wire wheel covers (included in SC, SD, SE pkgs) - all & SA or SB	183	215
A31	**Windows, Power** — (Coupes) Le Sabre & SB/SC	208	245
	- (Sedans) Custom & SA/SB/SC	264	310
Y56	**Gran Touring Package** — includes Gran Touring Suspension, 15" aluminum wheels (4), and P215/65R15 blackwall tires, 2:97 axle ratio & HD cooling leather-wrapped steering wheel and automatic level control		
	- all & SA	627	738
	- all & SB	563	662
	- all & SC/SD/SE	380	447
SA	**SA Package** — represents individual model w/standard equipment (see		

Mfgs. Code	Description	Base Cost	Sgstd. List
	listings)		
SB	**Le Sabre Coupe Popular Package —** includes windshield wipers with delay feature; cruise control, electronic; electric rear window defogger; white stripe tires; 55/45 split front seat with storage armrest; carpet savers, front; carpet savers, rear	620	729
SC	**Le Sabre Coupe Premium Package —** includes SB Le Sabre Coupe Popular Pkg equipment plus door locks, electric cassette tape player; locking wire wheel covers	1083	1274
SD	**Le Sabre Coupe Luxury Package —** includes SC Le Sabre Coupe Premium Pkg equipment plus power windows; 6-way power driver's seat; door edge guards; seat back recliner, passenger (manual); seat back recliner, driver (manual)	1627	1914
SE	**Le Sabre Coupe Prestige Package —** includes SD Le Sabre Coupe Luxury Pkg equipment plus electric trunk release; lighted visor vanity mirror, passenger; automatic power antenna; dual electric remote control mirrors; concert sound speakers	1921	2260
SB	**Le Sabre Custom Sedan Popular Package —** includes windshield wipers with delay feature; cruise control, electronic; electric rear window defogger; white stripe tires; 55/45 split front seat with storage armrest; carpet savers, front; carpet savers, rear	620	729
SC	**Le Sabre Custom Sedan Premium Package —** includes SB Le Sabre Custom Sedan Popular Pkg equipment plus door locks, electric; cassette tape player; locking wire wheel covers	1117	1314
SD	**Le Sabre Custom Sedan Luxury Package —** includes SC Le Sabre Custom Sedan Premium Pkg equipment plus power windows; 6-way power driver's seat; door edge guards; seat back recliner, passenger (manual); seat back recliner, driver (manual)	1725	2029
SE	**Le Sabre Custom Sedan Prestige Package —** includes SD Le Sabre Custom Sedan Luxury Pkg equipment plus electric trunk release; lighted visor vanity mirror, passenger; automatic power antenna; dual electric remote control mirrors; concert sound speakers	2019	2375
SB	**Le Sabre Limited Coupe Popular Package —** includes windshield wipers with delay feature; cruise control, electronic; electric rear window defogger; white stripe tires; carpet savers, front; carpet savers, rear; door locks, electric; cassette tape player; power windows; 6-way power driver's seat	1199	1411
SC	**Le Sabre Limited Coupe Premium Package —** includes SB Le Sabre Limited Coupe Popular Pkg equipment plus locking wire wheel covers; door edge guards; electric trunk release; lighted visor vanity mirror, passenger; automatic power antenna	1550	1824
SD	**Le Sabre Limited Coupe Luxury Package —** includes SC Le Sabre Limited Coupe Premium Pkg equipment plus dual electric remote control mirrors; electric recliner, passenger; deluxe trunk trim; electronic touch climate control air conditioner; front and rear reading lamps; front door courtesy lamps	1958	2303
SE	**Le Sabre Limited Coupe Prestige Package —** includes SD Le Sabre Limited Coupe Luxury Pkg equipment plus 6-way power passenger seat; graphic equalizer, cassette, AM stereo and concert sound speakers	2404	2828
SB	**Le Sabre Limited Sedan Popular Package —** includes windshield wipers with delay feature; cruise control, electronic; electric rear window defogger; white stripe tires; carpet savers, front; carpet savers, rear; door locks, electric; cassette tape player; power windows; 6-way power driver's seat	1289	1516
SC	**Le Sabre Limited Sedan Premium Package —** includes SB Le Sabre Limited Sedan Popular Pkg equipment plus locking wire wheel covers; door edge guards; electric trunk release; lighted visor vanity mirror, passenger; automatic power antenna	1648	1939

Mfgs. Code	Description	Base Cost	Sgstd. List
SD	**Le Sabre Limited Sedan Luxury Package** — includes SC Le Sabre Limited Sedan Premium Pkg equipment plus dual electric remote control mirrors; electric recliner, passenger; deluxe trunk trim; electronic touch climate control air conditioner; front & rear reading lamps; front door courtesy lamps	2055	2418
SE	**Le Sabre Limited Sedan Prestige Package** — includes SD Le Sabre Limited Sedan Luxury Pkg equipment plus 6-way power passenger seat; graphic equalizer; cassette, AM stereo and concert sound speakers	2502	2943

PARK AVENUE/ULTRA

PARK AVENUE (6 Cylinder)

W69	4 Dr Sedan	20800	24385

PARK AVENUE ULTRA (6 Cylinder)

U69	4 Dr Sedan	23389	27420

Destination Charge: All Models 580 580

STANDARD EQUIPMENT:

PARK AVENUE: Acoustical package, air conditioner, fixed-mast antenna, front-seat storage armrest, Delco Freedom II Plus battery, anti-lock brakes, power front disc/rear drum brakes, front bumper guards, front and rear bumper protective strips, carpeting, front and rear carpet savers, cruise control, front/side window outlet defogger, rear window defogger, electric door locks, front-wheel drive, electronic warning tone (seatbelt, ignition key and "headlamps on"), 3800 V6 engine with tuned port injection, electric remote release fuel filler door, solar control glass, composite tungsten-halogen headlamps, inside release hood lock, dual horns, lights (front and rear-door warning, front and rear seat reading and courtesy, front ashtray, trunk, engine compartment, instrument panel courtesy, glove box, front door courtesy), lighted visor vanity passenger mirror, mirrors (deluxe body-color, electric, outside, rearview (left remote and right remote), moldings (wheel opening, belt reveal, body-side), ETR AM/FM stereo radio cassette with seek and scan and clock, active front safety seatbelts, rear seat lap/shoulder seatbelts, 55/45 cloth seats with front storage armrest, manual reclining driver and passenger seats, 6-way power driver seat, dual-extended range speakers, tilt steering column, power rack and pinion steering, steering wheel with SIRS, body-side stripes, sunshade (slide-out extensions supplemental shades), automatic level control suspension, Dyna Ride suspension, front and rear independent suspension, P205/70R15 steel-belted, radial-ply, all-season blackwall tires, 4-speed automatic transmission with overdrive, trip odometer, full trunk trim, 15" aluminum wheels, power windows with driver express down, 2-speed delay wipers. **Park Avenue Ultra also has in addition to above standard equipment:** Specific grille, dual automatic comfortemp climate control, rear seat headrests, lighted driver visor/vanity mirror, two rear seat lighted mirrors, lower body-side moldings, specific lower accent moldings, seat recliner (6-way power driver and passenger with power recliners), 55/45 leather seats with front storage armrest, specific leather-wrapped (SIRS) steel wheel, specific 15" aluminum wheels.

ACCESSORIES

L27	**Engine** — 3.8 liter 3800 (231 CID) TPI V6	STD	STD
MX0	**Transmission** — automatic with overdrive	STD	STD
YF5	**California Assembly Line Emissions Equipment & Testing** — (req'd in California)	85	100
95U	**Firemist Paint**	179	210
D83	**Solid Color Paint** — Ultra	NC	NC

Mfgs. Code	Description	Base Cost	Sgstd. List
	BUICK		
—	**Radio Equipment**		
UX1	graphic equalizer, cassette tape with auto reverse and search/repeat, AM stereo, and concert sound speakers (included in SE) - all & SA/SB	187	220
	- all & SC/SD	128	150
	Bose music system (with AM stereo) (not available on Park Avenue) - Ultra & SA/SB	674	793
	- Ultra & SC/SD	615	723
	- Ultra & SE Pkg	487	573
U1A	compact disc player with graphic equalizer, AM stereo radio, and concert sound speakers - all & SA/SB	377	444
	- all & SC/SD	318	374
	- all & SE	190	224
—	**Astroroof** — electric sliding (includes driver side lighted visor vanity mirror, lamp monitors deleted from SD/SE packages) - Park Ave & SA/SB/SC	1095	1288
	- Ultra & SA/SB/SC	1046	1230
	- all with SD/SE	980	1153
—	**Stripes** — accent (select color)		
18A	slate		
21A	dark blue		
40A	white		
41A	black		
49A	taupe		
55A	gold		
66A	dark auburn		
72A	claret red		
75A	red		
85A	gray		
—	**Tires** — (all are steel belted radials)		
QGY	P205/70R15 blackwall - all & SA	STD	STD
	- all & SB/SC/SD	(65)	(76)
	- all & SE	(192)	(226)
QGZ	P205/70R15 whitewall - all & SB/SC/SD/SE (included in packages) - all & SA	65	76
CA9	**Top** — vinyl (select color also) - Park Avenue	170	200
28	blue		
40	white		
41	black		
66	dark auburn		
76	red		
85	gray		
95	taupe		
—	**Trailering Package** — includes: auxilary transmission oil and engine oil cooling, gran touring suspension and 3:06 axle ratio	128	150
—	**Trims**		
	Park Avenue		
56	cloth 55/45 with storage armrest - Park Avenue	STD	STD
96	leather/vinyl 55/45 with storage armrest - Park Avenue	383	450
	Ultra		
	ultra soft leather 55/45 with storage armrest	STD	STD
WDV	**Warranty Enhancement, New York** — (required in New York State)	55	65
N91	**Wheel Covers, Locking Wire**	NC	NC
C50	**Windshield** — electriclear heated	213	250
Y56	**Gran Touring Package** — includes: Gran Touring Suspension, P215/65R15 blackwall Eagle GT +4 tires, 3:06 axle ratio, and leather-wrapped steering wheel on Park Avenue (std Ultra) Note: packaged whitewalls are deleted from SB/SC/SD pkgs and self-sealing whitewalls are deleted from SE - Park Avenue & SA	161	189

Mfgs. Code	Description	Base Cost	Sgstd. List
	- Park Avenue & SB/SC/SD	96	113
	- Park Avenue & SE	(31)	(37)
	- Ultra & SA	79	93
	- Ultra & SB/SC/SD	14	17
	- Ultra & SE	(113)	(133)
SA	**SA Package** — represents individual model w/standard equipment (see listing)		
SB	**Park Avenue Popular Package** — includes 6-way power passenger seat adjuster; automatic power antenna; door edge guard molding; white stripe tires; tachometer & analog gauges; oil level monitor	535	629
SC	**Park Avenue Premium Package** — includes SB Park Avenue Popular Pkg equipment plus electric seat back recliner; comfortemp dual control air conditioner; concert sound speakers; illuminated entry; reminder package	875	1029
SD	**Park Avenue Luxury Package** — includes SC Park Avenue Premium Pkg equipment plus cornering lamps; twilight sentinel headlamp control; four note horn; lamp monitors (deleted when CF5 astroroof ordered); electric trunk pull-down; remote keyless entry; illuminated visor vanity mirror, driver's side; automatic electric door locks; theft deterrent system	1501	1766
SE	**Park Avenue Prestige Package** — includes SD Park Avenue Luxury Pkg equipment plus graphic equalizer, AM stereo, search/repeat cassette; automatic day/night mirror; heated left outside mirror; 2-position memory seat & mirrors; self-sealing tires; trunk mat	2015	2371
SB	**Park Avenue Ultra Popular Package** — includes automatic power antenna; door edge guard moldings; white stripe tires; tachometer, analog gauges, oil level monitor	288	339
SC	**Park Avenue Ultra Premium Package** — includes SB Park Avenue Ultra Popular Pkg equipment plus concert sound speakers; illuminated entry; reminder package	450	529
SD	**Park Avenue Ultra Luxury Package** — includes SC Park Avenue Ultra Premium Pkg equipment plus cornering lamps; twilight sentinel headlamp control; four note horn; lamp monitors (deleted when CF5 astroroof ordered); electric trunk pull-down; remote keyless entry; automatic electric door locks; theft deterrent system	1027	1208
SE	**Park Avenue Ultra Prestige Package** — includes SD Park Avenue Ultra Luxury Pkg equipment plus graphic equalizer, AM stereo, search/repeat cassette; automatic day/night mirror; heated left outside mirror; 2-position memory seat & mirrors; self-sealing tires; trunk mat	1541	1813

REATTA

REATTA (6 Cylinder)

Code	Description	Base Cost	Sgstd. List
C97	2 Dr Coupe	24993	29300
C67	2 Dr Convertible	30678	35965
	Destination Charge: All Models	580	580

STANDARD EQUIPMENT:

REATTA: Retained accessory power, electronic touch climate control air conditioner, automatic power antenna, heavy-duty battery, anti-lock four-wheel power disc brakes, rear bumper guards, bumper protection strips, front and rear storage area carpeting, front anti-slip carpet savers, full-length console, electronic cruise control, electric rear-window defogger, front, side-window outlet defoggers, automatic electric door locks, front-wheel drive, electronic warning tone chimes (seatbelt, ignition key, and "headlamps on"), 3800 V6 engine with tuned port injection, stainless steel dual outlet exhaust, electric remote fuel filler door release, soft-ray tinted glass, retractable dual headlamps, dual horns, illuminated driver door lock and interior light control, instrumentation (electronic digital - includes trip odometer, low fuel indicator, speedometer, tachometer, oil, temperature and fuel gauges), remote keyless entry system, cornering lamps, front fog lamps, door-operated courtesy and warning lights, lights (front ashtray, instrument panel courtesy, glove box, engine compartment and trunk), front-seat reading lights, mirrors (deluxe black electric outside, rearview mirror (left and right remote), lighted visor vanity driver and passenger mirrors, wide body-side molding (black unless color-coordinated is ordered), belt reveal molding, black rocker panel moldings, clearcoat paint with anti-chip primer, radio (graphic equalizer, cassette and ETR AM/FM stereo with seek and scan, auto reverse with search/repeat and clock), color-coordinated seat and shoulder safety belts, manual reclining leather bucket seats, 6-way power driver and passenger seats, 6-speaker Concert Sound II speakers, front and rear stabilizer bars, fast-ratio power steering, tilt steering column, leather-wrapped sport steering wheel with air bag, two lockable rear storage compartments, body-side accent stripes, extendable slide-out sunshades, independent 4-wheel Gran Touring suspension, Pass-key theft deterrent system with starter interrupt, P215/60R16 steel-belted, radial-ply, Eagle GT +4 blackwall tires, automatic electronically controlled transmission with overdrive, interior lockable trunk access door, electric remote trunk lock release, deluxe trunk trim, four 16" aluminum wheels, power windows with backlit controls, 2-speed wipers with low-speed delay feature,supplemental inflatable restraint.

ACCESSORIES

Code	Description	Base Cost	Sgstd. List
LN3	**Engine** — 3.8 litre (231 CID) 3800 SFI V6	STD	STD
MX0	**Transmission** — automatic with overdrive	STD	STD
YF5	**California Assembly Line Emission Equipment & Testing** — (req'd in California	85	100
B84	**Molding** — matching wide body side	NC	NC
41Q	**Molding** — black	STD	STD
U1H	**Radio Equipment** — compact disc player - added to base graphic equalizer, cassette tape, and AM stereo/FM stereo ETR radio	337	396
CA1	**Sunroof** — sliding electric (steel) - Reatta Coupe	761	895
—	**Stripes: Body Side** — (select by color)	STD	STD
18A	slate		
21A	dark blue		
40A	white		
41A	black		
55A	gold		
75A	red		
85A	dark gray		
YL6	**Stripe Delete**	(38)	(45)
C05	**Top Color, Convertible** — (selection required)	STD	STD
40	white		
41	black		
58	saddle		
74	flame red		
—	**Trims**		
99	leather buckets	STD	STD
98	leather buckets with 16-way adjustable driver side	506	595
WDV	**Warranty Enhancement** — New York State (required in New York)	55	65

REGAL

REGAL CUSTOM (6 Cylinder)

Code	Description	Base Cost	Sgstd. List
B19	4 Dr Sedan	13730	15910

Mfgs. Code	Description	Base Cost	Sgstd. List
	BUICK		
B57	2 Dr Coupe	13540	15690
	REGAL LIMITED (6 Cylinder)		
D19	4 Dr Sedan	14442	16735
D57	2 Dr Coupe	14201	16455
	Destination Charge: All Models	485	485

STANDARD EQUIPMENT:

REGAL: Air conditioner, fixed-mast antenna, power four-wheel disc brakes, front and rear bumper guards, front and rear bumper protective strips, front/side window outlet defoggers, front-wheel drive, electronic warning tone (seatbelt, ignition key and "headlamps on"), 3.1L V6 engine with MFI stainless steel exhaust system, soft-ray tinted glass, composite tungsten-halogen headlamps, adjustable front-seat headrests, rear seat ventilation heat ducts, inside floor-mounted release hood lock release, dual horns, instrumentation (digital speedometer with analog fuel gauge), lights (door-operated dome, front ashtray, instrument panel courtesy, trunk and engine compartment, glove box), driver's side map strap, mirrors (deluxe, outside, rearview - left remote and right manual), moldings (black windshield and back window, rear quarter window, belt reveal and front and rear wheel opening), lower bodyside black moldings (Custom), bright narrow rocker panel moldings (Custom), Plastisol protection paint, ETR AM/FM stereo radio with seek and scan and clock, automatic front safety system seatbelts, rear seat lap/shoulder seatbelts, cloth reclining bucket seats (Gran Sport), cloth reclining 55/45 seats with storage armrest (Custom, Limited), tilt steering column, power steering, slide-out extension sunvisors, DynaRide suspension (except Gran Sport), independent front and rear suspension, P205/70R14 steel-belted, radial-ply, all-season blackwall tires (Custom, Limited), P225/60R16 steel-belted radial-ply Touring blackwall tires (Gran Sport), 4-speed automatic transmission with overdrive, trunk trim, deluxe wheelcovers (Custom, Limited), four 16" aluminum wheels (Gran Sport), 2-speed wipers.

ACCESSORIES

Code	Description	Base Cost	Sgstd. List
—	**Engines**		
LH0	3.1 litre (191 CID) V6 with MFI - Custom/Limited		
L27	3.8 litre 3800 (231 CID) V6 with SFI (requires N91, PH6, or Y56) (std Gran Sport) - Custom/Limited	336	395
MX0	**Transmission** — automatic with overdrive	STD	STD
JL9	**Anti-Lock Brake System**	786	925
BF9	**Carpet Savers Delete (from packages)** — all except SA	(38)	(45)
K34	**Cruise Control, Electronic** — (with resume) - Custom & SB	179	210
C47	**Defogger Delete (from packages)** — all except SA	(136)	(160)
AU3	**Door Locks, Electric** — (Coupe) - Custom & SB	162	190
	- Sedan	196	230
YF5	**Emission System** — California assembly line emission equipment and test (required in California)	85	100
U21	**Instrumentation** — analog gauges and tachometer (std Limited, includes Y56 or with Gran Sport (Z13) - Custom		
AU0	**Keyless Entry, Remote Control** — (not available with SA or SB)	106	125
V56	**Luggage Rack** — deck lid (black) - Coupe	98	115
V58	**Luggage Rack** — deck lid (bright) - Sedan	98	115
B5Z	**Molding, Wide Black With Red Stripe** — (included in Gran Sport Coupe)		
	- Custom Coupe	60	70
	- Limited Coupe	NC	NC
B93	**Moldings, Door Edge Guards** — (not available with B5Z) - (Sedan)		
	- Custom/Limited	21	25
	- (Coupe) - Custom/Limited	13	15
D84	**Paint, Lower Accent** — (Coupes only) - Custom Limited	174	205

Mfgs. Code	Description **BUICK**	Base Cost	Sgstd. List
—	**Radio Equipment**		
UM6	cassette tape player - Custom & SB Pkg	119	140
UX1	graphic equalizer, AM stereo for Radio and search/repeat for cassette		
	- all & SB pkg	247	290
	- all & SC/SD/SE	128	150
U1C	compact disc player - all & SB	352	414
	- all & SC/SD/SE	233	274
U75	power antenna (included SD/SE) - all & SB/SC	64	75
UW6	speakers, concert sound (included SE)	60	70
CF5	**Roof** — electric sliding sunroof, glass (A31 power windows required)	553	650
UK3	**Steering Wheel Mounted Radio Controls** — (note: steering wheel is not leather-wrapped) - Gran Sport	25	29
A	**Stripes, Body Side** — (Coupes) Custom/Limited	38	45
21A	dark blue		
40A	white		
41A	black		
55A	gold		
66A	dark auburn		
75A	red		
85A	dark gray		
—	**Tires** — all are steel belted radials		
QHX	P205/70R14 blackwall tires (standard) - all w/SB or SC	(65)	(76)
QHY	P205/70R14 whitewall tires - all & SA	65	76
QGY	P205/70R15 blackwall tires (included in SD/SE) - all & SA	17	20
	- all & SB or SC	(48)	(56)
QGZ	P205/70R15 whitewall tires - all & SA	82	96
	- all & SB or SC	17	20
	- all & SD or SE	65	76
—	**Trims**		
	Custom		
16	cloth 55/45 with storage armrest - Custom	STD	STD
39	cloth reclining buckets & console - Custom Coupe	NC	NC
	Limited		
56	cloth 55/45 with storage armrest - Limited	STD	STD
96	leather/vinyl 55/45 - Limited	383	450
99	leather/vinyl buckets & console - Limited	383	450
BIB	four seater package - Sedan less Y56/SE	429	505
	- Sedan & Y56 or SE	348	409
	Gran Sport (&Z13)		
38	cloth reclining buckets & console - Gran Sport	STD	STD
98	leather/vinyl buckets & console - Gran Sport	383	450
BIB	four seater package - (includes reclining cloth bucket seats with operating console, rear "bucket" seats & console with storage, and rear headrests) - Gran Sport	348	409
—	**Wheels and Wheel Covers**		
PC7	styled steel wheels (4) - all less SD or SE	98	115
N91	locking wire wheelcovers - all with SB or SC	(183)	(215)
	- all with SD or SE	(72)	(85)
PG4	14" styled aluminum wheels (4) - all with SB or SC	230	270
PH6	15" styled aluminum wheels (4) - all less SB or SC	255	300
A31	**Windows** — power, driver's express-down (included various packages)		
	- Coupe	217	255
	- Sedan	272	320
WDV	**New York Warranty Enhancement** — required in New York State	55	65
Y56	**Gran Touring Package** — Gran Tour Suspension 16" aluminum wheels and P225/60R16 tires, leather-wrapped steering wheel and analog gauges and tach (note: with SE pkg, steering wheel is not leather-wrapped)		

Mfgs. Code	Description	Base Cost	Sgstd. List
	- Custom & SB/SC	556	654
	- Custom & SD	349	410
	- Custom & SE	267	314
	- Limited & SB/SC	505	594
	- Limited & SD	298	350
	- Limited & SE	216	254
Z13	**Gran Sport** — includes Gran Touring Pkg (Y56 above), bucket seats & console (AR9), analog gauges and tach, 3800 TPI V6 engine, and specific exterior appearance (included in SC or SE pkgs) - Limited Sedan/Custom Coupe		
SA	**SA Package** — represents individual model w/standard equipment (see listings)		
SB	**Regal Custom Sedan Popular Package** — includes electric rear window defogger; white stripe tires; delay feature w/s wipers; carpet saver, front; carpet saver, rear	286	336
SC	**Regal Custom Sedan Premium Package** — includes SB Regal Custom Sedan Popular Pkg equipment plus cassette tape player (with auto reverse); electronic cruise control; power door locks (electric)	779	916
SD	**Regal Custom Sedan Luxury Package** — includes SC Regal Custom Sedan Premium Pkg equipment plus dual control comfortemp air conditioner; power windows with express down driver's window; automatic power antenna; 15" aluminum wheels (4); tires - P205/70R15 blackwall all - season radial	1360	1600
SE	**Regal Custom Sedan Prestige Package** — includes SD Regal Custom Luxury Pkg equipment plus illuminated visor vanity mirror, passenger side; remote trunk lid release; front seat reading & courtesy lamps; 6-way power seat adjuster, driver; dual electric remote control mirrors; concert sound speakers; radio controls - steering wheel mounted	1956	2301
SB	**Regal Custom Coupe Popular Package** — includes electric rear window defogger; white stripe tires; delay feature w/s wipers; carpet saver, front; carpet saver, rear	286	336
SC	**Regal Custom Coupe Premium Package** — includes SB Regal Custom Coupe Popular Pkg equipment plus cassette tape player (with auto reverse) electronic cruise control; power door locks (electric)	745	876
SD	**Regal Custom Coupe Luxury Package** — includes SC Regal Custom Coupe Premium Pkg equipment plus dual control comfortemp air conditioner; power windows with express down driver's window; automatic power antenna; 15" aluminum wheels (4); tires - P205/70R15 blackwall all season radial	1271	1495
SE	**Regal Custom Coupe Prestige Package** — includes SD Regal Custom Coupe Luxury Pkg equipment plus illuminated visor vanity mirror, passenger side; remote trunk lid release; front seat reading & courtesy lamps; 6-way power seat adjuster, driver; dual electric remote control mirrors; concert sound speakers; radio controls - steering wheel mounted	1867	2196
SB	**Regal Limited Sedan Popular Package** — includes electric rear window defogger; white stripe tires; delay feature w/s wipers; carpet saver, front; carpet saver, rear; dual control comfortemp air conditioner; electronic cruise control with resume; power door locks (electric)	698	821
SC	**Regal Limited Sedan Premium Package** — includes SB Regal Limited Sedan Popular Pkg equipment plus cassette tape player (with auto reverse, and power windows with express down driver's window	1089	1281
SD	**Regal Limited Sedan Luxury Package** — includes SC Regal Limited Sedan Premium Pkg equipment plus dual electric remote control mirrors; remote trunk release; automatic power antenna; 15" aluminum wheels (4); tires - P205/70R15 blackwall all season radial	1469	1728
SE	**Regal Limited Sedan Prestige Package** — includes SD Regal Limited		

Mfgs. Code	Description	Base Cost	Sgstd. List
	Sedan Luxury Pkg equipment plus illuminated visor vanity mirror, passenger side; 6-way power seat adjuster, driver; concert sound speakers; radio controls - steering wheel mounted	1930	2271
SB	**Regal Limited Coupe Popular Package —** includes electric rear window defogger; white stripe tires; delay feature w/s wipers; carpet saver, front; carpet saver, rear; dual control comfortemp air conditioner; electronic cruise control with resume; power door locks (electric)	664	781
SC	**Regal Limited Coupe Premium Package —** includes SB Regal Limited Coupe Popular Pkg equipment plus cassette tape player (with auto reverse); power windows with express down driver's window	1000	1176
SD	**Regal Limited Coupe Luxury Package —** includes SC Regal Limited Coupe Premium Pkg equipment plus dual electric remote control mirrors; remote trunk lid release; automatic power antenna; 15" aluminum wheels (4); tires - P205/70R15 blackwall all season radial	1380	1623
SE	**Regal Limited Coupe Prestige Package —** includes SD Regal Limited Coupe Luxury Pkg equipment plus illuminated visor vanity mirror, passenger side; 6-way power seat adjuster, driver; concert sound speakers; radio controls - steering wheel mounted	1841	2166
SC	**Regal Gran Sport Sedan Premium Package —** includes Gran Sport Pkg: includes specific exterior, 3800 TPI V6 engine, Gran Touring Pkg, bucket seats with full length operating console; electric rear window defogger; delay feature windshield wipers; electronic cruise control with resume; carpet savers, front; carpet savers, rear; cassette tape player with auto reverse; power door locks (electric); power windows with express down driver's window; dual control comfortemp air conditioner	2029	2387
SE	**Regal Gran Sport Sedan Prestige Package —** includes SC Regal Gran Sport Sedan Premium Pkg equipment plus automatic power antenna; illuminated visor vanity mirror, passenger side; remote trunk lid release; 6-way power seat adjuster, driver's seat; dual electric remote control mirrors; concert sound speakers	2557	3008
SC	**Regal Gran Sport Coupe Premium Package —** includes Gran Sport Pkg: includes specific exterior; 3800 TPI V6 engine; Gran Touring Pkg; analog gauges and tachometer; bucket seats (cloth) with full length operating console; electric rear window defogger; delay feature windshield wipers; electronic cruise control with resume; carpet savers, front; carpet savers, rear; cassette tape player with auto reverse; power door locks (electric); power windows with express down driver's window; dual control comfortemp air conditioner	2199	2587
SE	**Regal Gran Sport Coupe Prestige Package —** includes SC Regal Gran Sport Coupe Premium Pkg equipment plus automatic power antenna; illuminated visor vanity mirror, passenger side; remote trunk lid release; front seat reading and courtesy lamps; 6-way power seat adjuster, driver's seat; dual electric remote control mirrors; concert sound speakers	2752	3238

RIVIERA

RIVIERA (6 Cylinder)

Z57	2 Dr Coupe	20950	24560
Destination Charge:		580	580

STANDARD EQUIPMENT:

RIVIERA: Retained accessory power, acoustical package, electronic touch climate control air conditioner, automatic power antenna, passenger assist straps, automatic level control, heavy-duty battery, color-coordinated front/rear seat and shoulder belts, four-wheel power disc brakes with anti-lock, front and rear bumper guards, front and rear bumper protective strips, front and rear carpet savers, carpeting, full-length console with armrest, heavy-duty engine and transmission cooling, electronic cruise control, front side-window outlet defoggers, electric rear window defogger, door-edge guards, electric door locks, front-wheel drive, electronic warning tone (seatbelt, ignition key and "headlamps on"), 3800 V6 engine with tuned port injection, electric remote release fuel filler door, soft-ray tinted glass, composite tungsten-halogen headlamps, rear seat ventilation heat ducts, inside release hood lock, dual horns, illuminated entry, instrumentation (electronic digital includes trip odometer, low fuel indicator, tachometer, voltmeter), cornering lamps, electroluminescent coach lamps, front seat reading lights, lights (front ashtray, instrument panel courtesy, glove box, engine compartment and trunk), mirrors (deluxe electric, body-color, outside rearview mirror (left and right remote), lighted driver and passenger visor vanity mirrors, moldings (belt reveal, wheel opening, rocker panel), protective body-side chrome molding, cassette tape and ETR AM/FM stereo radio with seek and scan, auto-reverse with search/repeat and clock, manual reclining cloth bucket - driver and passenger seats, 6-way power driver seats, Concert Sound II speakers, power steering, tilt steering column, leather-wrapped steering wheel with air bag, body-side accent stripe, slide-out extension sunshade, automatic level control suspension, DynaRide suspension, 4-wheel independent suspension, P205/70R15 steel-belted, radial-ply, all-season whitewall tires, electronically controlled automatic transmission with overdrive, electric remote control trunk release, deluxe trunk trim, custom locking wire wheelcovers, power windows with floodlit controls, 2-speed wipers with low-speed delay feature.

ACCESSORIES

Code	Description	Base Cost	Sgstd. List
LN3	**Engine** — 3.8 litre 3800 (231 CID) SFI V6	STD	STD
MX0	**Transmission** — automatic with overdrive	STD	STD
YF5	**California Assembly Line Emission Equipment & Testing** — (required in California)	85	100
—	**Paint** — Firemist (83U or 95U)	178	210
93U	- Pearlescent white diamond	178	210
D84	**Paint** — lower accent	162	190
U16	**Radio** — Delco Bose music system - compact disc player, cassette tape, AM stereo/FM stereo with Dolby	1189	1399
U1H	**Radio** — graphic equalizer, compact disc, cassette player, AM stereo	439	516
CF5	**Roof** — Astroroof, electric sliding sun	1046	1230
—	**Stripes** — body side (color must be chosen) (included with D84)	STD	STD
18A	slate		
21A	dark blue		
22A	light blue		
40A	white		
49A	taupe		
55A	gold		
64A	light auburn		
66A	dark auburn		
72A	claret red		
75A	red		
85A	dark gray		
C04	**Top** — heavily padded vinyl (choose color also)	591	695
13T	silver		
28T	dark blue		
40T	slate		
41T	black		
56T	alabaster		
66T	dark auburn		
72T	red		
76T	dark red		

Mfgs. Code	Description	Base Cost	Sgstd. List
	BUICK		
83T	medium sapphire		
85T	dark gray		
95T	taupe		
—	**Trim, Interior**		
19	bucket - cloth	STD	STD
99	leather & suede	468	550
98	bucket seats, 14-way adjustable driver - leather & suede	761	895
PH6	**Styled Aluminum Wheels** — 15" (4)	47	55
WDV	**Warranty Enhancement** — New York State (required in New York)	55	65
Y56	**Gran Touring Package** — includes Gran Touring Suspension, 2:97 axle ratio, 15" aluminum wheels, leather wrapped sport steering wheel and shift handle, fast ratio power steering, and P215/65R15 steel belted radial ply blackwall Eagle GT +4 tires	88	104
R1V	**Riviera Appearance Package** — includes platinum beige firemist lower accent paint, body side stripe, and painted aluminum wheels (4)	174	205
SD	**Luxury Package** — includes 6-way power passenger seat adjuster and electric recliner, automatic day/night mirror and twilight sentinel headlamp control	429	505
SE	**Prestige SE Package** — includes power trunk pull-down, heated left outside mirror, remote keyless entry and automatic electric door locks and theft deterrent system	887	1044

ROADMASTER ESTATE WAGON

ROADMASTER ESTATE WAGON (8 Cylinder)

Code	Description	Base Cost	Sgstd. List
R35	4 Dr 3 Seat Wagon	18507	21445
B90	4 Dr CoachBuilder's Wagon	17213	19945
	Destination Charge: All Models	535	535

STANDARD EQUIPMENT:

ROADMASTER ESTATE WAGON: Acoustical package, air conditioner, fixed-mast antenna, third-seat assist handles, heavy-duty battery, power front disc/rear drum brakes with anti-lock, front bumper guards, front bumper protective strips, dual function convenience net, front, rear and load area carpeting, front, side-window defoggers, door-edge guards, remote tailgate door lock releases, electronic warning tone (seatbelts, ignition key, turn signal and "headlamps on"), 5.0L V8 engine with electronic fuel injection, soft-ray tinted glass, lockable glove box, composite tungsten-halogen headlamps, 4-way headrests, dual horns, instrumentation (gauge cluster includes oil, coolant temperature, volts, trip odometer, and tachometer), rear roof rail lights with integral reading lights, integral luggage rack with vista roof, inside day/night mirror, cloth covered driver and passenger vanity mirrors, mirrors (deluxe body-color, outside, rearview (left remote, right manual), protective body-side moldings, wheel opening moldings, ETR AM/FM stereo radio with seek and scan and clock, manual driver and passenger recliners, seat (second, fold-down seatback), seat (third, rear-facing vinyl), 55/45 cloth seats with armrest, "active" front safety system seatbelts, rear-seat shoulder belts, speakers (dual front standard range, dual extended range rear), power steering, tilt steering column, deluxe steering wheel with air bag, front and rear door lower built-in storage compartments, lockable hidden storage compartments, front seatback storage pockets, instrument panel pull-out storage tray with two cupholders, heavy-duty suspension, two-way manual tailgate, compact spare tire, P225/75R15 steel-belted, radial-ply, all-season whitewall tires, automatic electronically controlled transmission with overdrive, vista tinted glass roof, four 15" aluminum wheels, power windows with driver's "express down", 2-speed wipers with low-speed delay, rear window wipers with washer, woodgrain vinyl applique (delete option available).

Mfgs. Code	Description	Base Cost	Sgstd. List

BUICK

ACCESSORIES

L03	**Engine** — 5.0 litre (305 CID) V8 with TBI	STD	STD
MX0	**Transmission** — automatic with overdrive	STD	STD
YF5	**California Assembly Line Emission Equipment and Testing** — (required in California)	85	100
C49	**Rear Window Defogger** — includes heated o/s mirrors with SE Pkg - Estate & SA/SC/SD	136	160
	- Estate & SE	166	195
—	**Radio Equipment**		
U1A	compact disc, graphic equalizer, & AM stereo radio & premium speakers - Estate & SC/SD/SE	365	429
UX1	radio - graphic equalizer, cassette tape & ETR AM stereo - FM stereo with seek & scan, auto reverse with search/repeat clock, & premium speakers (*receive C-Quam Broadcasts) - Estate & SC/SD/SE	157	185
AG1	**6-Way Power Driver's Seat** — Coachbuilder's	247	290
6Y2	**Delete Third Seat** — Estate	(183)	(215)
V92	**Trailer Towing Package** — consists of 3.23 axle ratio, heavy duty engine and transmission cooling, automatic level control & engine oil cooler - Estate	276	325
—	**Trim**		
16	cloth 55/45 with armrest - Estate	STD	STD
96	leather/vinyl 55/45 - Estate	417	490
G80	**Limited Slip Differential** — (V92 required) - Estate	85	100
N91	**Wheel Covers** — custom locking wire - Estate	NC	NC
WB4	**Woodgrain Delete** — Estate	(234)	(275)
WDV	**Warranty Enhancement — New York State** — (req'd in New York)	55	65
SA	**SA Package** — includes cornering lights; cruise control, electronic; door locks, electric; lamps, front door courtesy & warning; electric dual remote control mirrors; automatic power antenna; full size spare tire; trailer towing package; locking wire wheel covers; woodgrain delete	651	766
SB	**Popular Package** —	NC	NC
SC	**Premium Package** — includes armrest, front seat storage; carpet savers, front & rear; cruise control, electronic; door locks, electric; power antenna, automatic; cassette tape player	697	820
SD	**Luxury Package** — includes SC Premium Pkg equipment plus air conditioner, electronic touch climate control; lamps, front door courtesy & warning; mirror, lighted visor vanity - right; mirror, lighted visor vanity - left; mirror, rear view with reading lights & compass; 6-way power seat, driver's side; security cover, rear storage area	1326	1560
SE	**Prestige Package** — includes SD Luxury Pkg equipment plus cornering lamps; twilight sentinel headlamp control; electric dual remote control mirrors; 6-way power passenger seat; remote keyless entry	1846	2172

SKYLARK

SKYLARK (4 Cylinder)

V69	4 Dr Sedan	9899	10725
V27	2 Dr Coupe	9991	10825

SKYLARK CUSTOM (4 Cylinder)

C69	4 Dr Sedan	10734	12020
J27	2 Dr Coupe	10734	12020

SKYLARK LUXURY EDITION (4 Cylinder)

D69	4 Dr Sedan	12381	13865

Mfgs. Code	Description	Base Cost	Sgstd. List

BUICK

SKYLARK GRAN SPORT (4 Cylinder)

M27	2 Dr Coupe	12203	13665
	Destination Charge: All Models	455	455

STANDARD EQUIPMENT:

SKYLARK: Fixed-mast antenna, front and rear console mounted ashtray, Delco Freedom II Plus battery, power front disc/rear drum brakes, body-color front and rear bumper protective strips, body-color bumpers, carpeting, front-wheel drive, electronic warning tone (seatbelts, ignition key, "headlamps on", turn signal), 2.5 liter Tech IV engine with EFI, soft-ray tinted glass, lockable glove box tray, composite tungsten-halogen headlamps, rear-seat ventilation heat ducts, dual horns, analog cluster instrumentation with trip odometer, lights (ashtray, glove compartment, engine compartment, instrument panel courtesy, trunk compartment), driver's sunvisor with map strap, belt reveal and roof drip moldings, clearcoat Plastisol protection paint, ETR AM/FM stereo radio with seek and scan, dual speakers and clock, automatic front safety system seatbelts, cloth split bench seats, power rack and pinion steering, DynaRide suspension, front, independent MacPherson strut suspension, compact spare tire, P185/75R14 steel-belted, radial-ply all-season blackwall tires, automatic transmission, deluxe 14" wheelcovers, roll-down rear windows (Sedan). **Skylark Custom also has in addition to above standard equipment:** Front and rear seat center armrests, dome light, front and rear courtesy lights, visor vanity passenger mirror, narrow rocker panel moldings, trunk trim, remote fuel filler door release.

ACCESSORIES

Mfgs. Code	Description	Base Cost	Sgstd. List
—	**Engines**		
LG8	2.5 litre (151 CID) EFI L4	STD	STD
LD2	2.3 litre (138 CID) DOHC QUAD 4	561	660
LG7	3.3 litre (204 CID) MFI V6	604	710
WDV	**Warranty Enhancement — New York State —** (req'd in New York)	55	65
MX1	**Automatic Transmission**	STD	STD
C67	**Air Conditioning —** (included SB/SC/SD/SE) - Skylark, Custom	612	720
JM4	**Anti-Lock Brake System —** (included SE) - Gran Sport	786	925
B37	**Carpet Savers, Front & Rear —** Skylark, Custom	38	45
K34	**Cruise Control, Electronic —** Skylark (included SE)	179	210
C49	**Defogger, Rear Window —** Skylark	136	160
C47	**Delete Defogger (from package) —** all except Skylark	(136)	(160)
AU3	**Door Locks, Electric —** (2 door) - Skylark, Custom	162	190
	- (4 door) Skylark, Custom	196	230
YF5	**California Emissions —** (required in California)	85	100
K05	**Heater, Engine Block —**	15	18
V58	**Luggage Rack, Deck Lid (Chrome) —** Custom, Luxury	98	115
D35	**Mirrors, Dual —** left remote, right manual - Skylark & SA/SB	45	53
D89	**Paint —** lower accent - Custom	166	195
—	**Radio Equipment**		
UM6	cassette tape player - Skylark	119	140
	- Custom & SA/SB/SC	119	140
—	**Stripes, Body Side —** Custom, Gran Sport	38	45
18A	light gray		
21A	dark blue		
40A	white		
41A	black		
55A	gold		
66A	dark auburn		
75A	red		
85A	gray		

Mfgs. Code	Description **BUICK**	Base Cost	Sgstd. List
—	**Tires** — (steel belted radials)		
QFF	P185/75R14 whitewall (STD on Luxury) - Skylark & Custom	58	68
—	**Trims**		
	Skylark		
13	cloth bench - Skylark Sedan	STD	STD
13	cloth split bench with recliners - Skylark Coupe	STD	STD
	Custom		
18	cloth split bench with recliners - Custom	STD	STD
59	cloth bucket seats with full length operating console - Custom	179	210
	Luxury Sedan		
18	cloth split bench with recliners - Luxury Secan	STD	STD
59	cloth bucket seats with full length operating console - Luxury Sedan	179	210
	Gran Sport Coupe		
59	cloth bucket seats with full length operating console - Gran Sport Coupe	STD	STD
—	**Wheels & Wheelcovers**		
N91	locking wire wheel covers - Custom & SA/SB/SC	150	177
	- Luxury Sedan	STD	STD
PD8	**Styled Aluminum Wheels (4)** — includes P195/70R14 touring B/W tires except on Gran Sport - Custom & SA/SB/SC	294	346
	- Custom & SD/SE/SF	144	169
	- Gran Sport	NC	NC
PC4	**Styled Hubcap & Trim Ring** — Skylark	32	38
A31	**Windows, Power** — with express down driver's (2 Door) - Skylark, Custom	217	255
	- (4 Door) - Skylark, Custom	272	320
CD4	**Windshield Wipers With Delay Feature** — Skylark, Custom	47	55
Y56	**Gran Touring Package** — includes styled aluminum wheels (4) and P215/60R14 blackwall tires, Gran Touring Suspension and leather - wrapped sport steering wheel - Custom & SA/SB/SC	480	565
	- Custom & SD/SE/SF	330	388
SA	**SA Package** — represents individual model w/standard equipment (see listings)		
SB	**Skylark Sedan Popular Package** — includes air conditioner; rocker panel moldings; protective body side moldings; wheel opening moldings	728	856
SC	**Skylark Sedan Premium Package** — includes SB Skylark Sedan Popular Pkg equipment plus dual mirrors, left remote & right manual; tilt steering column	887	1044
SD	**Skylark Sedan Luxury Package** — includes SC Skylark Sedan Premium Pkg equipment plus front seat armrest; remote fuel filler door release; seat back recliners; trunk trim, deluxe; visor vanity mirror (passenger)	1058	1245
SE	**Skylark Sedan Prestige Package** — includes SD Skylark Sedan Luxury Pkg plus electronic cruise control; electric door locks; power windows (express down driver); delay feature windshield wipers	1751	2060
SB	**Skylark Coupe Popular Package** — includes air conditioner; rocker panel moldings; protective body side moldings; wheel opening moldings	728	856
SC	**Skylark Coupe Premium Package** — includes SB Skylark Coupe Popular Pkg equipment plus dual mirrors, left remote & right manual; tilt steering column	887	1044
SD	**Skylark Coupe Luxury Package** — includes SC Skylark Coupe Premium Pkg equipment plus front seat armrest; remote fuel filler door release; trunk trim, deluxe; visor vanity mirror (passenger)	982	1155
SE	**Skylark Coupe Prestige Package** — includes SD Skylark Coupe Luxury Pkg equipment plus electronic cruise control; electric door locks; power windows (express down driver); delay feature windshield wipers	1585	1865
SB	**Skylark Custom Sedan Popular Package** — includes air conditioner; electric rear window defogger; protective body side moldings; wheel opening moldings; dual mirrors, left remote & right manual; tilt steering column	1001	1178

Mfgs. Code	Description **BUICK**	Base Cost	Sgstd. List
SC	**Skylark Custom Sedan Premium Package** — includes SB Skylark Custom Sedan Popular Pkg equipment plus electronic cruise control and delay feature windshield wipers	1227	1443
SD	**Skylark Custom Sedan Luxury Package** — includes SC Skylark Custom Sedan Premium Pkg equipment plus cassette tape player; seat adjuster, 4-way manual (driver); locking wire wheel covers	1526	1795
SE	**Skylark Custom Sedan Prestige Package** — includes SD Skylark Custom Sedan Luxury Pkg equipment plus electric door locks and power windows	1993	2345
SF	**Skylark Custom Sedan Elite Package** — includes SE Skylark Custom Sedan Prestige Pkg equipment plus reading lights, mirror mounted; lights, rear door rail courtesy; wide rocker panel molding; automatic power antenna; 6-way power seat, driver; electric remote trunk lock release; lighted visor vanity mirror (passenger)	2428	2857
SB	**Skylark Custom Coupe Popular Package** — includes air conditioner; electric rear window defogger; protective body side moldings; wheel opening moldings; dual mirrors, left remote & right manual, tilt steering column	1001	1178
SC	**Skylark Custom Coupe Premium Package** — includes SB Skylark Custom Coupe Popular Pkg equipment plus electronic cruise control and delay feature windshield wipers	1227	1443
SD	**Skylark Custom Coupe Luxury Package** — includes SC Skylark Custom Coupe Premium Pkg equipment plus cassette tape player; seat adjuster, 4-way manual (driver); locking wire wheel covers	1526	1795
SE	**Skylark Custom Coupe Prestige Package** — includes SD Skylark Custom Coupe Luxury Pkg equipment plus electric door locks and power windows	1904	2240
SF	**Skylark Custom Coupe Elite Package** — includes SE Skylark Custom Coupe Prestige Pkg equipment plus reading lights, mirror mounted; lights, rear door rail courtesy; wide rocker panel molding; automatic power antenna; 6-way power seat, driver; electric remote trunk lock release; lighted visor vanity mirror (passenger)	2339	2752
SB	**Skylark Luxury Sedan Popular Package** — includes air conditioner; electric rear window defogger; tilt steering column	863	1015
SC	**Skylark Luxury Sedan Premium Package** — includes SB Skylark Luxury Sedan Popular Pkg equipment plus electronic cruise control; delay feature windshield wipers; cassette tape player; seat adjuster, 4-way manual (driver); carpet savers, front & rear	275	1500
SD	**Skylark Luxury Sedan Luxury Package** — includes SC Skylark LuxurySedan Premium Pkg equipment plus electric door locks and power windows	1743	2050
SE	**Skylark Luxury Sedan Prestige Package** — includes SD Skylark Luxury Sedan Luxury Pkg equipment plus reading lights, mirror mounted; lights, rear door rail courtesy; automatic power antenna; 6-way power seat, driver; electric remote trunk lock release; lighted visor vanity mirror (passenger)	2135	2512
SB	**Skylark Gran Sport Coupe Popular Package** — includes air conditioning; electric rear window defogger and tilt steering column	863	1015
SC	**Skylark Gran Sport Coupe Premium Package** — includes SB Skylark Gran Sport Coupe Popular Pkg equipment plus electronic cruise control; delay feature windshield wipers; seat adjuster, 4-way manual (driver); carpet savers, front & rear	1156	1360
SD	**Skylark Gran Sport Coupe Luxury Package** — includes SC Skylark Gran Sport Coupe Premium Pkg equipment plus electric door locks; power windows (express down driver); automatic power antenna; 6-way power seat adjuster driver	1815	2135
SE	**Skylark Gran Sport Coupe Prestige Package** — includes SD Skylark Gran		

		Base Cost	Sgstd. List
	Sport Coupe Luxury Pkg equipment plus anti-lock brake system and 2.3 liter quad L4 DOHC MI engine	3162	3720

1991 cadillac

CADILLAC

Mfgs. Code	Description	Base Cost	Sgstd. List
DE VILLE (8 Cylinder)			
6CD47 J	Coupe De Ville	25765	30205
6CD69 B	Sedan De Ville	25978	30455
FLEETWOOD (8 Cylinder)			
6CB47 W	Coupe	29595	34695
6CB69 P	Sedan	29808	34945
6CG69 N	Sixty Special	32708	38345
ELDORADO (8 Cylinder)			
6EL57 H	Coupe	26652	31245
SEVILLE (8 Cylinder)			
6KS69 M	Sedan	28947	33935
6KY69 G	Touring Sedan	31676	37135
BROUGHAM (8 Cylinder)			
6DW69 L	Sedan	25782	30225
6DW69 L	Sedan w/5.7 liter engine (includes gas guzzler tax of $650)	26432	30875
ALLANTE (8 Cylinder)			
6VR67 V	Convertible Hardtop (includes gas guzzler tax of $650	52512	61450
6VS67 F	Convertible (includes gas guzzler tax of $650)	47778	55900
Destination Charge:	All models except Allante-no charge on the Allante	580	580

STANDARD EQUIPMENT:

DEVILLE-COUPE & SEDAN: Side and decklid accent striping, power antenna, anti-lock braking system, flip-open storage-type armrest (center front seat), center rear seat armrest, overhead assist handles, audible reminders for headlights on, key in ignition, seatbelts; front power disc brakes, front bumber guards, accent-colored rear bumber rub strips, cigarette lighters (one front and two rear), electronic climate control with outlets and outside temperature display, digital display clock in radio, on-board computer diagnostics, controlled cycle wiper system, cruise control, front side window defogger including heated outside mirrors, door edge guards, power door locks, electronic level control, 4.9L V8 sequential port fuel injection engine, engine oil life indicator, stainless steel exhaust system, front-wheel drive, fuel data center, digital fuel gauge, garage door opener retainer, gold key delivery system, adjustable front seat headrests, integral rear seat headrests (Sedan), front and rear lamp monitors, front cornering lamps, tungsten halogen composite headlamps, interior lights (including underhood, glove compartment, front ash receivers, sunshade support, door courtesy and warning, sail panel courtesy, luggage compartment), low brake fluid warning indicator, low fuel warning indicator, low windshield washer fluid level indicator, visor vanity mirrors (driver and passenger), electrically powered mirrors (integrally mounted right and left outside rearview - car color), moldings (including lower accent color and wheel openings), rear package shelf with storage compartment (Sedan), clearcoat paint, automatic parking brake release, PASS-key system, front seatback pockets, AM/FM stereo radio (signal seeking and scanner with digital display, cassette player and 5-band graphic equalizer-ETR), manual recliners (driver and passenger seats), retained accessory power, 6-way power seat adjuster (driver seat), front dual comfort 44/55 seats (three passenger), solar-control tinted glass, compact high-pressure type laydown spare tire, spare tire cover, power assisted rack and pinion steering, leather-trimmed tilt steering wheel, supplemental inflatable restraint system (driver side), independent four-wheel suspension, steel-belted all-season radial whitewall tires (P205/70R15), 4-speed automatic transmission with overdrive, power trunk release lid, twilight sentinel, padded dual sun visors with extensions, cast aluminum wheels, electrically powered windows.

FLEETWOOD - COUPE & SEDAN: Side and decklid accent striping, power antenna, anti-lock braking system, flip-open storage type armrest (center front seat), center rear seat armrest, overhead assist handles, audible reminders for headlights on, key in ignition, seatbelts; power front disc brakes, front bumper guards, accent-colored rear bumper rub strips, cigarette lighters (one front and two rear), electronic climate control with outside temperature display, digital display clock (in radio), computer command ride system, on-board computer diagnostics, controlled cycle wiper system, cruise control, front side window defoggers, rear window defogger (including heated outside mirrors), door edge guards, electrically powered door locks, electronic level control, 4.9L V8 sequential port fuel injection engine, engine oil life indicator, stainless steel exhaust system, fender skirts, front and rear carpeted floor mats, front-wheel drive, fuel data center, remote release fuel filler door, digital fuel gauge, garage door opener retainer, gold key delivery system, adjustable front seat headrests, integral rear seat headrests (Sedan), illuminated entry system, digital instrument cluster (speedometer and odometer), front and rear lamp monitors, exterior lights (including front cornering and tungsten halogen composite headlamps), interior lights (including underhood, glove compartment, front ash receiver, sunshade support, door courtesy and warning, rear reading, sail panel courtesy, luggage compartment), low brake fluid warning indicator, low fuel warning indicator, low windshield washer fluid level indicator, carpeted luggage compartment, automatic day/night electrochromic mirror, driver and passenger illuminated visor vanity mirrors, overhead illuminated vanity mirrors in rear compartment (Sedan - except with astroroof option), electrically powered right and left outside rearview mirrors (car color), moldings (including lower accent color and wheel openings), opera lamps (Coupe), rear package shelf with storage compartment (Sedan), clearcoat paint, automatic parking brake release, PASS-key system, front seatback pockets, AM/FM stereo radio (signal seeking and scanner with digital display, cassette player and 5-speed graphic equalizer (ETR), manual reclining driver and passenger seats, retained accessory power, formal Cabriolet roof (Coupe), fully padded vinyl roof (Sedan), 6-way power seat adjusters (driver and passenger seats), front dual comfort 45/55 seats (three passenger), solar-control tinted glass, laydown compact high-pressure type spare tire, spare tire cover, power assisted rack and pinion steering, leather-trimmed tilt steering wheel, supplemental inflatable restraint system (driver side), independent four-wheel suspension, steel-belted all-season radial whitewall tires (P205/70R15), 4-speed automatic transmission with overdrive, power trunk lid release and pull-down, trunk mat, twilight sentinel, padded dual sun visors with extensions, cast aluminum wheels, electrically powered windows.

FLEETWOOD SIXTY SPECIAL: Side and decklid accent striping, power antenna, anti-lock braking system, flip-open storage-type armrest (center front seat), center rear seat armrest, overhead assist handles, audible reminders for headlights on, key in ignition, seatbelts; power front disc brakes, front bumper guards, accent-colored rear bumper rub strips, cigarette lighters (one front and two rear), electronic climate control with outside temperature display, digital display clock (in radio), computer command ride system, on-board computer diagnostics, controlled cycle wiper system, cruise control, front side window defogger, rear window defogger (including heated outside mirrors), door edge guards, electrically powered door locks, electronic level control, 4.9L V8 sequential port fuel injection engine, engine oil life indicator, stainless steel exhaust system, fender skirts, carpeted front and rear floor mats, front-wheel drive, fuel data center, remote control fuel filler door, digital fuel gauge, garage door opener retainer, gold key delivery system, adjustable power headrests (front seats), integral rear seat headrests, heated front seats, illuminated entry system, digital instrument cluster (speedometer and odometer), front and rear lamp monitors, ultrasoft leather seating areas, exterior lights (including front cornering and tungsten halogen composite headlamps), interior lights (including underhood, glove compartment, front ash receiver, sunshade support, door courtesy and warning, rear reading, sail panel courtesy, luggage compartment), low brake fluid warning indicator, low fuel warning indicator, low windshield wiper fluid level indicator, power lumbar supports (driver and passenger seats), two-seating position memory seat, electrochromic automatic day/night mirror, driver and passenger illuminated visor vanity mirrors, overhead rear compartment illuminated vanity mirrors (except with astroroof option), electrically powered integrally mounted right and left outside rearview mirrors (car color), moldings (including lower accent color and wheel openings), rear package shelf with storage compartment, clearcoat paint, automatic parking brake release, PASS-key system, front seatback pockets, AM/FM stereo radio (signal seeking and scanner with digital display, cassette player and 5-band graphic equalizer), driver and passenger seat power recliners, retained accessory power, full padded vinyl roof, 6-way power seat adjusters (driver and passenger seats), front, unique split-frame dual comfort 45/55 seats (three passenger), power side bolsters (driver and passenger seats), solar-control tinted glass, compact high-pressure type laydown spare tire, spare tire cover, power-assisted rack and pinion steering, leather-trimmed tilt steering wheel, supplemental inflatable restraint system (driver side), independent four-wheel suspension, power thigh supports (driver and passenger seats), steel-belted all-season radial whitewall (P205/70R15) tires, automatic 4-speed transmission with overdrive, power trunk lid release and pull-down, trunk mat, twilight sentinel, padded dual sun visors with extensions, cast aluminum wheels, electrically powered windows.

ELDORADO: Accent molding, side accent striping, power antenna, anti-lock braking system, center front and rear seat armrests, overhead assist handles, audible reminders for headlights on, key in ignition, seatbelts; four-wheel disc power brakes, front and integral rear bumper guards, front and rear bumper rub strips, cigarette lighters (one front and two rear), electronic climate control, computer command ride system, on-board computer diagnostics, front floor console, controlled cycle wiper system, cruise control, front side window defogger, rear window defogger including heated outside mirrors, door edge guards, electrically powered door locks, driver information center, electronic level control, 4.9L V8 sequential port fuel injection engine, engine oil life indicator, front and rear carpeted floor mats, front-wheel drive, remote release fuel filler door, digital fuel gauge, garage door opener retainer, gold key delivery system, adjustable front seat headrests, illuminated entry system, electronic instrument cluster, front and rear lamp monitors, exterior lights (including tungsten halogen front cornering and tungsten halogen composite headlamps), interior lights (including underhood, glove compartment, front ash receiver, instrument panel courtesy, overhead dual map, door courtesy and warning, rear reading, sail panel courtesy, luggage compartment), low brake fluid warning indicator, low windshield washer fluid level indicator, driver and passenger illuminated visor vanity mirrors, electrically powered right and left outside rearview mirrors (car color), moldings (including lower body side, rocker panel, wheel openings), clearcoat paint, automatic parking brake release, PASS-key system, AM/FM stereo radio with signal seeking and scanner with digital display, cassette player and 5-band graphic equalizer (ETR), driver and passenger manual reclining seats, retained accessory power, 6-way power seat adjusters (driver and passenger seats), cloth and leather combination seating areas, front bucket (two passenger), seats, soft ray tinted glass, compact high-pressure type spare tire, spare tire cover, power-assisted rack and pinion steering, leather-trimmed tilt steering wheel, supplemental inflatabe restraint system (driver side), independent four-wheel suspension, steel-belted all-season whitewall tires (P205/70R15), automatic 4 speed transmission with overdrive, power trunk lid release and pull-down, trunk mat, twilight sentinel, padded dual sun visors with extensions, cast aluminum wheels (Snowflake), electrically powered windows with driver side express-down feature.

SEVILLE & SEVILLE TOURING SEDAN (STS): Side and decklid accent striping (Seville), power antenna, anti-lock braking system, genuine Birdseye Maple Wood appliques (Seville), genuine Elm Burl Wood appliques (STS), center front and rear seat armrests, front and rear door armrests, overhead assist handles, audible reminders for headlights on/key in ignition/seatbelts; four-wheel disc power brakes, front and integral rear bumper guards, front and rear bumper rub strips, front and two-rear cigarette lighters, electronic climate control, computer command ride system, cruise control, front side window defoggers, rear window defogger (including heated outside mirrors), door edge guards (Seville), electrically powered door locks, automatic door locks system (STS), central door unlocking system (STS), remote keyless entry system (STS), door pull straps, driver information center, electronic level control, 4.9L V8 sequential port fuel injection engine, engine oil life indicator, dual exhaust outlet (STS), carpeted front and rear floor mats, front wheel drive, remote release fuel filler door, digital fuel gauge, garage door opener retainer, gold key delivery system, adjustable front seat headrests, integral rear seat headrests (STS), illuminated entry system, electronic instrument cluster, front lamp monitors (Seville), rear lamp monitors, ultrasoft leather seating areas (STS), exterior lights (including tungsten halogen front cornering and tungsten halogen composite headlamps), interior lights (including underhood, glove compartment, front ash receiver, instrument panel courtesy, overhead dual map, door courtesy and warning, rear reading, sail panel courtesy, luggage compartment), low brake fluid level indicator, low windshield washer fluid level indicator, power lumbar supports for driver and passenger seats, illuminated visor vanity mirrors (driver and passenger), electrically powered right and left outside rearview mirrors (car color), moldings (including lower body side, rocker panel, wheel openings), clearcoat paint, automatic parking brake release, PASS-key system, front seatback pockets, AM/FM stereo radio (signal seeking and scanner with digital display, cassette player and 5-band equalizer), power reclining driver and passenger seats, retained accessory power, 6-way power seat adjusters (driver and passenger seats), cloth and leather combination seating areas (Seville), front bucket two passenger seats, soft ray tinted glass, compact high-pressure type spare tire, spare tire cover, power assisted rack and pinion steering, leather-trimmed tilt steering wheel, driver side supplemental inflatable restraint system, independent four-wheel suspension, theft-deterrent system (STS), Goodyear Eagle GT & 4 Blackwall P215/60R16 tires (STS), steel-belted all-season radial whitewall P205/70R15 tires (Seville), touring suspension (STS), automatic 4 speed transmission with overdrive, power trunk lid release and pull-down, trunk mat, twilight sentinel, padded dual sun visors with extensions, cast aluminum lace wheels (Seville), diamond finish forged aluminum 16" wheels (STS), electrically powered windows with driver side express-down feature.

BROUGHAM: Accent molding, side and decklid accent striping, power antenna, anti-lock braking system, flip open storage-type armrest (center front seat), center rear seat armrest, assist handles on front seatbacks, audible reminders for headlights on/key in ignition/seatbelts, power front disc brakes, front bumper guards, front and rear bumper rub strips, front cigarette lighter, two rear cigarette lighters, electronic climate control with outside temperature display, digital display clock in radio, controlled cycle wiper system, cruise control, rear window defogger (including heated outside mirrors), door edge guards, electrically powered door locks, door pull swing handles, electronic level control, 5.0L V8 throttle body injection engine, carpeted front and rear floor mats, electronic fuel gauge, garage door opener retainer, gold key delivery system, adjustable front seat headrests, illuminated entry system, digital instrument cluster, front and rear lamp monitors, (including front cornering lights), tungsten halogen composite headlamps, interior lights (including underhood, glove compartment, sunshade support, door courtesy and warning, rear sail panel reading, luggage compartment), low fuel warning indicator, passenger visor vanity mirror, electrically powered mirrors (left and right outside rearview-chrome), moldings (including lower accent color, belt, wheel openings), opera lamps, clearcoat paint, automatic parking brake release, front seatback pockets, AM/FM stereo radio with signal seeking, digital clock/scanner display, cassette player and preset graphic equalizer (ETR), power reclining driver and passenger seats, formal full padded vinyl roof, automatic driver and right front passenger safety belts, 6-way power adjusters for driver and passenger seats, front dual comfort 55/45 (three passenger) seats, soft ray tinted glass, compact high-pressure type spare tire, spare tire cover, electronic variable power steering, leather-trimmed tilt and telescope steering wheel, Uniroyal Royal Seal puncture sealing whitewall tires (P225/75R15), 4-speed automatic transmission with overdrive, power trunk lid release, trunk mat, wheel discs, electrically powered windows.

ALLANTE - CONVERTIBLE AND CONVERTIBLE HARDTOP: Accent molding, power antenna, anti-lock braking system, leather-trimmed center armrest, audible reminders for headlights on, key in ignition, seatbelts; four-wheel disc power brakes, electronic climate control with outside temperature display, on-board computer diagnostics, center console, cigar lighter, controlled cycle wiper system, cruise control, front side window defogger, electric rear window defogger, electrically powered door locks (central door unlocking system), driver information center, high-output 4.5L V8 sequential port fuel injection engine, engine oil life indicator, carpeted floor mats, front-wheel drive, remote release fuel filler door, gold key delivery system, headlamp washer system, adjustable headrests (vertical and tilt), illuminated entry system, electronic instrument cluster (Convertible Hardtops only), driver side knee bolster, durosoft leather seating areas, tungsten halogen composite headlamps, interior lights (including underhood, footwell, pass-through area, overhead courtesy/map, door courtesy and warning, luggage compartment), power lumbar supports (driver and passenger seats), memory seat with two-seating positions, electrically powered heated mirrors, illuminated visor vanity mirrors (driver and passenger), clearcoat paint, automatic parking brake release, PASS-key system, seatback pockets, AM/FM stereo radio (symphony sound system - Delco - Bose gold series - signal seeking and scanner with digital display, cassette player and compact disc player); power recliners (driver and passenger seats), retained accessory power, folding convertible top with three glass windows, removable aluminum hardtop with three glass windows (Convertible Hardtop only), 6-way power seat adjusters (driver and passenger seats), Recaro bucket seats (two passenger), soft ray tinted glass, compact high-pressure type spare tire, variable-assisted power rack and pinion steering, leather-trimmed tilt steering wheel, supplemental inflatable restraint system (driver side), independent four-wheel suspension with speed-dependent damping system, theft-deterrent system, Goodyear Eagle VL steel-belted radial blackwall tires (P225/55 VR16), traction control, automatic 4-speed transmission with overdrive, power trunk lid release, twilight sentinel, padded dual sun visors, forged aluminum alloy 16" wheels, electrically powered windows with driver and passenger side express-down feature.

ACCESSORIES

Code	Description	Base Cost	Sgstd. List
B20	**Appliques** — Birdseye Maple Wood-H (incl. on YP3 and YP5)	206	245
CF5	**Astroroof** — WPJBLHMGN	1138	1355
YP3	**Biarritz-Eldorado** — H	2671	3180
NB2	**California Emmissions Equipment & Testing** — WPNJBHM (B w/o R1P, H w/o YP5)	84	100
NN5	**California Emissions Label** — BLHGFV (B with R1P, H with YP5)	84	100
V4F	**Coachbuilder Package** — L	(117)	(139)
R1P	**Coachbuilder Package** — B	840	1000
FX3	**Computer Command Ride System** — JB	319	380
V4S	**d'Elegance-Broughman (Cloth)** — L	1514	1802
V4S	**d'Elegance-Broughman (Leather)** — L	1992	2372
YP5	**Eldorado Touring Coupe** — H	1722	2050
L05	**Engine 5.7 Liter V8 TBI** — L (incl. with V4F or V92)	210	250
B94	**Gold Ornamentation Package** — WPNJBLHM	332	395
C50	**Heated Windshield System** — HMG (incl. in V10 on WPNJB)	260	309
FE7	**H.D. Livery Package** — B	840	1000
U02	**Instrument Cluster-Digital** — F (std. on WPNLHMGV)	416	495
UY9	**Instrument Cluster-Analog** — V (std. on F)	NC	NC
YL1	**Leather Seating Area** — L (without V4S)	479	570
YL1	**Leather Seating Area** — WPJB (std. on N)	479	570
YL1	**Leather Seating Area** — M (std. on G)	386	460
YL1	**Leather Seating Area** — H (incl. in YP3 and YP5) (incl. power pass. recliner on H)	466	555
VK3	**License Plate Front Mount Provisions** — FV (std. on WPNJBLHMG)	NC	NC
R1P	**Livery Package** — L	251	299
DD8	**Mirror-Automatic Day/Night** — LHMG (std. on WPN) (incl. on YP5)	83	99
YL2	**Paint-Firemist** — WPNJBLHM (LHM monotone)	202	240
YL2	**Paint-Firemist-Primary** — LHM (primary color firemist)	160	190
YL2	**Paint-Firemist-Secondary** — LHM (lower color firemist)	42	50
YL3	**Paint-Pearl White** — F	588	700
V1F	**Paint-White Diamond** — HM	202	240
D84	**Paint-Two Tone** — M	189	225
D83	**Monotone Lower Accent Color** — WPNJBLH (H with YP3)	NC	NC
—	**Radios** — All radios (including base UUO/UXI) are AM/FM stereo, electronically tuned, digital display with signal seeking & scanner, cassette tape player, and graphic equalizer)		
UU8	Delco-Bose sound system - WPNJB	484	576

Mfgs. Code	Description	Base Cost	Sgstd. List
	CADILLAC		
UU2	Delco-Bose sound system - HMG	484	576
1H	radios with compact disc music system - L	333	396
U1B	with Delco-Bose sound system - WPNJB	732	872
U1E	with Delco-Bose sound system - HMG	732	872
—	**Warranty Enhancement** — requ'd in New York State	55	65
CA9	**Roof-Full Padded Vinyl** — H (n/a with YP3 or YP5)	920	1095
CB4	**Roof-Formal Cabriolet** — J (std. on W)	693	825
CB5	**Roof-Full Padded Vinyl** — B (std. on PNL)	693	825
CF8	**Roof-Full Cabriolet Roof** — JH (n/a with CF5/YP3/YP5)	920	1095
C27	**Phaeton Roof** — M (n/a with CF5)	1004	1195
T2G	**Phaeton Roof** — B (n/a with CF5)	920	1095
CA2	**Vinyl Roof Delete** — PN	NC	NC
QNR	**Tire Option** — whitewall P215/65R15 - HM (with FE2)	64	76
FE2	**Touring Suspension** — HM (incl. in YP5, std. on G)	130	155
V92	**Trailer Towing Package** — L (incl. L05)	461	549
N91	**Wheel Discs** — wire locking - JBHM (incl. in YP3)	197	235
N91	**Wheel Discs** — wire locking - WPN	NC	NC
N91	**Wheel Discs** — wire locking - L	374	445
PH6	**Cast Aluminum Snowflake Wheels** — M (incl. with FE2, std. on H)	NC	NC
PW8	**Cast Aluminum Wheels** — H	97	115
PH3	**Cast Aluminum Lace Wheels** — JB (std. on M, n/c on WPN)	197	235
PH8	**Wire Wheels** — L	840	1000
1SB	**Deville Option Pkg B** — includes front and rear carpeted floor mats, 6-way power passenger seat adjuster	269	320
1SC	**Deville Option Pkg C** — includes items in Deville Option Pkg B plus driver and passenger illuminated vanity mirrors, power trunk lid pull down and trunk mat	492	586
1SD	**Deville Option Pkg D** — includes items in Deville Option Pkg C plus remote release, fuel filler door, digital instrument cluster, electrochromic automatic day/night mirror and trumpet horn	878	1045
V4R	**Deville Security Pkg** — includes illuminated entry system, remote keyless entry and theft deterrent system	323	385
V10	**Deville Cold Weather Pkg** — includes engine block heater and heated windshield system	310	369
V4R	**Fleetwood Security Pkg** — includes remote keyless entry and theft deterrent system	248	295
V10	**Fleetwood Cold Weather Pkg** — includes engine block heater and heated windshield system	310	369
V4H	**Fleetwood Custom Seating Pkg** — includes driver memory seat and driver and passenger power recliners	357	425
1SB	**Brougham Option Pkg B** — includes driver and passenger illuminated vanity mirrors, power trunk lid pull down and twilight sentinel	273	325
1SC	**Brougham Option Pkg C** — includes items in Broughman Option Pkg B (except with V4S) plus remote release fuel filler door and theft deterrent system	575	685
1SC	**Brougham Option Pkg C (d'Elegance)** — includes remote release fuel filler door (with V4S) and theft deterrent system	302	360
	Eldorado & Seville Security Pkg — includes automatic door locks, central door unlocking system, remote keyless entry system, and theft deterrent system	403	480

1991 chevrolet

BERETTA

		Base Cost	Sgstd. List
BERETTA (4 Cylinder)			
1LV37	2 Dr Coupe	9256	10365
1LZ37	2 Dr GTZ Coupe	12993	14550
BERETTA (6 Cylinder)			
1LW37	2 Dr GT Coupe	11743	13150
Destination Charge:	All models	455	455

STANDARD EQUIPMENT:
BERETTA: 2.2 liter, 4 cylinder engine with electronic fuel injection (Base Coupe), 3.1 liter V6 engine with multi-port fuel injection (GT), 2.3 liter high-output quad 4 engine with multi-port fuel injection (GTZ), 5-speed manual transmission with overdrive, composite halogen headlamps, dual sport mirrors (LH and RH remote), body-color body side moldings and bumper facia rub strips, tinted glass, full console (GT,GTZ), 60/40 split-folding rear seat with armrest (GT, GTZ), radio (AM/FM stereo with seek-scan, digital clock and ERS™), air conditioning (GT, GTZ), driver's side supplemental inflatable restraint system (air bag), tachometer(GT, GTZ), gauge package (GT, GTZ), instrument panel courtesy lamps, P185/75R14 tires (Base Coupe with 4-cylinder engine), P20560R15 tires (GT), P205/55R16 performance radial tires (GTZ), 14" styled steel wheels (Base Coupe with 6-cylinder engine), 15" aluminum-laced wheels (GT), 16" cast aluminum wheels (GTZ), level I sport suspension (Base Coupe), level III sport suspension (GT), level IV sport suspension (GTZ), Scotchgard™ fabric protector, stainless steel exhaust system, power front disc/rear drum brakes, power rack and pinion steering, gloss black remote sport mirrors (Base Coupe), body color remote sport mirrors (GT), leather-wrapped sport steering wheel (GTZ).

ACCESSORIES

Code	Description	Base Cost	Sgstd. List
—	**Beretta Base Equipment Group** — (included with model)		
UM6	- with UM6 radio, add	119	140
U1C	- with U1C radio, add	337	396
UL5	- with UL5 radio delete; deduct	(140)	(165)
—	**Beretta Preferred Equipment Group 1** — includes intermittent windshield wiper system; floor covering - carpeted mats, front and rear, color-keyed; rear view mirrors with reading lamps; visor mirrors with sunshade extensions	111	131
UM6	- with UM6 radio, add	119	140
U1C	- with U1C radio, add	337	396
—	**Beretta Preferred Equipment Group 2** — (includes air conditioning; electronic speed control with resume speed; comfortilt steering wheel; intermittent windshield wiper system; floor covering - carpeted mats, front and rear, color-keyed; rear view mirror with reading lamps; visor mirrors with sunshade extensions)	1068	1256
UM6	- with UM6 radio, add	119	140
U1C	- with U1C radio, add	337	396
—	**Beretta Preferred Equipment Group 3** — (includes air conditioning;electronically tuned AM/FM stereo radio with seek and scan, stereo cassette tape and digital clock - includes extended range sound system; power windows with driver's express down; power door lock		

Mfgs. Code	Description	Base Cost	Sgstd. List
	system; electronic speed control, with resume speed; comfortilt steering wheel; intermittent windshield wiper system; console; power trunk opener; floor covering - carpeted mats, front and rear, color-keyed; rear view mirror with reading lamps; visor mirrors with sunshade extensions)	1658	1951
U1C	- with U1C radio, add	218	256
—	**Beretta GT Base Equipment Group —** (included with model)	NC	NC
UM6	- with UM6 radio, add	119	140
U1C	- with U1C radio, add	337	396
UL5	- with UL5 radio delete; deduct	(140)	(165)
—	**Beretta GT Preferred Equipment Group 1 —** (includes electronic speed control with resume speed; comfortilt steering wheel; intermittent windshield wiper system; floor covering - carpeted mats, front and rear, color-keyed; rear view mirror with reading lamps)	388	456
UM6	- with UM6 radio, add	119	140
U1C	- with U1C radio, add	337	396
—	**Beretta GT Preferred Equipment Group 2 —** (includes electronically tuned AM/FM stereo radio with seek and scan, stereo cassette tape and digital clock - includes extended range sound system; power windows with driver's express down; power door lock system; electronic speed control, with resume speed; comfortilt steering wheel; intermittent windshield wiper system; power trunk opener; floor covering - carpeted mats, front and rear, color-keyed; rear view mirror with reading lamps)	927	1091
U1C	- with U1C radio, add	218	256
—	**Beretta GTZ Base Equipment Group —** (included with model)	NC	NC
UM6	- with UM6 radio, add	119	140
U1C	- with U1C radio, add	337	396
UL5	- with UL5 radio delete; deduct	(140)	(165)
—	**Beretta GTZ Preferred Equipment Group 1 —** (includes electronic speed control with resume speed; comfortilt steering wheel; floor covering - carpeted mats, front and rear, color-keyed)	321	378
UM6	- with UM6 radio, add	119	140
U1C	- with U1C radio, add	337	396
—	**Beretta GTZ Preferred Equipment Group 2 —** (includes electronically tuned AM/FM stereo radio with seek and scan, stereo cassette tape and digital clock - includes extended range sound system; power windows, with driver's express down; power door lock system; electronic speed control with resume speed; comfortilt steering wheel; power trunk opener; floor covering - carpeted mats, front and rear, color-keyed)	861	1013
U1C	- with U1C radio, add	218	256
—	**Interior Trim**		
C2	cloth bucket seats	NC	NC
L2	sport cloth bucket seats - included with GTZ	NC	NC
—	**Exterior Color —** paint, solid	NC	NC
—	**Engines**		
LM3	2.2 liter EFI L4		
LH0	3.1 liter MFI V6 (included with GT) - Base Beretta only	582	685
	- GTZ only	(119)	(140)
LG0	2.3 liter quad 4 (H.O.) MFI - standard on GTZ	NC	NC
C60	**Air Conditioning —** includes increased cooling (included with GT and GTZ)	663	780
VK3	**Bracket, Front License Plate**	NC	NC
V56	**Carrier, Deck Lid —** Black	98	115
D55	**Console —** floor mounted (standard on GT and GTZ)	51	60
C49	**Defogger, Rear Window —** electric	136	160
AU3	**Door Lock System, Power —** electric	162	190
—	**Floor Covering, Mats —** carpeted, color-keyed		
B34	front	15	18

Mfgs. Code	Description	Base Cost	Sgstd. List
B35	rear	13	15
YF5	**California Emission Requirements** — includes all testing equipment and/or certification necessary for registration in the State of California	85	100
NA5	**Standard Emission Equipment**	NC	NC
UB3	**Gauge Package with Tachometer** — includes voltmeter, oil pressure, temperature gauges and trip odometer - Std on GT and GTZ	118	139
DC4	**Mirror, Rear View** — with reading lamps - included with GTZ	20	23
D34	**Mirrors, Visor** — with sunshade extensions (included with GT and GTZ)	17	20
—	**Radio Equipment** — for specific radio pricing, refer to radio information included with each preferred equipment group.		
UM6	electronically tuned AM/FM stereo radio with seek and scan, stereo cassette tape and digital clock (includes extended range sound system)		
U1C	electronically tuned AM stereo/FM stereo radio with seek and scan, compact disc player and digital clock (includes extended range sound system)		
UL5	radio delete		
K34	**Speed Control, Electronic** — with resume speed	179	210
D52	**Spoiler, Rear** — included with GTZ	59	69
N33	**Steering Wheel, Comfortilt**	115	135
AD3	**Sun Roof** — manual, removable	298	350
F41	**Suspension, Sport**	42	49
QME	**Tires** — P195/70R14 all season steel belted radial ply blackwall	79	93
—	**Transmissions**		
MM5	5-speed manual, standard	NC	NC
MX1	automatic	459	540
A90	**Trunk Opener, Power**	43	50
A31	**Windows, Power** — with driver's express down	217	255
CD4	**Windshield Wiper System** — intermittent	47	55
—	**Warranty Enhancement** — req'd in New York State	55	65

CAMARO

Model	Base Cost	Sgstd. List
CAMARO (6 Cylinder)		
1FP87 2 Dr RS Coupe	10877	12180
1FP67 2 Dr RS Convertible	16038	17960
CAMARO (8 Cylinder)		
1FP87/Z28 2 Dr Z28 Coupe	13792	15445
1FP67/Z28 2 Dr Z28 Convertible	18588	20815
Destination Charge: All Models	469	469

STANDARD EQUIPMENT:

CAMARO: 3.1 liter V6 engine with multi-port fuel injection (RS Coupe), 5.0 liter V8 engine with electronic fuel injection (RS Convertible), 5.0 liter V8 engine with tuned-port fuel injection (Z28), 5-speed manual transmission, body-color lower aero panels and facias, halogen headlamps, body-color dual sport mirrors (LH remote), black grille (RS), halogen fog lamps in grille openings (Z28), hood power dome (Z28), tinted glass, power automatic hatch, glass latch closure (Coupes), rear deck spoiler, comfortilt steering wheel, base-coat/clear-coat paint, Scotchgard™ fabric protector, leather-wrapped steering wheel (Z28), integral center console, full floor console with hidden stowage compartment, PASS-Key anti-theft ignition system, radio (AM/FM stereo with seek-scan, digital clock and ERS™), driver's side supplemental inflatable restraint system, full floor carpeting, 15" spoked aluminum wheels with body-color accents (RS), 16" aluminum wheels (Z28), all-season steel belted P215/65R-15 touring tires (RS), all-season steel belted P235/55R-16 performance tires (Z28 Coupe), all-season steel belted P245/50ZR-16 performance tires (Z28 Convertible), power front disc/rear drum brakes, power steering, front and rear stabilizer bars, side window defoggers, auxiliary lighting.

ACCESSORIES

Mfgs. Code	Description	Base Cost	Sgstd. List
—	**RS Coupe Base Equipment Group** — (included with model)	NC	NC
UN6	- with UN6 radio, add	136	160
U1C	- with U1C radio, add	337	396
UL5	- with UL5 radio delete; deduct	(140)	(165)
—	**RS Coupe Preferred Equipment Group 1** — (includes air conditioning; electronically tuned, AM/FM stereo radio with seek and scan, stereo cassette tape with search and repeat and digital clock - includes extended range sound system; bodyside moldings; floor covering - carpeted mats, front and rear, color-keyed)	901	1060
U1C	- with U1C radio, add	201	236
—	**RS Coupe Preferred Equipment Group 2** — (includes air conditioning; electronically tuned, AM/FM stereo radio with seek and scan, stereo cassette tape with search and repeat and digital clock - includes extended range sound system; power windows; power door lock system; electronic speed control with resume speed; power hatch release; rear compartment; cover; bodyside moldings; floor covering - carpeted mats, front and rear, color-keyed; mirror with dual reading lamps)	1570	1847
U1C	- with U1C radio, add	201	236
—	**Z28 Base Equipment Group** — (included with model)	NC	NC
UN6	- with UN6 radio, add	136	160
U1C	- with U1C radio, add	337	396
UL5	- with UL5 radio delete; deduct	(140)	(165)
—	**Z28 Preferred Equipment Group 1** — (includes air conditioning; bodyside moldings; floor covering - carpeted mats, front and rear,color-keyed)	765	900
UN6	- with UN6 radio, add	136	160
U1C	- with U1C radio, add	337	396
—	**Z28 Preferred Equipment Group 2** — (includes air conditioning; electronically tuned AM/FM stereo radio with seek and scan, stereo cassette tape with search and repeat and digital clock - includes extended range sound system; power windows; power door lock system; electronic speed control with resume speed; power hatch release; rear compartment cover; bodyside moldings; floor covering - carpeted mats, front and rear, color-keyed; mirror, with dual reading lamps)	1570	1847
U1C	- with U1C radio, add	201	236
—	**Z28 Preferred Equipment Group 3** — (includes air conditioning; electronically tuned AM/FM stereo radio with seek and scan, stereo cassette tape with search and repeat and digital clock - includes extended range sound system; power windows; power seat driver's side only; power door lock system; electronic speed control with resume speed; power hatch release; electric twin remote sport mirrors; rear compartment cover; bodyside moldings; floor covering -carpeted mats, front and rear, color -keyed; mirror with dual reading lamps)	1894	2228
U1C	- with U1C radio, add	201	236
—	**RS Convertible Base Equipment Group** — (included with model)	NC	NC
UN6	- with UN6 radio, add	136	160
U1C	- with U1C radio, add	337	396
UL5	- with UL5 radio delete, deduct	(140)	(165)
—	**RS Convertible Preferred Equipment Group 1** — (includes air conditioning; electronically tuned AM/FM stereo radio with seek and scan, stereo cassette tape with search and repeat and digital clock -includes extended range sound system; bodyside moldings; floor covering -		

Mfgs. Code	Description	Base Cost	Sgstd. List
	carpeted mats, front and rear, color-keyed)	901	1060
U1C	- with U1C radio, add	201	236
—	**RS Convertible Preferred Equipment Group 2** — includes air conditioning; electronically tuned AM/FM stereo radio with seek and scan, stereo cassette tape with search and repeat and digital clock -includes extended range sound system; power windows; power door lock system; electronic speed control with resume speed; bodyside moldings; floor covering - carpeted mats, front and rear, color-keyed)	1449	1705
U1C	- with U1C radio, add	201	236
—	**Z28 Convertible Base Equipment Group** — included with model	NC	NC
UN6	- with UN6 radio, add	136	160
U1C	- with U1C radio, add	337	396
UL5	- with UL5 radio, delete; deduct	(140)	(165)
—	**Z28 Convertible Preferred Equipment Group 1** — (includes air conditioning; bodyside moldings; floor covering - carpeted mats, front and rear, color-keyed)	765	900
UN6	- with UN6 radio, add	136	160
U1C	- with U1C radio, add	336	396
—	**Z28 Convertible Preferred Equipment Group 2** — (includes air conditioning; electronically tuned AM/FM stereo radio with seek and scan, stereo cassette tape with search and repeat and digital clock -includes extended range sound system; power windows; power door lock system, electronic speed control with resume speed, bodyside moldings; floor covering - carpeted mats, front and rear, color-keyed)	1449	1705
U1C	- with U1C radio, add	201	236
—	**Z28 Convertible Preferred Equipment Group 3** — (includes air conditioning; electronically tuned AM/FM stereo radio with seek and scan, stereo cassette tape with search and repeat and digital clock -includes extended range sound system; power windows; power seat (driver's side only); power door lock system; electronic speed control with resume speed; electric, twin remote sport mirrors; bodyside moldings; floor covering - carpeted mats, front and rear, color-keyed)	1773	2086
U1C	- with U1C radio, add	201	236
—	**Interior Trim**		
C2	cloth bucket seats	NC	NC
F2	custom cloth bucket seats	278	327
A2	custom leather bucket seats	680	800
—	**Exterior Color** — paint, solid	NC	NC
—	**Engines**		
LH0	3.1 liter MFI V6 (std on RS Coupe and Convertible)	NC	NC
LB9	5.0 liter TPI V8 (std on Z28 Coupe and Convertible)	NC	NC
L03	5.0 liter EFI V8	298	350
B2L	5.7 liter TPI V8	255	300
C60	**Air Conditioning** — includes increased cooling	684	805
G92	**Axle, Performance Ratio** — included performance exhaust - without C60 air conditioning	574	675
	- with C60 air conditioning	244	287
VK3	**Bracket, Front License Plate**	NC	NC
C49	**Defogger, Rear Window** — electric	136	160
AU3	**Door Lock System, Power** — electric	162	190
YF5	**California Emission Requirements** — includes all testing, equipment and/or certification necessary for registration in the State of California	85	100
NA5	**Standard Emission Equipment**	NC	NC
A90	**Hatch Release, Power**	43	50
K05	**Heater, Engine Block**	17	20
DE1	**Louvers, Rear Window**	179	210

Mfgs. Code	Description **CHEVROLET**	Base Cost	Sgstd. List
DG7	**Mirrors, Sport, Twin Remote** — electric	77	91
—	**Radio Equipment** — all stereo radios include extended range sound system. For specific radio pricing refer to radio information included with each preferred equipment group.		
UN6	electronically tuned AM/FM stereo radio with seek and scan, stereo cassette tape with search and repeat and digital clock.		
U1C	electronically tuned AM/FM stereo radio with seek and scan, compact disc player and digital clock.		
UL5	radio delete		
CC1	**Roof Panels** — removable glass - includes locks	736	866
—	**Tires**		
QMT	P235/55R16 steel belted radial ply blackwall - standard on Z28 Coupe and Convertible	145	170
QLC	P245/50ZR16 steel belted radial ply blackwall	340	400
—	**Transmissions**		
MM5	5-speed manual, standard on Z28 Coupe and Convertible	(438)	(515)
MX0	automatic w/overdrive, standard on RS Coupe and Convertible	438	515
N96	**Wheels, Aluminum Cast** — 16" (standard on Z28) includes wheel locks	NC	NC
—	**Warranty Enhancement** — req'd in New York State	55	65

CAPRICE, CAPRICE CLASSIC

CAPRICE (8 Cylinder)			
1BL19	4 Dr Sedan	14252	16515
1BL35	4 Dr Wagon	15426	17875
CAPRICE CLASSIC (8 Cylinder)			
1BN19	4 Dr Sedan	15940	18470
Destination Charge:	All Models	535	535

STANDARD EQUIPMENT:
CAPRICE: 5.0 liter V8 engine with electronic fuel injection, 4-speed automatic overdrive transmission, composite halogen headlamps, tinted glass, base coat/clear coat exterior finish, body-side moldings, dual outside rearview mirrors (LH remote), cornering lamps (Caprice Classic), four-wheel anti-lock brake system (ABS), 15" x 7" steel wheels with full wheel covers (Caprice), 15" x 7" aluminum wheels (Caprice Classic), P205/75R-15 all-season steel belted radial blackwall tires (Sedans), P225/70R-15 white-stripe all-season steel-belted radial tires (Wagon), power steering, air conditioning, intermittent windshield wipers, driver's side supplemental inflatable restraint system, 55/45 split front cloth seat with armrest and reclining seat-backs (Caprice Classic Sedan), seat-back storage pockets (Caprice Classic Sedan), rear center armrest (Caprice Classic Sedan), Scotchgard™ fabric protector, radio (AM/FM stereo with seek-scan, digital clock and dual rear speakers), built-in front and rear-door storage compartments, visor vanity mirrors (LH & RH), child security rear door locks, trip odometer, diagnostic system — indicates low levels of coolant, fuel, engine oil and windshield washer fluid (Caprice Classic Sedan), hold-down cargo net, rear single wet arm wiper (Wagon), luggage rack (Wagon), manual rear vent rear windows (Wagon), power windows (Caprice Classic Sedan), power door locks (Caprice Classic Sedan), front door courtesy lamps (Caprice Classic Sedan), dual rearview mirror mounted reading lamps (Caprice Classic Sedan).

ACCESSORIES

—	**Caprice Sedan Base Equipment** — (included with Model)	NC	NC
UM6	- with UM6 radio, add	140	165

CHEVROLET

Mfgs. Code	Description	Base Cost	Sgstd. List
U1C	- with U1C radio, add	358	421
—	**Caprice Sedan Preferred Equipment Group 1** — (includes power door lock system; power windows with driver's express down; electronic speed control with resume speed; comfortilt steering wheel; inside power trunk opener; floor covering - carpeted mats, color-keyed, front and rear)	842	990
UM6	- with UM6 radio, add	140	165
U1C	- with U1C radio, add	358	421
—	**Caprice Sedan Preferred Equipment Group 2** — (includes electronically tuned AM/FM stereo radio with seek and scan, stereo cassette tape with auto-reverse and digital clock - includes extended range sound front and rear speakers; power windows with driver's express down; six-way driver's side only power seat; power door lock system; electronic speed control, with resume speed; comfortilt steering wheel; electric twin remote sport mirrors; inside power trunk opener; power antenna; dual reading lamps in rearview mirror; mirror - RH visor, illuminated; floor covering - carpeted mats, color-keyed, front and rear) - with 55/45 seat - includes driver's power seats	1416	1666
	- with bench seat	1170	1376
UU8	- with UU8 radio, add	285	335
U1B	- with U1B radio, add	502	591
U1C	- with U1C radio, add	218	256
—	**Caprice Classic Sedan Base Equipment Group** — (included with model)	NC	NC
UM6	- with UM6 radio, add	140	165
U1C	- with U1C radio, add	358	421
—	**Caprice Classic Sedan Preferred Equipment Group 1** — (includes electronically tuned AM/FM stereo radio with seek and scan, stereo cassette tape with auto-reverse and digital clock - includes extended range sound front and rear speakers; six-way driver's side only power seat; electronic speed control with resume speed; comfortilt steering wheel; inside power trunk opener; illuminated RH visor mirror; floor covering - carpeted mats, color-keyed, front and rear)	793	933
U1C	- with U1C radio, add	218	256
—	**Caprice Classic Sedan Preferred Equipment Group 2** — (includes Delco/Bose sound system, electronically tuned AM/FM stereo radio with seek and scan, stereo cassette tape with auto-reverse and digital clock; six-way driver and passenger power seats; keyless remote door locks and trunk opener; electronic speed control with resume speed; comfortilt steering wheel; electric twin remote mirrors; inside power trunk opener; power antenna; twilight sentinel headlamp system; dual reading lamps with electronic compass in rearview mirror; illuminated RH visor mirror; floor covering - carpeted mats, color-keyed, front and rear)	1667	1961
U1B	- with U1B radio, add	218	256
—	**Caprice Wagon Base Equipment Group** — (included with model)	NC	NC
UM6	- with UM6 radio, add	140	165
U1C	- with U1C radio, add	358	421
—	**Caprice Wagon Preferred Equipment Group 1** — (includes electronically tuned AM/FM stereo radio with seek/scan stereo cassette tape with auto-reverse and digital clock - includes extended range sound front and rear speakers; power windows with driver's express down; power door lock system (includes tailgate lock); electronic speed control with resume speed; comfortilt steering wheel; floor covering - carpeted mats, color keyed, front and rear)	1003	1180
U1C	- with U1C radio, add	218	256
—	**Caprice Wagon Preferred Equipment Group 2** — (includes electronically tuned AM/FM stereo radio with seek and scan, stereo cassette tape with auto-reverse and digital clock - includes extended range sound front and		

Mfgs. Code	Description **CHEVROLET**	Base Cost	Sgstd. List
	rear speakers; power windows with driver's express down; power door lock system (includes tailgate lock); six-way driver's side only power seats; electronic speed control with resume speed; deluxe rear compartment decor; comfortilt steering wheel; electric twin remote mirrors; security rear compartment cover; power antenna; dual reading lamps in rearview mirror; illuminated RH visor mirror; floor covering - carpeted mats, color-keyed front and rear) - with 55/45 seats (includes driver's power seats)	1530	1800
	- with bench seat	1284	1510
U1C	- with U1C radio, add	218	256
—	**Interior Trim**		
C1	cloth bench seat	NC	NC
C5	cloth 55/45 seat - standard on Caprice Classic	190	223
A5	leather 55/45 seat	506	595
F5	custom cloth 55/45 seat - Caprice Wagon only	255	300
—	**Paint**		
—	solid	NC	NC
D84	custom two-tone (includes lower body accent and outside door handle inserts	120	141
L03	**Engine —** 5.0 liter EFI V8 - standard	NC	NC
G80	**Axle, Rear —** limited slip differential with V92 suspension equipment	85	100
	- without V92 suspension equipment	119	140
VK3	**Bracket, Front License Plate**	NC	NC
C49	**Defogger, Rear Window —** electric - with B*A2 PEG - includes twin remote heated electric mirrors	166	195
	- without B*A2 PEG	136	160
AU3	**Door Lock System, Power —** electric - Sedans (standard on Caprice Classic)	196	230
	- Wagon (includes tailgate lock)	259	305
YF5	**California Emission Requirements —** includes all testing equipment and/or certification necessary for registration in the State of California	85	100
NA5	**Standard Emission Equipment**	NC	NC
—	**Radio Equipment —** for specific radio pricing, refer to radio information included with each preferred equipment group		
UM6	electronically tuned AM/FM stereo radio with seek and scan, stereo cassette tape with auto-reverse and digital clock - includes extended range sound front and rear speakers		
UU8	Delco/Bose sound system, electronically tuned AM/FM stereo radio with seek and scan, stereo cassette tape with auto-reverse and digital clock		
U1B	Delco/Bose sound system silver series, electronically tuned AM/FM stereo radio with seek-scan, compact disc player and digital clock		
U1C	electronically tuned AM/FM stereo radio with seek-scan, compact disc player and digital clock - includes extended range sound front and rear speakers		
D85	**Striping, Pin —** body side and rear (standard on Caprice Classic)	52	61
—	**Suspension Equipment**		
G67	auto leveling suspension - Caprice Wagon only	149	175
F41	ride/handling suspension - includes increased capacity front and rear shock absorbers, front and rear springs, rear stabilizer and large front stabilizer bar	42	49
V92	trailering package - includes HD cooling, engine oil cooler (Sedan includes 3.08 and Wagon includes 3.23 rear radio performance axle		
	- Sedans	187	220
	- Wagon	145	171
N81	**Spare Tire, Full Size —** Caprice Classic includes aluminum wheel		
	with QCU tires		
	- Caprice Sedan	52	61
	- Caprice Classic	94	111
	with QCV tires		

Mfgs. Code	Description	Base Cost	Sgstd. List
	- Caprice Sedan	66	78
	- Caprice Classic	109	128
	with QNP tires		
	- Caprice Sedan	76	89
	- Caprice Classic	118	139
	with QEU tires		
	- Caprice Wagon	76	89
—	**Tires**		
QCU	P215/75R15 all seasons steel belted radial ply blackwall (standard)	NC	NC
QCV	P215/75R15 all seasons steel belted radial ply white stripe	68	80
QNP	P225/70R15 all seasons steel belted radial ply white stripe	150	176
QEU	P225/175R15 all seasons steel belted radial ply white stripe (standard on Wagon)	NC	NC
N91	**Wheel Covers with Locks, Wire** — Caprice Sedan and Wagon only	183	215
—	**Warranty Enhancement** — req'd in New York State	55	65

CAVALIER

CAVALIER (4 Cylinder)

Code	Description	Base Cost	Sgstd. List
1JC37/WV9	2 Dr VL Coupe	7539	7995
1JC69/WV9	4 Dr VL Sedan	7799	8270
1JC35/WV9	4 Dr VL Wagon	8699	9225
1JC37	2 Dr RS Coupe	8367	9065
1JC69	4 Dr RS Sedan	8552	9265
1JC35	4 Dr RS Wagon	9479	10270

CAVALIER (6 Cylinder)

Code	Description	Base Cost	Sgstd. List
1JF37	2 Dr Z24 Coupe	10761	12050

Destination Charge: All models 455 455

STANDARD EQUIPMENT:
CAVALIER: 2.2 liter 4 cylinder engine with turbo body injection (except Z24), 3.1 liter 6 cylinder engine with multi-port fuel injection (Z24), 5-speed manual transmission (except Wagons), 3-speed automatic transmission (Wagons), body-color grille panel, black bumper facias and body-side moldings (VL), body-color bumper facias, aero package (Z24), color-coordinated bumper facia and body-side moldings (RS, Z24), composite halogen headlamps, tinted glass (except VL Coupes & Sedans), self-aligning feature steering wheel, carpeting, full-length floor console with integral armrest, radio [AM/FM stereo with seek-scan, digital clock and ERS™] (RS, Z24), headlamps-on reminder buzzer (RS, Z24), easy entry passenger seat (RS Coupe, Z24 Coupe), trunk/rear compartment lamp, P185/75R14 blackwall radial ply tires (all except Z24), P205/60R15 black lettered performance radial tires (Z24), 14" styled steel wheels (except Z24), 15" cast aluminum wheels (Z24), level III sport suspension (Z24), power front disc/rear drum brake system, power steering, map pockets (Coupes), trunk tie downs (Z24), stainless steel exhaust system.

ACCESSORIES

Mfgs. Code	Description	Base Cost	Sgstd. List
—	**Cavalier VL Base Equipment Group** — 1JC35-1JC69-1JC37/WV9 only (included with model)	NC	NC
UM7	- with UM7 radio, add	282	332
UM6	- with UM6 radio, add	401	472
—	**Cavalier VL Preferred Equipment Group 1** — 1JC69-1JC37/WV9 only - (includes electronically tuned AM/FM stereo radio with seek and scan and digital clock - includes extended range sound system; all windows tinted glass; sport mirrors - LH remote and RH manual; floor covering - carpeted		

Mfgs. Code	Description	Base Cost	Sgstd. List
	mats, color-keyed front and rear)	425	500
UM6	- with UM6 radio, add	119	140
—	**Cavalier VL Preferred Equipment Group 1 —** 1JC35/WV9 only - (includes electronically tuned AM/FM stereo radio with seek and scan and digital clock - includes extended range sound system; sport mirrors - LH remote and RH manual; floor covering - carpeted mats, color-keyed front and rear)	336	395
UM6	- with UM6 radio, add	119	140
—	**Cavalier RS Base Equipment Group —** 1JC35-1JC37-1JC69 only (included with model)	NC	NC
UM6	- with UM6 radio, add	119	140
—	**Cavalier RS Preferred Equipment Group 1 —** 1JC37-1JC69 only - (includes split back folding rear seat; intermittent windshield wiper system; sport mirrors - LH remote and RH manual; reading lamp; mounted instrument panel; dual covered visor vanity mirrors; floor covering - carpeted mats, color-keyed front and rear; cargo retaining net)	269	317
UM6	- with UM6 radio, add	119	140
—	**Cavalier RS Preferred Equipment Group 1 —** 1JC35 only - (includes split back folding rear seat; intermittent windshield wiper system; sport mirrors - LH remote and RH manual; dual covered visor vanity mirrors; floor covering - carpeted mats, color-keyed front and rear; reading lamps; mounted instrument panel)	159	187
UM6	- with UM6 radio, add	119	140
—	**Cavalier RS Preferred Equipment Group 2 —** 1JC37-1JC69 only - (includes air conditioning; electronic speed control with resume speed; comfortilt steering wheel; split back folding rear seat; intermittent windshield wiper system; sport mirrors - LH remote and RH manual; mounted instrument panel reading lamp; dual covered visor vanity mirrors; floor covering - carpeted mats, color-keyed front and rear; cargo retaining net)	1183	1392
UM6	- with UM6 radio, add	119	140
—	**Cavalier RS Preferred Equipment Group 2 —** 1JC35 only - (includes air conditioning; electronic speed control with resume speed; comfortilt steering wheel; roof carrier; split back folding rear seat; intermittent windshield wiper system; sport mirrors - LH remote and RH manual; mounted instrument panel reading lamp; dual covered visor vanity mirrors; floor covering - carpeted mats, color-keyed front and rear)	1170	1377
UM6	- with UM6 radio, add	119	140
—	**Cavalier RS Preferred Equipment Package 3 —** 1JC37-1JC69 only - (includes air conditioning, electronically tuned AM/FM stereo radio with seek and scan, stereo cassette tape and digital clock - includes extended range sound system; power windows; power door lock system; electronic speed control with resume speed; comfortilt steering wheel; split back folding rear seat; intermittent windshield wiper system; sport mirrors - LH remote and RH manual; power trunk opener; mounted instrument panel reading lamp; dual covered visor vanity mirrors; floor covering - carpeted mats, color-keyed front and rear; cargo retaining net) - Coupe	1714	2017
	- Sedan	1804	2122
—	**Cavalier RS Preferred Equipment Group 3 —** 1JC35 only - (includes air conditioning; electronically tuned AM/FM stereo radio with seek and scan, stereo cassette tape and digital clock - includes extended range sound system; power windows; power door lock system; electronic speed control with resume speed; comfortilt steering wheel; roof carrier; split back folding rear seat; intermittent windshield wiper system; sport mirrors - LH remote and RH manual; mounted instrument panel reading lamp; dual covered visor vanity mirrors; floor covering - carpeted mats, color-keyed front and rear)	1748	2057

CHEVROLET

Mfgs. Code	Description	Base Cost	Sgstd. List
—	**Cavalier Z24 Coupe Base Equipment Group** — 1JF37 only (included with model)	NC	NC
UM6	- with UM6 radio, add	119	140
U1C	- with U1C radio, add	337	396
—	**Cavalier Z24 Coupe Preferred Equipment Group 1** — 1JF37 only - (includes air conditioning; electronically tuned AM/FM stereo radio with seek and scan, stereo cassette tape and digital clock - includes extended range sound system; electronic speed control with resume speed; comfortilt steering wheel; intermittent windshield wiper system; floor covering - carpeted mats, color-keyed front and rear; dome reading lamp)	1128	1327
U1C	- with U1C radio, add	218	256
—	**Cavalier Z24 Coupe Preferred Equipment Group 2** — 1JF37 only - (includes air conditioning; electronically tuned AM/FM stereo radio with seek and scan, stereo cassette tape and digital clock - extended range sound system; power windows; power door lock system; electronic speed control with resume speed; comfortilt steering wheel; intermittent windshield wiper system; power trunk opener; floor covering - carpeted mats, color-keyed front and rear; dome reading lamp)	1540	1812
U1C	- with U1C radio, add	218	256
—	**Interior Trim**		
C2	cloth bucket seats	NC	NC
J2	sport cloth bucket seats (includes AM9 split folding)	NC	NC
—	rear seat - standard on Z24 Coupe	NC	NC
—	**Exterior Color** — paint, solid	NC	NC
—	**Engines**		
LM3	2.2 liter EFI L4	NC	NC
LH0	3.1 liter MFI V6 (includes with Z24 Coupe)	582	685
C60	**Air Conditioning**	621	730
VK3	**Bracket, Front License Plate**	NC	NC
AP9	**Cargo Retaining Net**	26	30
V54	**Carriers** — roof	98	115
C49	**Defogger, Rear Window** — electric	136	160
C95	**Dome Reading Lamp**	20	24
AU3	**Door Lock System; Power** — Coupes only	162	190
	- Sedans and Wagon only	196	230
B37	**Floor Mats, Carpeted, Front and Rear**	28	33
A01	**Glass, Tinted**	89	105
K05	**Heater, Engine Block**	17	20
—	**Emissions Systems**		
YF5	**California Emission Requirements** — includes all testing, equipment and/or certification necessary for registration in the State of California	85	100
NA5	**Standard Emission Equipment**	NC	NC
D35	**Mirrors, Sport, LH Remote, RH Manual**	26	30
DD2	**Mirrors, Dual Visor Vanity**	12	14
—	**Radio Equipment** — for specific radio pricing, refer to radio information included with each preferred equipment group		
UM7	electronically tuned AM/FM stereo radio with seek and scan and digital clock - includes extended range sound system		
UM6	electronically tuned AM/FM stereo radio with seek and scan, stereo cassette tape and digital clock - includes extended range sound system		
U1C	electronically tuned AM stereo and FM stereo radio with seek and scan, compact disc player and digital clock - includes extended range sound system		
UL5	radio delete - standard on VL models		
Z51	**Performance Handling Package** — includes P195/70R14 blackwall tires, level II sport suspension and gauge package with tachometer	174	205

Mfgs. Code	Description CHEVROLET	Base Cost	Sgstd. List
CR3	**Reading Lamp, Instrument Panel**	4	5
AM9	**Seat, Rear, Split Folding** — Coupe and Sedan	128	150
	- Wagons	43	50
K34	**Speed Control, Electronic with Resume Speed**	179	210
N33	**Steering Wheel** — comfortilt	115	135
AD3	**Sun Roof** — removable	298	350
—	**Tires**		
QFE	P185/75R14 all seasons steel belted radial ply blackwall - standard on all models except Z24 Coupe	NC	NC
QHF	P205/60R15 steel belted radial ply blackwall - standard on Z24 Coupe	NC	NC
QHH	P205/60R15 steel belted radial ply white outline lettered	83	98
—	**Transmissions** — floor mounted control		
MX1	automatic - standard on Wagons	395	465
MM5	5-speed manual - standard on Coupes and Sedans	NC	NC
A90	**Trunk Opener, Power**	43	50
A31	**Windows, Power** — Coupes only	208	245
	- Sedans and Wagons	264	310
CD4	**Wiper System** — intermittent	47	55
—	**Warranty Enhancement** — req'd in New York State	55	65

CORSICA

CORSICA (4 Cylinder)

Code	Description	Base Cost	Sgstd. List
1LT69	4 Dr LT Notchback Sedan	8993	10070
1LT68	4 Dr LT Hatchback Sedan	9595	10745
	Destination Charge: All models	455	455

STANDARD EQUIPMENT:

CORSICA: 2.2 liter 4 cylinder engine with electronic fuel injection, 5-speed manual with overdrive transmission, halogen headlamps, gloss black grille, gloss black door handles and lock cylinders, gloss black window reveal and door moldings, gloss black body-side moldings and bumper facia rub strips with black inserts, radio (AM/FM stereo with seek-scan, digital clock and ERS™), tinted glass, base coat/clear-coat exterior finish, depressed-park windshield wipers with wet-arm washers, gloss black dual remote sport mirrors, fingertip-control instrument panel cluster pods, side window defoggers, supplemental inflatable restraint system with air bag for driver, full-folding rear seat-back (Hatchback Sedan), lift-out package tray for ease of access to cargo area (Hatchback Sedan), retracting roller package screen for cargo area (Hatchback Sedan), 14" steel wheels with full covers (styled steel wheels required with 3.1 liter V6 engine), P185/75R14 tires, soft ride suspension, power front disc/rear drum brakes, power steering, stainless steel exhaust, Scotchgard™ fabric protector.

ACCESSORIES

Code	Description	Base Cost	Sgstd. List
—	**Corsica LT Base Equipment Group** — (included with model)	NC	NC
UM6	- with UM6 radio, add	119	140
U1C	- with U1C radio, add	337	396
UL5	- with UL5 radio delete; deduct	(140)	(165)
—	**Corsica LT Preferred Equipment Group 1** — (includes intermittent windshield wiper system; floor covering - carpeted mats, color-keyed front and rear; rear view mirror with reading lamps)	94	111
UM6	- with UM6 radio, add	119	140
U1C	- with U1C radio, add	337	396
—	**Corsica LT Preferred Equipment Group 2** — (includes air conditioning; electronic speed control with resume speed; comfortilt steering wheel;		

Mfgs. Code	Description	Base Cost	Sgstd. List
	intermittent windshield wiper system; floor covering -carpeted mats, color -keyed front and rear; rear view mirror with reading lamps)	1051	1236
UM6	- with UM6 radio, add	119	140
U1C	- with U1C radio, add	337	396
—	**Corsica LT Preferred Equipment Group 3** — (includes air conditioning; electronically tuned AM/FM stereo radio with seek and scan, stereo cassette tape and digital clock - includes extended range sound system; power windows with driver's express down; power door lock system; electronic speed control with resume speed; comfortilt steering wheel; console; intermittent windshield wiper system; power trunk/hatch opener; floor covering - carpeted mats, color-keyed front and rear; rear view mirror with reading lamps)	1731	2036
U1C	- with U1C radio, add	218	256
C2	**Interior Trim** — C2 cloth bucket seats	NC	NC
—	**Paint, Solid**	NC	NC
D84	**Custom Two-Tone Paint**	105	123
—	**Engines**		
LM3	2.2 liter EFI L4	NC	NC
LH0	3.1 liter MFI V6	582	685
C60	**Air Conditioning** — includes increased cooling	663	780
VK3	**Bracket, Front License Plate**	NC	NC
V56	**Carrier, Deck Lid** — black	98	115
B19	**Comfort Convenience Package** — includes luggage area cargo net, 4-way passenger seat adjuster, sliding sunshade extensions and visor mirrors		
	- 1LT68 only	72	85
	- 1LT69 only (also includes split folding rear seat	200	235
D55	**Console** — floor mounted	51	60
C49	**Defogger, Rear Window** — electric	136	160
AU3	**Door Lock System, Power** — electric	196	230
YF5	**California Emission Requirements** — includes all testing, equipment and/or certification necessary for registration in the State of California	85	100
NA5	**Standard Emission Equipment**	NC	NC
—	**Floor Covering** — carpeted mats, color-keyed		
B34	front	15	18
B35	rear	13	15
UB3	**Gauge Package with Tachometer** — includes voltmeter, oil pressure, temperature gauges and trip odometer	118	139
DC4	**Mirror, Rear View** — with reading lamps	20	23
—	**Radio Equipment** — for specific radio pricing, refer to radio information included with each preferred equipment group		
UM6	electronically tuned AM/FM stereo radio with seek and scan, stereo cassette tape and digital clock - includes extended range sound system		
U1C	electronically tuned AM/FM stereo radio with seek and scan, compact disc player and digital clock - includes extended range sound system		
UL5	Radio Delete		
K34	**Speed Control, Electronic** — with resume speed	179	210
N33	**Steering Wheel, Comfortilt**	115	135
Z52	**Sport Handling Package** — includes 15" aluminum wheels, 15" tires, level III sport suspension, bodyside molding with red inserts and sport steering wheel	336	395
—	**Tires**		
QFF	P185/75R14 all seasons steel belted radial ply white stripe	58	68
—	**Transmissions**		
MM5	5-speed manual	NC	NC
MX1	automatic	459	540
A90	**Trunk/Hatch Release, Power**	43	50
PC4	**Wheels, Styled Steel**	48	56

A31	**Windows, Power** — with driver's express down	272	320
CD4	**Windshield Wiper System** — intermittent	47	55
—	**Warranty Enhancement** — req'd in New York State	55	65

CORVETTE

CORVETTE (8 Cylinder)

1YY07 2 Dr Hatchback Coupe	27360	32455
1YY67 2 Dr Convertible Coupe	32683	38770
Destination Charge: All models	530	530

STANDARD EQUIPMENT:

CORVETTE: 5.7 liter V8 engine with tuned-port fuel injection, choice of 4-speed automatic overdrive transmission or 6-speed manual transmission, power-operated retractable halogen headlamps, halogen fog lamps, dual electrically adjusted and heated outside rearview mirrors, full-glass rear hatch with roller cargo cover (Coupe), one-piece removable fiberglass roof panel (Coupe), full-folding roof (Convertible), PASS-Key anti-theft system, intermittent wipe system, electronic speed control with resume speed, air conditioning, heated rear window (Coupe), leather-wrapped steering wheel with supplemental inflatable restraint system, radio (AM/FM stereo with seek-scan, cassette, four speakers and automatic power antenna), power door locks, power windows, cloth bucket seats with lateral support and back angle adjustment plus wool-pad comfort liner, outside engine air induction, P275/40ZR-17 Eagle radial tires, 17" x 9½" cast aluminum wheels, power 4-wheel disc brakes, Bosch ABS IIS anti-lock braking system, power rack-and-pinion steering, Bilstein gas-charged shock absorbers, underhood lamps, acoustical insulation package, uniframe-design body structure with corrosion-resistant coating, independent front and rear suspension with transverse fiberglass leaf springs and forged aluminum A-arms, body-color body-side moldings, low oil indicator lamp.

ACCESSORIES

—	**Corvette Coupe Base Equipment Group** — (included with model)	NC	NC
UU8	- with UU8 radio, add	683	823
U1F	- with U1F radio, add	1012	1219
—	**Corvette Coupe Preferred Equipment Group 1** — (includes electronic air conditioning; electronically tuned Delco Bose music system, AM/FM stereo radio with seek and scan, stereo cassette tape and digital clock, special tone and balance control and four speakers; six-way driver's side only power seat)	1073	1293
U1F	- with U1F radio, add	329	396
—	**Corvette Convertible Base Equipment Group** — (included with model)	NC	NC
UU8	- with UU8 radio, add	683	823
U1F	- with U1F radio, add	1012	1219
—	**Corvette Convertible Preferred Equipment Group 1** — (includes electronic air conditioning; electronically tuned Delco Bose music system includes AM/FM stereo radio with seek and scan, stereo cassette tape and digital clock, special tone and balance control and four speakers; six-way driver's side only power seat)	1073	1293
U1F	- with U1F radio, add	329	396
—	**Interior Trim**		
H2	cloth bucket seats	NC	NC
A2	leather buckets seats	353	425
A8	leather adjustable sport bucket seat	872	1050

Mfgs. Code	Description	Base Cost	Sgstd. List
—	**Exterior Color** — paint, solid	NC	NC
L98	5.7 liter TPI V8 engine	NC	NC
C68	**Air Conditioning, Electronic Control**	149	180
—	**Axle, Performance Ratio**	18	22
J55	**Brakes, Heavy-Duty** — included with Z07 adjustable performance handling package	NC	NC
V56	**Carrier, Luggage** — black	116	140
KC4	**Cooler, Engine Oil** — included with Z07 performance handling package	91	110
NN5	**California Emission Requirements** — includes all testing necessary for registration in the state of California	83	100
NA5	**Standard Emission Equipment**	NC	NC
—	**Adjustable Handling Package**		
Z07	performance includes engine oil cooler, heavy-duty brakes, heavy-duty power steering cooler, Bilstein adjustable ride control system with performance oriented calibration, stiffer springs, shocks, stabilizer bars and bushings	1789	2155
FX3	selective ride and handling - electronic	1407	1695
UJ6	**Low Tire Pressure Warning Indicator**	270	325
—	**Radio Equipment** — for specific radio pricing, refer to radio information included with each preferred equipment group		
UU8	electronically tuned Delco/Bose music system - includes AM/FM stereo radio with seek and scan, stereo cassette tape and digital clock, special tone and balance control and four speakers		
U1F	electronically tuned Delco/Bose music system - includes AM/FM stereo radio with seek and scan, stereo cassette tape, compact disc player and digital clock, special tone and balance control and four speakers		
—	**Roof Panels** — removable		
24S	blue tint - transparent	510	615
64S	bronze tint - transparent	510	615
C2L	dual - includes body color-keyed roof panel and 24S blue or 64S bronze transparent roof panel	759	915
CC2	hard top - removable	1656	1995
—	**Seats, Power** — six-way		
AC3	driver's side only	241	290
AC1	passenger side only	241	290
ZR1	**Special Performance Package** — includes 5.7 liter MPFI DOHC 32 valve V8 engine, P315/35ZR17 tires (rear), 17 x 9.5 front and 17 x 11 rear styled aluminum wheels, specific rear fascia and stop lamps, side body panels, selective ride and handling package, leather adjustable sport seats, six-way passenger and driver power seats, electronic air conditioning, low tire pressure warning, Delco/Bose gold series music system with CD and cassette player and solar glass	26297	31683
—	**Transmissions**		
MX0	automatic with overdrive (standard)	NC	NC
MN6	6-speed manual	NC	NC
—	**Warranty Enhancement** — req'd in New York State	55	65

LUMINA APV

LUMINA APV (6 Cylinder)			
1UM06	Base APV Passenger	13154	14730
1UM06	CL APV Passenger	14690	16450

Destination Charge: All models	485	485

Mfgs. Code	Description	Base Cost	Sgstd. List

CHEVROLET

STANDARD EQUIPMENT:
LUMINA APV: Independent front suspension with MacPherson struts, power front disc/rear drum brakes, power rack and pinion steering, rear window wiper/washer, all tinted glass with solar windshield, stainless steel exhaust, remote left hand-manual right hand outside rearview mirrors, halogen headlamps, P205/70R14 all season radial tires, 3.1 liter TBI V6 engine, 3-speed automatic transmission.

ACCESSORIES

Mfgs. Code	Description	Base Cost	Sgstd. List
—	**Lumina APV Base Equipment Group —** (included with model)	NC	NC
UM6	- with UM6 radio, add	119	140
U1C	- with U1C radio, add	337	396
—	**Lumina APV Preferred Equipment Group 1 —** (includes air conditioning, comfortilt steering wheel, auxiliary lighting)	850	1000
UM6	- with UM6 radio, add	119	140
U1C	- with U1C radio, add	337	396
—	**Lumina APV Preferred Equipment Group 2 —** (includes air conditioning; electronically tuned AM/FM stereo with seek/scan, stereo cassette tape and digital clock - extended range sound system; power windows with driver's express down; power door/tailgate locks with side door delay; electronic speed control with resume speed; comfortilt steering wheel; twin remote sport mirrors; auxiliary lights; floor covering - carpeted mats, front and rear) - with 5-person seating	1649	1940
	- with 6 or 7-person seating	1662	1955
U1C	- with U1C radio, add	218	256
—	**Lumina APV CL Base Equipment Group —** (included with model)	NC	NC
UM6	- with UM6 radio, add	119	140
	- with U1C radio, add	337	396
—	**Lumina APV CL Preferred Equipment Group 1 —** (includes electronically tuned AM/FM stereo with seek/scan, stereo cassette tape and digital clock - extended range sound system; power windows with driver's express down; power door/tailgate locks with side door delay; electronic speed control with resume speed; twin remote sport mirrors; floor covering - carpeted mats, front and rear) - with 5-person seating	799	940
	- with 7-person seating	812	955
U1C	- with U1C radio, add	218	256
—	**Interior Trim**		
C2	cloth bucket seats - standard	NC	NC
F2	custom cloth buckets seats - standard on CL	NC	NC
—	**Exterior Color —** paint		
—	solid	NC	NC
D84	custom two-tone	126	148
LG6	**Engine —** 3.1 liter EFI V6	NC	NC
C67	**Air Conditioning —** standard on CL	684	805
VK3	**Bracket, Front License Plate**	NC	NC
V54	**Carrier, Roof**	123	145
C49	**Defogger, Rear Window —** electric	136	160
YF5	**California Emission Requirements —** includes all testing, equipment and/or certification necessary for registration in the state of California	85	100
NA5	**Standard Emission Equipment**	NC	NC
—	**Floor Covering - Carpeted Mats**		
B32	- front only	17	20
B33	- rear only with 5-person seating	13	15
B33	- rear only with 6 or 7-person seating	26	30
AJ1	**Glass, Deep Tinted**	208	245
K05	**Heater, Engine Block**	17	20

Mfgs. Code	Description **CHEVROLET**	Base Cost	Sgstd. List
TR9	**Lighting, Auxiliary**	51	60
AB5	**Locks, Power** — door and tailgate	230	270
D68	**Mirrors, Twin Remote, Sport**	26	30
—	**Radio Equipment** — for specific radio pricing, refer to radio information included with each preferred equipment group		
UM6	electronically tuned AM/FM stereo radio with seek and scan, stereo cassette tape and digital clock - includes extended range sound system		
U1C	electronically tuned AM/FM stereo radio with seek and scan, compact disc player and digital clock - includes extended range sound system		
AG9	**Seating, Power** — driver's side only; electric 6-way control	247	290
—	**Seating Arrangements** — one of the following seat options must be specified		
—	five passenger seating - standard		
ZP5	- w/o CL; includes two front bucket seats and three passenger bench seat; also includes seat belts	NC	NC
AB4	- w/CL; includes two front bucket seats and three modular rear seats; also includes seat belts	NC	NC
AB3	six passenger seating; includes two front bucket seats and four modular rear seats; also includes seat belts	434	510
ZP7	seven passenger seating; includes two front bucket seats and five modular rear seats; also includes seat belts - w/o CL	561	660
	- w/CL	361	425
G67	**Suspension, Load Leveling**	145	170
K34	**Speed Control, Electronic with Resume Speed**	179	210
N33	**Steering Wheel, Comfortilt**	115	135
XMR	**Tires** — P205/65R15 all seasons steel belted radial ply blackwall	62	73
MX1	**Transmission** — automatic	NC	NC
—	**Wheels**		
PH3	aluminum cast with locks 15"	225	265
PD7	aluminum cast with locks 14"	225	265
A31	**Windows, Power with Driver's Express Down**	217	255

LUMINA

LUMINA (4 Cylinder)

1WL27	2 Dr Coupe	10934	12670
1WL69	4 Dr Sedan	11107	12870

LUMINA (6 Cylinder)

1WN27/ZV8	2 Dr Euro Coupe	12768	14795
1WN69/ZV8	4 Dr Euro Sedan	12941	14995

Destination Charge: All models 485 485

STANDARD EQUIPMENT:

LUMINA: 2.5 liter 4 cylinder engine with electronic fuel injection (Base Models), 3.1 liter 6 cylinder engine with multi-port fuel injection (Euro Models), composite halogen headlamps, body-color grille, soft body-color facias, black facia rub strips and body-side moldings with bright inserts (Base Models), black facia rub strips and body-side moldings with red inserts (Euro Models), black wheelhousing rub strips (Base Models), black exterior accent color (Euro Models), body-color wheelhousing rub strips (Euro Models), air conditioning (Euro Models), tinted glass, black door glass and beltline moldings (Euro Models), black rear roof trim pillar plates and sport mirror backs (Euro Models), illuminated door lock cylinders (Coupes), inside day/night mirror with integral courtesy lamps, visor vanity mirrors (LH and RH), sport steering wheel, black instrument panel facia and door panel appliques (Euro Models), full floor carpeting including trunk, P195/75R14 blackwall radial tires

(Base Models), 14" full wheel covers (Base Models), 15" aero wheel covers (Euro Models), firm ride sport suspension (Euro Models), soft ride suspension (Base Models), rear spoiler (may be deleted).

ACCESSORIES

Mfgs. Code	Description	Base Cost	Sgstd. List
—	**Lumina Base Equipment Group —** (included with model)	NC	NC
UM6	- with UM6 radio, add	119	140
—	**Lumina Preferred Equipment Group 1 —** (includes air conditioning; comfortilt steering wheel; floor covering - carpeted mats, front and rear)	837	985
UM6	- with UM6 radio, add	119	140
UU8	- with UU8 radio, add	404	475
—	**Lumina Preferred Equipment Group 2 —** (includes air conditioning; electronic speed control with resume speed; comfortilt steering wheel; black deck lid carrier; luggage area cargo retaining net; floor covering - carpeted mats, front and rear)	1139	1340
	- without deck-lid carrier	1041	1225
UM6	- with UM6 radio, add	119	140
UU8	- with UU8 radio, add	404	475
—	**Lumina Preferred Equipment Group 3 —** (includes air conditioning; power windows; power door lock system; electronic speed control with resume speed; comfortilt steering wheel; power trunk opener; luggage area cargo retaining net; black deck lid carrier; twin remote sport mirrors; floor covering - carpeted mats, front and rear) - Coupe	1577	1855
	- Sedan	1666	1960
	without deck lid carrier		
	- Coupe	1479	1740
	- Sedan	1568	1845
UM6	- with UM6 radio, add	119	140
UU8	- with UU8 radio, add	404	475
—	**Lumina Euro Base Equipment Group —** (included with model)	NC	NC
UM6	- with UM6 radio, add	119	140
—	**Lumina Euro Preferred Equipment Group 1 —** (includes electronic speed control with resume speed; comfortilt steering wheel; gauge package with tachometer; luggage area cargo retaining net; floor covering - carpeted mats, front and rear)	442	520
UM6	- with UM6 radio, add	119	140
UU8	- with UU8 radio, add	404	475
—	**Lumina Euro Preferred Equipment Group 2 —** (includes electronically tuned, AM/FM stereo radio with seek and scan, stereo cassette tape and digital clock - includes extended range sound system; power windows, power door lock system; electronic speed control with resume speed; comfortilt steering wheel; power trunk opener; gauge package with tachometer; twin remote sport mirrors; luggage area cargo retaining net; floor covering - carpeted mats, front and rear) - Coupe	999	1175
	- Sedan	1088	1280
UU8	- with UU8 radio, add	285	335
—	**Interior Trim**		
C1	cloth bench seat	NC	NC
F2	custom cloth bucket seats with console	254	299
F3	custom cloth 60/40 seat	169	199
—	**Exterior Color —** paint, solid	NC	NC
—	**Engines**		
LR8	2.5 liter EFI L4	NC	NC
LH0	3.1 liter MFI V6 (standard on Euro)	561	660
C67	**Air Conditioning —** standard on Euro	684	805
VK3	**Bracket, Front License Plate**	NC	NC

Mfgs. Code	Description **CHRYSLER**	Base Cost	Sgstd. List
AP9	**Cargo Retaining Net, Luggage Area**	26	30
V56	**Carrier, Deck Lid** — black	98	115
C49	**Defogger, Rear Window** — electric	136	160
AU3	**Door Lock System, Power** — electric - Coupe	162	190
	- Sedan	196	230
YF5	**California Emission Requirements** — includes all testing, equipment and/or certification necessary for registration in the state of California	NC	NC
NA5	**Standard Emission Equipment**	NC	NC
—	**Floor Covering, Carpeted Mats**		
B34	front only	21	25
B35	rear only	17	20
UB3	**Gauge Package with Tachometer**	85	100
D68	**Mirrors, Sport, Twin Remote**	26	30
—	**Radio Equipment** — for specific radio pricing, refer to radio information included with each preferred equipment group		
UM6	electronically tuned AM/FM stereo radio with seek and scan, stereo cassette tape and digital clock - includes extended range sound system		
UU8	Delco/Bose sound system - electronically tuned AM/FM stereo radio with seek and scan, stereo cassette tape and digital clock		
WG1	**Seat, Power** — six-way control - driver's side only	247	290
K34	**Speed Control, Electronic with Resume Speed**	179	210
D58	**Spoiler, Rear Delete**	(109)	(128)
N33	**Steering Wheel, Comfortilt**	115	135
—	**Tires**		
QMX	P195/75R14 all season steel belted radial ply white stripe	61	72
QPE	P215/60R16 all seasons steel belted radial ply blackwall	95	112
—	**Transmissions**		
MX0	automatic with overdrive	170	200
MX1	automatic	NC	NC
A90	**Trunk Opener, Power**	43	50
A31	**Windows, Power** — Coupe	208	245
	- Sedan	264	310
—	**Warranty Enhancement** — req'd in New York State	55	65

1991 chrysler

IMPERIAL

		Base Cost	Sgstd. List
IMPERIAL (6 Cylinder)			
P41	4 Dr Sedan	22937	26925
Destination Charge:		590	590

STANDARD EQUIPMENT:

IMPERIAL: Automatic temperature control air conditioning, 500 ampre battery, bumpers (bright bumper bar - 5 mph protection & rear bumper guards), full carpeting, chimes (warning for key in ignition, headlights and turn signal on, seat belt), front and rear cigarette lighter, electric rear window defroster, 3.8 liter V6 MPI engine, front wheel drive, front and rear floor mats, tinted glass, concealed halogen headlamps with auto delay, crystalline pentastar hood ornament, dual horns, instrument panel (analog cluster includes: speedometer, odometer, and trip odometer; gauges for fuel, voltage, oil pressure and temperature), lights (cornering, fender mounted, door courtesy, underhood, trunk, front and rear courtesy/reading, illuminated entry), mirrors (inside day/night, dual illuminated visor vanity), moldings (bodyside bodycolor, bright windshield, wheel lip, wide lower body door-brushed chrome), power antenna, 4-wheel disc anti-lock power brakes, power deck lid pulldown, power door lock, power mirrors (outside dual heated with 2-position memory), power seats (8-way driver and passenger with recliner and 2 position memory on driver seat), rack and pinion power steering, power windows, AM/FM stereo cassette radio with seek and scan, graphic equalizer plus 4 Infinity speakers; restraint system (passive driver air bag, active 3-point unibelts), vinyl body color Landau roof, security features (interior remote release for deck lid and hood), electronic speed control, tilt steering column, leather-wrapped steering wheel, bodyside and decklid stripes, gas charged struts and shocks, automatic load leveling suspension, P195/75R14 steel belted radial tires (WSW with compact spare), automatic 4 speed ultradrive transmission, trunk dress up, wire wheel covers, deluxe windshield wiper/washer with intermittent wipe.

ACCESSORIES

Code	Description	Base Cost	Sgstd. List
HGB	**Engine** — 3.8 liter V6 MPI	STD	STD
AFC	**Mark Cross Package** — includes leather interior, 50/50 front bench seat with center armrest and rear cupholders, total retail price - 649, discount - 0, net price	552	649
AJB	**Security Alarm Package** — includes security alarm panel warning light, keyless remote entry for door locks and decklid, total retail price - 277, discount - 0, net price	235	277
ADN	**Electronic Feature Package** — includes overhead console (includes electronic vehicle information center, electronic instrument cluster, automatic adjustment rearview day/night mirror, pre-wired harness for cellular phone and radio ("Infinity RS" speakers (10) and trunk mounted amplifier), total retail price - 1689, discount - 0, net price	1436	1689
MDA	**Bracket** — front license plate	NC	NC
NAE	**Emissions** — California	87	102
P	**Paint** — extra cost pearl coat/clear coat	65	77
TBB	**Spare Tire** — conventional	72	85
SLA	**Suspension** — electronically controlled air suspension	553	650
—	**New York Warranty Enhancement** — required in New York State	106	125

LEBARON CONVERTIBLE

LEBARON CONVERTIBLE (4 Cylinder)

Code	Description	Base Cost	Sgstd. List
CH27	2 Dr High Convertible	14085	15925

LEBARON CONVERTIBLE (6 Cylinder)

Code	Description	Base Cost	Sgstd. List
CP27	2 Dr LX Premium Convertible	16912	19175
CH27 w/ALJ	2DR GTC High Convertible	15977	18100

Destination Charge: All models 490 490

STANDARD EQUIPMENT:

LE BARON CONVERTIBLE: Manual air conditioning (Premium Convertible, High Convertible GTC), power assisted front disc/rear drum brakes (High Convertible, Premium Convertible), 4-wheel disc high performance brakes (High Convertible GTC), soft fascia bumpers with 5 mph protection, chimes (seat belt warning, key in ignition, headlights "on", turn signal cancel), center console, power operated convertible top, lower body urethane coating, remote decklid release, electric rear window defroster, power door locks (Premium Convertible, High Convertible GTC), 2.2 liter 4 cylinder MPI intercooled Turbo IV engine (High Convertible GTC), 2.5 liter 4 cylinder electronic fuel injection engine (High Convertible), 3.0 liter 6 cylinder multi point injection engine (Premium Convertible), front and rear floor mats (Premium Convertible, High Convertible GTC), tinted glass, inside hood release, instrument panel cluster (mechanical cluster includes analog speedometer, odometer and trip odometer, fuel, low washer fluid, deck lid ajar and door ajar; gauges - temperature, voltage (High Convertible, High Convertible GTC), tachometer and oil pressure gauge (Premium Convertible, High Convertible GTC), warning lights (air bag, gauge alert, low fuel), decklid mounted luggage rack (High Convertible GTC), outside dual remote control mirrors (High Convertible), outside dual power heated remote control mirrors (Premium Convertible, High Convertible GTC), right and left illuminating vanity mirrors (Premium Convertible, High Convertible GTC), AM mono/FM stereo radio with digital clock, restraint system (passive driver air bag, active 3-point unibelts), front low back reclining bucket seats, fixed rear bench seats, electronic speed control (Premium Convertible, High Convertible GTC), power assisted rack and pinion type steering, tilt steering column (Premium Convertible, High Convertible GTC), luxury steering wheel (High Convertible), leather-wrapped steering wheel (Premium Convertible, High Convertible GTC), upper bodyside stripes (Premium Convertible), sport handling-includes firm feel power steering, upgraded swaybars, P195/70R14 SBR black sidewall tires (High Convertible), P205/60R15 SBR black sidewall touring tires (Premium Convertible), P205/60R15 SBR all-season performance tires (High Convertible GTC), compact type spare tire, 5-speed manual transmission (High Convertible GTC), automatic 3-speed transmission (High Convertible), automatic 4-speed electronic transmission (Premium Convertible), lace 14" wheel covers (High Convertible), luxury 15" wheel covers (Premium Convertible), cast aluminum 15" lace road wheels (High Convertible GTC), power windows, deluxe windshield wiper/washer with intermittent wipe.

ACCESSORIES

Code	Description	Base Cost	Sgstd. List
AAM	**Popular Equipment Discount Package —** (not available with GTC model) (includes air conditioning, front and rear floor mats, electronic speed control, tilt steering wheel, upper bodyside stripe) - High Convertible, total retail price - 1268, discount - 150, net price	950	1118
AJK	**Deluxe Convenience Package —** (included in AAM Popular Equipment Package on High Convertible) (includes electronic speed control and tilt steering wheel) - High Convertible	299	352
ADA	**Light Package —** (includes illuminated entry and illuminated visor vanity mirrors) - High Convertible, LX Convertible, GTC	167	197
AJW	**Power Convenience Package —** (standard w/GTC & LX Convertible) (includes power automatic door locks and black outside dual power heated remote control mirrors) - High Convertible	283	333
AGT	**"GTC" Performance Package —** (not available w/AAM Popular Equipment Package) includes 2.5 liter MPI turbo I 5-speed manual heavy duty transmission, XLD5 enthusiast sport bucket seats (driver's side includes: power recliner backwing, lumbar and 6-way track), power assisted high performance 4-wheel disc brakes, turbo boost gauge, performance handling suspension (upgrade shocks, sway bars and firm feel power steering) P205/55R16 all season performance tires, 16" x 6" cast aluminum wheels - GTC, total retail price - 2017, discount - 194, net price	1550	1823
EDM	**Engine —** 2.5 liter electronic fuel injection - High Convertible	STD	STD
EDT	**Engine —** 2.5 liter multi-point fuel injection high torque turbo I (requires/AGT - GTC	NC	NC
EDT	**Engine —** 2.5 liter multi-point fuel injection high torque turbo I - High Convertible	590	694
EFA	**Engine —** 3.0 liter V6 multi-point injection - High Convertible	590	694
DDV	**Transmission —** 5-speed manual heavy duty (requires/AGT) - GTC	NC	NC
DDN	**Transmission —** 5-speed manual (w/3.0 liter V6 engine includes tachometer on High Convertible) - High Convertible	(465)	(547)
DGA	**Transmission —** 3-speed automatic - High Convertible	STD	STD
DGA	**Transmission —** 3-speed automatic (requires/AGT) - GTC	325	382

Mfgs. Code	Description **CHRYSLER**	Base Cost	Sgstd. List
DGB	**Transmission** — 4-speed automatic - High Convertible	79	93
DGB	**Transmission** — 4-speed automatic (requires 3.0 liter V6) - GTC	544	640
HAA	**Air Conditioning** — manual (in AAM) - High Convertible	698	821
MDA	**Bracket** — front license plate	NC	NC
BRE	**Brakes** — power assisted high performance 4-wheel disc (requires AY3 on High Convertible)	156	183
NAE	**Emission** — California control and testing	87	102
JAF	**Electronic Instrument Cluster** — (requires AAM on High Convertible) - High Convertible, LX Convertible	259	305
LEA	**Electronic Vehicle Info Center** — monitors over 20 functions (requires AGT on "GTC" or JAF on LX Convertible) - LX Convertible, GTC	587	690
P	**Paint** — extra cost - High Convertible, LX Convertible	65	77
RAS	**Radio** — AM mono/FM stereo, cassette, non seek & scan w/4 speakers - High Convertible, LX Convertible	131	155
RAN	**Radio** — Infinity - AM stereo/FM stereo cassette, seek/scan & 6 Infinity speakers; includes power antenna (requires AAM on High Convertible)	485	570
RAY	**Radio** — Infinity II - AM stereo/FM stereo cassette, seek and scan, & 5-band graphic equalizer; includes power antenna and 6 infinity speakers (requires AAM on High Convertible)	666	783
RDP	**Compact Disc Audio System** — requires RAN or RAY	382	449
JPS	**Seat** — power 6-way driver (requires AJW on High Convertible, GTC)	252	296
D8	**Seat Trim** — vinyl - High Convertible, GTC	87	102
SL	**Seat Trim** — leather & power 8-way driver seat - GTC	1040	1223
LSA	**Security Alarm** — includes function light (requires AJW on High Convertible)	127	149
TKT	**Tire** — P195/70R14 whitewall touring (NA w/AY3) - High Convertible	62	72
TPJ	**Tire** — P205/60R15 whitewall touring (NA w/AY3) - LX Convertible	66	78
LET	**Trip Computer** — includes average fuel economy, instant fuel economy, distance to empty and elapsed time (NA w/LEA) - LX Convertible, GTC	79	93
AY3	**Wheel Handling, Aluminum 15"** — cast aluminum, includes sport handling suspension and P205/60R15 performance tires (requires AAM on High Convertible) - LX Convertible	452	532
	- High Convertible	550	647
WHE	**Wheels** — road cast aluminum, 14"; NA w/AY3 (requires AAM) - High Convertible	279	328
ALJ	**GTC Body**		

LEBARON COUPE

LEBARON COUPE (4 Cylinder)			
CH21	2 Dr High Coupe	11536	12995
LEBARON COUPE (6 Cylinder)			
CP21	2 Dr LX Premium Coupe	13732	15520
CH21 w/ALJ	2 Dr GTC High Coupe	13798	15595
Destination Charge:	All models	490	490

STANDARD EQUIPMENT:

LE BARON COUPE: Air conditioning (Premium Coupe, High Coupe GTC), power assisted front disc, rear drum brakes (High Coupe, Premium Coupe), 4-wheel disc high performance brakes (High Coupe GTC), soft fascia bumpers with 5 mph protection, chimes (seat belt warning, key in ignition, headlights "on", turn signal cancel), center console, overhead console (Premium Coupe, High Coupe GTC), stainless steel exhaust, remote decklid release, electric rear window defroster (Premium Coupe, High Coupe GTC), power door locks (Premium Coupe, High Coupe GTC), 2.5 liter 4 cylinder electronic fuel injection engine (High Coupe), 3.0 liter 6 cylinder multi port injection engine (Premium Coupe, High Coupe GTC), front and rear floor mats (Premium Coupe, High Coupe GTC), tinted glass, instrument panel cluster - mechanical cluster includes analog speedometer, odometer, trip odometer, tachometer (High Coupe, High Coupe GTC), gauges - temperature, voltage, fuel (High Coupe, High Coupe GTC), tachometer, oil pressure gauge (Premium Coupe, High Coupe GTC), deck lid mounted luggage rack (High Coupe GTC), outside dual remote control mirrors (High Coupe), outside dual power heated remote control mirrors (Premium Coupe, High Coupe GTC), vanity right and left non-illuminating mirrors (High Coupe, Premium Coupe), AM mono/FM stereo radio with digital clock; restraint system (passive driver air bag, active 3-point unibelts), front low back bucket reclining seats, fixed bench rear seats (High Coupe), 60/40 fold down rear seat with armrest (Premium Coupe, High Coupe GTC), electronic speed control (High Coupe GTC), power assisted rack and pinion type steering, tilt steering column (High Coupe GTC), luxury steering wheel (High Coupe), leather-wrapped steering wheel (Premium Coupe, High Coupe GTC), bodyside stripes (Premium Coupe), P195/70R14 SBR black sidewall touring tires (High Coupe), P205/60R15 SBR black sidewall touring tires (Premium Coupe), P205/60R15 SBR all-season performance tires (High Coupe GTC), compact type spare tire, 5-speed manual transmission (High Coupe GTC), automatic 3-speed transmission (High Coupe), automatic 4-speed ultradrive transmission (Premium Coupe), lace 14" wheel covers (High Coupe), 15" luxury wheel covers (Premium Coupe), cast aluminum 15" lace road wheels (High Coupe GTC), power windows, deluxe windshield wiper/washer with intermittent wipe, sport handling suspension - includes firm feel power steering (High Coupe GTC).

ACCESSORIES

Mfgs. Code	Description	Base Cost	Sgstd. List
AAM	**Popular Equipment Discount Package** — not available with GTC model or AFF luxury equipment package (includes air conditioning, electronic speed control, tilt steering wheel and front and rear floor mats) - CH21, total retail price - 1250, discount - 700, net price	468	550
AFF	**Luxury Equipment Discount Package** — (not available with GTC model or AAM Popular Equipment Package) includes AAM Popular Equipment Package plus illuminated entry, dual illuminated vanity mirrors, overhead console, power door locks (standard on CP21), black dual power heated remote control outside mirrors (standard on CP21), power driver's seat, leather-wrapped steering wheel (standard on CP21), upper bodyside stripe (standard on CP21), front and rear floor mats (available on CP21 only)		
	- CH21, total retail price - 2449, discount - 700, net price	1487	1749
	- CP21, total retail price - 874, discount - 75, net price	679	799
AJK	**Deluxe Convenience Package** — (included in AAM Popular Equipment Package and AFF Luxury Equipment Package) includes electronic speed control and tilt steering wheel - CH21	299	352
ADA	**Light Package** — (included in AFF Luxury Equipment Package) includes illuminated entry and illuminated visor vanity mirrors		
	- CH21	167	196
	- CP21	167	196
AJW	**Power Convenience Package** — (included in AFF Luxury Equipment Package; requires AMM Popular Equipment Package) includes automatic power door locks and black outside dual power heated remote control mirrors - CH21	283	333
AGT	**"GTC" Performance Package** — (not available with AAM Popular Equipment Package or AFF Luxury Equipment Package) includes 2.5 liter MPI turbo I engine, 5-speed manual heavy duty transmission X7D5 enthusiast sport bucket seats (driver's side includes: power recliner, backwing, lumbar and 6-way track), power assisted high performance four		

Mfgs. Code	Description CHRYSLER	Base Cost	Sgstd. List
	wheel disc brakes, turbo boost gauge, performance handling suspension (upgraded shocks, sway bars and firm feel power steering), P205/55R16 SBR BSW all season performance tires, 16" x 6" cast aluminum wheels - CH21 w/ALJ, total retail price - 1161, discount - 109, net price	894	1052
EDM	**Engine** — 2.5 liter electronic fuel injection - CH21	STD	STD
EDT	**Engine** — 2.5 liter multi-point fuel injection high torque turbo I; requires ALJ w/AGT - CH21 w/ALJ	NC	NC
EDT	**Engine** — 2.5 liter multi-point fuel injection high torque turbo I - CH21	590	694
EFA	**Engine** — 3.0 liter V6 multi-point injection - CH21	590	694
DDV	**Transmission** — 5-speed manual heavy duty; requires ALJ w/AGT - CH21 w/ALJ	NC	NC
DDN	**Transmission** — 5-speed manual (w/3.0 liter V6 engine includes tachometer on CH21) - CH21	(465)	(547)
DGA	**Transmission** — 3-speed automatic - CH21	STD	STD
DGA	**Transmission** — 3-speed automatic; requires ALJ w/AGT - CH21 w/ALJ	325	382
DGB	**Transmission** — 4-speed automatic - CH21	79	93
DGB	**Transmission** — 4-speed automatic, requires 3.0 liter V6 w/ALJ - CH21 w/ALJ	544	640
HAA	**Air Conditioning** — manual (in AAM or AFF on CH21) - CH21	698	821
MDA	**Bracket** — front license plate	NC	NC
BRE	**Brakes** — power assisted high performance 4-wheel disc (requires AY3 on CH21)	156	183
CUN	**Console** — overhead; in pkg AFF; requires AAM on CH21 - CH21, CH21 w/ALJ	225	265
NAE	**Emission** — California control and testing (required in California)	87	102
JAF	**Electronic Instrument Cluster** — requires AFF on CH21 - Ch21, CP21	259	305
LEA	**Electronic Vehicle Info Center** — monitors over 20 functions; requires AGT on "GTC" or AFF & JAF on CP21 - CP21, CH21 w/ALJ	587	690
P	**Paint** — extra cost - CH21, CP21	65	77
RAS	**Radio** — AM mono/FM stereo, cassette, non seek & scan w/4 speakers - CH21	132	155
RAN	**Radio** — Infinity I - AM stereo/FM stereo cassette, seek/scan & 6 Infinity speakers, includes power antenna; requires AAM or AFF on CH21	485	570
RAY	**Radio** — Infinity II - AM stereo/FM stereo cassette, seek/scan, 5-band graphic equalizer and 6 Infinity speakers, includes power antenna; requires AAM or AFF on CH21	666	783
RDP	**Compact Disc Audio System** — requires RAN or RAY	382	449
JPS	**Seat** — power 6-way, driver; requires AJW or AFF; in AFF on CH21 - CH21	252	296
JPV	**Seat** — power 8-way, driver; in AFF on CP21 - CP21, CH21	312	367
SL	**Seat Trim** — leather and power 8-way driver seat - CP21, CH21 w/ALJ	855	1006
XL	**Seat Trim** — leather, enthusiast and power 12-way driver seat; requires AGT - CH21 w/ALJ	543	639
LSA	**Security Alarm** — includes function light requires AJW on CH21	127	149
GWB	**Sunroof** — glass - removable, deletes overhead console; includes removable sunshade	344	405
GWB	**Sunroof** — glass - removable, deletes overhead console; includes removable sunshade; requires AFF - CH21, CP21	196	230
TKT	**Tire** — P195/70R14 whitewall touring; NA w/AY3 - CH21	62	73
TPJ	**Tire** — P205/60R15 whitewall touring; NA w/AY3 - CP21	66	78
LET	**Trip Computer** — includes average fuel economy, instant fuel economy, distance to empty and elasped time; NA w/LEA - CP21, CH21 w/ALJ	79	93
WHE	**Wheels** — road, cast aluminum, 14"; NA w/AY3; requires AAM or AFF on CH21 - CH21	279	328
ALJ	**GTC Body Model** — (must code)		
AY3	**Wheel Handling, Aluminum, 15"** — cast aluminum, includes: sport handling suspension and tires - P205/60R15 performance; requires		

		Base Cost	Sgstd. List
	AAM or AFF on CH21 - CH21	550	647
	- CP21	452	532

LE BARON SEDAN

LE BARON (6 Cylinder)

P41	4 Dr Sedan	14562	16450
Destination Charge:		465	465

STANDARD EQUIPMENT:

LE BARON SEDAN: Air conditioning, maintenance free battery, brakes (power disc front, drum rear), soft fascia front and rear bumpers with 5 mph protection, full passenger compartment premium carpeting, chimes (headlights on, seatbelt and key in ignition), lower body protective urethane coating, electric rear window defroster, side window demisters, 3.0 liter V6 multi-port injection engine (including front air dam), tinted glass, single halogen aero style headlights, inside hood release, instrument panel (mechanical cluster includes 120 mph speedometer, odometer, trip odometer; gauges for oil pressure, voltometer, fuel, temperature, warning lights for turn signal, high beam, seatbelt, brake, check engine, check gauges, air bag and tachometer), premium sound insulation, Landau roof, front and rear carpeted mats, message center, mirrors (outside dual remote control, bright; vanity visor), moldings (bright, wheel lip, bodyside-narrow, bodyside-(lower)-bright, (upper) grooved quartz lower), AM mono/FM stereo/cassette radio with digital clock and 4 speakers, restraint system (passive driver air bag and 3-point unibelts), electronic speed control, tilt steering column, power rack and pinion type steering, luxury steering wheel, bodyside and deck color-keyed stripe, gas shocks, position sensitive struts, front and rear sway bars, P195/70R14 SBR WSW all-season touring tires, compact T125/70D14 spare tire, automatic 4-speed electronic transmission, dress up trunk, remote trunk release, premium 14" wheel treatment cover, deluxe windshield wiper/washer system with intermittent wipe.

ACCESSORIES

AFF	**Luxury Equipment Discount Package** — (includes power equipment -AJP and over convenience - AFH), includes overhead console, dual illuminated visor vanity mirrors, power door locks with ignition interlock, dual remote heated mirrors, power driver's seat, power windows, luxury leather-wrapped steering wheel, wire wheelcovers, total retail price -1643, discount - 755, net price	738	868
AJP	**Power Equipment Discount Package** — (included in luxury equipment - AFF), includes power door locks with ignition interlock, dual remote heated mirrors and power windows, total retail price - 676, discount - 676, net price	NC	NC
AFH	**Overhead Convenience Package** — (included in luxury equipment - AFF), includes overhead console and dual illuminated visor vanity mirror, total retail price - 383, discount - 0, net price	325	383
ADM	**Electronic Display Package** — includes electronic cluster instrument panel and trip computer, total retail price - 317, discount - 0, net price	269	317
AGB	**Engine** — 3.0 liter V6 MPI	STD	STD
MDA	**Bracket** — front license plate	NC	NC
BRF	**Brakes** — four wheel disc w/anti-lock	764	899
JPB	**Door Locks** — power w/ignition interlock (in AJP, AFF)	208	245
NAE	**Emissons** — California control and testing	87	102
P	**Paint** — extra cost	65	77
RAN	**Radio** — Infinity I AM stereo/FM stereo w/cassette, digital clock,		

Mfgs. Code	Description	Base Cost	Sgstd. List
	seek/scan, 4 Infinity speakers	260	306
RAY	**Radio** — Infinity II AM stereo/FM stereo w/cassette, digital clock seek/scan, 4 Infinity speakers, graphic equalizer	442	520
JPS	**Seat** — power driver side (in AFF)	252	296
SCL	**Steering wheel** — leather-wrapped (in AFF)	51	60
TBB	**Tire** — conventional spare 14"	81	95
W4L	**Wheel Covers** — wire (in AFF)	194	228
CP	**Seats** — leather w/Ultrahyde trim; includes leather-wrapped steering wheel (requires AJP and JPS)	568	668
—	**Windows** — power (only available in AFF or AJP)		
—	**New York Warranty Enhancement** — required in New York State	106	125

NEW YORKER FIFTH AVENUE

NEW YORKER FIFTH AVENUE (6 Cylinder)

S41	4 Dr Sedan	18064	20875
Destination Charge:		590	590

STANDARD EQUIPMENT:

NEW YORKER FIFTH AVENUE: Air conditioning, 5 mph protection and rear bumper guards, full carpeting, chimes (warning for: key in ignition, headlights and turn signal on, seatbelt), 500 amp battery, front cigarette lighter, electric rear window defroster, 3.3 liter V6 MPI engine, front wheel drive, tinted glass, concealed halogen headlamps with auto delay, crystalline pentastar hood ornament, dual horns, instrument panel (analog cluster includes: speedometer, odometer, and trip odometer; gauge display for fuel, voltage, oil pressure and temperature), message center, inside day/night and visor vanity mirrors, moldings (bright windshield, wheel lip, wide lower body/door-bright), power front disc/rear drum brakes, power door locks, power outside dual heated mirrors, 6-way power driver seat, power rack and pinion steering, power windows, AM mono/FM stereo ETR with digital clock and four speakers, restraint system (passive driver air bag, active 3-point unibelts left and right), Landau vinyl body color roof, security features (interior remote release for deck lid, fuel door and hood), electronic speed control, tilt steering column, luxury steering wheel, upper bodyside and decklid stripes, gas charged struts and shocks, P195/75R14 steel-belted radial WSW tires with compact spare, automatic 4-speed electronic transmission, trunk dress up, luxury wheel covers, deluxe windshield wiper/washer with intermittent wipe.

ACCESSORIES

AFF	**Luxury Equipment Discount Package** — includes bodyside moldings, front and rear floor mats, illuminated entry, cornering lights, illuminated visor vanity mirrors, dual outside mirrors (power, heated with 2 position memory), driver and passenger 8-way seats with recliner and 2-position driver memory, rear seat center armrest w/cupholder, leather-wrapped steering wheel, undercoating, pre-wired for cellular phone wiring harness, wire wheel covers, total retail price - 1712, discount - 0, net price	1285	1512
AFC	**Mark Cross Discount Package** — contains all equipment in luxury equipment - AFF, plus leather interior, 50/50 front bench seat with center armrest, total retail price - 2289, discount - 200, net price	1776	2089
AJB	**Security Package** — includes security alarm with panel warning light, keyless remote illuminated entry and illuminated visor vanity mirror -New Yorker Fifth Avenue w/o AFF Package, total retail price - 473, discount - 0, net price	402	473
	- New Yorker Fifth Avenue w/AFF Package, total retail price - 277,		

Mfgs. Code	Description	Base Cost	Sgstd. List
	discount - 0, net price	235	277
AJW	**Power Accessories Package** — (requires luxury equipment Package - AFF), includes power decklid pulldown, power antenna, total retail price - 159, discount - 0, net price	135	159
ADM	**Electronic Features Package** — includes overhead console (includes electronic vehicle information center), electronic instrument cluster and automatic adjustment day/night rearview mirror, total retail price - 1241, discount - 0, net price	1055	1241
26B	**Customer Preferred Equipment Package 26B** — includes air conditioning, floor mats, undercoating, bodyside moldings, cellular phone pre-wire, illuminated entry, vanity mirrors, cornering lamps, 8-way power seats with driver memory, wire wheel covers, rear seat armrest with cupholder, leather steering wheel - prices include total cost for base model w/3.3 liter V6 engine and option package	19349	22387
26C	**Customer Preferred Equipment Package 26C** — includes customer preferred equipment pkg 26B items plus leather seat trim -- prices include total cost for base model w/3.3 liter V6 engine and option package	19839	22964
28B	**Customer Preferred Equipment Pkg 28B** — includes customer preferred equipment package 26B items - prices include total cost for base model w/3.8 liter V6 engine and option package	19572	22649
28C	**Customer Preferred Equipment Pkg 28C** — includes customer preferred equipment package 26C - prices include total cost for base model w/3.8 liter V6 engine and option package	20062	23226
EGA	**Engine** — 3.3 liter V6 multi-point fuel injection	STD	STD
EGH	**Engine** — 3.8 liter V6 multi-point fuel injection	223	262
DGB	**Transmission** — automatic 4-speed ultradrive	STD	STD
HAB	**Air Conditioning** – automatic temperature control	129	152
MDA	**Bracket** — front license plate	NC	NC
NAE	**Emissions** — California	87	102
P	**Paint** — extra cost pearl coat/clear coat	65	77
BRF	**Power Brakes** — 4 wheel disc anti-lock	764	899
RAY	**Radio** — AM stereo/FM stereo cassette w/seek/scan, graphic equalizer & 4 speakers	364	428
ARB	**Radio** — "Infinity RS" includes RAY Radio and 10 Infinity speakers in 6 locations and a trunk mounted amplifier (req. AFF or AFC)	690	812
SLA	**Suspension** — electronically controlled air suspension	553	650
TBB	**Spare Tire** — conventional	72	85
GWA	**Sunroof** — power operated	673	792
WHE	**Wheels** — cast aluminum (req. AFF or AFC)	43	50
W4L	**Wheel Covers** — wire	194	228
—	**New York Warranty Enhancement** — required in New York State	106	125

NEW YORKER SALON

NEW YORKER SALON (6 Cylinder)

S41	4 Dr Sedan	15491	17919
Destination Charge:		545	545

STANDARD EQUIPMENT:

NEW YORKER SALON: Manual air conditioning, power brakes (front disc, rear drum), 5 mph front and rear bumpers, rear bumper guards, chimes (warning for: key in ignition, headlights and turn signal on, seatbelt), lower body protective coating, electric rear window defroster, front and side window demisters, 3.3 liter V6 multi-port injection front-wheel drive engine, aluminized steel exhaust system, tinted glass, locking glove box, concealed halogen headlights, inside hood release, crystalline pentastar hood ornament, dual horns, instrument panel (mechanical includes: speedometer, odometer and trip odometer; gauges for fuel, voltage, oil pressure and temperature), message center, mirrors (inside day/night; visor vanity - cloth covered left and right; outside dual power remote control bright, heated), moldings (windshield, upper doors, decklid, wheel opening - bright, lower body/wide bright, sill and backlight-black), front seat back storage pockets, AM mono/FM stereo ETR radio with digital clock and 4 speakers, passive driver air bag and active 3-point restraint system, power steering, luxury steering wheel, bodyside and decklid stripes, P195/75R14 whitewall steel-belted radial tires with compact spare, automatic 4-speed ultradrive transmission, remote release power trunk, trunk (carpeted floor, tire cover, sides and lower deck trunk), 14" premium wheel covers, power windows, deluxe windshield wiper/washer with intermittent wipe.

ACCESSORIES

Code	Description	Base Cost	Sgstd. List
AAB	**Popular Equipment Discount Package** — (includes deluxe convenience package - AJK), includes power door locks, front and rear floor mats, electronic speed control, tilt steering column and undercoating, total retail price - 768, discount - 400, net price	313	368
AFF	**Luxury Equipment Discount Package** — contains all equipment in popular equipment - AAB plus automatic headlamp delay system, illuminated entry, cornering lights, dual illuminated visor vanity mirrors, automatic day/night rearview mirror, bodyside molding, rear seat center armrest w/cupholder, power 6-way driver and passenger seats, leather-wrapped steering wheel, pre-wire wiring harness for cellular phone and wire wheel covers, total retail price - 2264, discount - 550, net price	1457	1714
AJK	**Deluxe Convenience Package** — (included in popular equipment - AAB and luxury equipment - AFF), includes electronic speed control, tilt steering wheel, total retail price - 352, discount - 0, net price	299	352
AJB	**Security Package** — (requires popular equipment package - AAB), includes security alarm with panel warning light, keyless remote entry (door locks and decklid), illuminated entry and dual illuminated visor vanity mirror - Salon w/o AFF package, total retail price - 473, discount - 0, net price	402	473
	- Salon w/AFF package, total retail price - 277, discount - 0, net price	235	277
AJW	**Power Accessories Package** — (requires luxury equipment package - AFF), includes automatic decklid pulldown and power antenna, total retail price - 159, discount - 0, net price	135	159
26B	**Customer Preferred Equipment Package 26B** — includes air conditioning, floor mats and undercoating, power door locks - prices include total cost for base model and option package	15787	18267
26C	**Customer Preferred Equipment Package 26C** — includes air conditioning, floor mats and undercoating, speed control and tilt column, power door locks, cellular phone pre-wire and headlamp delay, illuminated entry, vanity mirrors, cornering lamps, automatic adjustable rearview mirror, 6-way driver and passenger power seat, leather steering wheel and bodyside moldings, rear seat armrest with cupholder and wire wheel covers - prices include total cost for base model and option package	16931	19613
EGA	**Engine** — 3.3 liter V6 multi-point fuel injection	STD	STD
DGB	**Transmission** — electronic 4 speed	STD	STD
MDA	**Bracket** — front license plate	NC	NC
BRF	**Brakes** — 4 wheel disc anti-lock	764	899
JPH	**Door Locks** — power; (in AAB or AFF)	277	326
NAE	**Emissions** — California; req. in CA, N/A otherwise	87	102
P	**Paint** — extra cost pearl coat/clear coat	65	77
RAS	**Radio** — AM mono/FM stereo w/cassette non seek & scan &		

Mfgs. Code	Description	Base Cost	Sgstd. List
	4 speakers	132	155
RAY	**Radio** — AM stereo/FM stereo cassette radio w/seek/scan, graphic equalizer and 4 speakers (req's. AAB or AFF)	364	428
ARB	**Radio** — "Infinity RS" (includes: RAY Radio and 10 Infinity speakers in 6 locations and a trunk mounted amplifier), req's. AFF	690	812
HP	**Seat Trim** — leather 50/50 front bench (req's AFF)	502	590
JPS	**Seat** — power 6-way driver only; req's AAB	252	296
JPP	**Seat** — Power 8-way, driver/pass with memory & power recliners, includes 2 position memory mirrors (req's AFF)	337	396
GWA	**Sunroof** — Power (req's AFF)	673	792
SER	**Suspension** — rear automatic load leveling (req's AAB)	191	225
TBB	**Spare Tire** — conventional	72	85
W46	**Wheelcovers** — wire (req's AAB); (in AFF)	194	228
WHE	**Wheels** — cast aluminum (req's AFF)	43	50
—	**New York Warranty Enhancement** — required in New York State	106	125

TOWN & COUNTRY

TOWN & COUNTRY (6 Cylinder)

P53	4 Dr Wagon	21426	23905
Destination Charge:		520	520

STANDARD EQUIPMENT:

TOWN & COUNTRY: Air conditioning, maintenance-free battery, power assisted brakes (front disc and rear drum with anti-lock), headlamps on, seatbelt and key in ignition chimes, console (forward storage, overhead long), body protective urethane coating, stainless steel exhaust, front door window demisters, electric rear window defroster, 3.3 liter 6 cylinder multi-port injection engine, floor mats, inside fuel filler door remote release, windshield and front door tinted glass, glass sunscreen on remaining windows, glass vented (4-passenger compartment), bright grille, cloth covered headliner, crystal pentastar hood ornament, inside hood release, dual note horns, instrument panel (includes: speedometer, odometer, trip odometer with reset; graphic displays for tachometer, oil pressure, fuel, temperature; graphic message for low fuel, low washer fluid, liftgate and door ajar; warning lights for check engine and check gauges), deluxe body sound insulation, roof mounted luggage rack, mirrors (outside - dual power remote control body color, visor vanity illuminated, right and left), lower bodyside and sill applique body color moldings, front and side power door locks, power driver's seat, power liftgate release, power windows (front door and rear quarter vent), AM/FM stereo with cassette, seek and scan (includes Infinity I sound system), active 3-point restraint system, seating (7-passenger, high-back driver and passenger reclining buckets with 2-passenger and 3-passenger quick release rear bench seats), electronic speed control, rack and pinion type power steering, tilt steering column, leather-wrapped steering wheel, P205/70R15 steel-belted radial tires (BSW with compact spare), spare tire carrier (underslung with cable winch), automatic 4-speed electronic transmission, 15" cast aluminum lace wheels (painted body color with white exterior), rear window wiper/washer with intermittent wipe, woodgrain bodyside and liftgate with unique wood color moldings.

ACCESSORIES

HBB	**Air Conditioning** — rear passenger compartment; includes 120 Amp. Alt.	396	466
MDA	**Bracket** — front license plate	NC	NC
NAE	**Emissions** — California control & testing; req. in CA; N/A otherwise	87	102
RAY	**Radio Infinity II** — AM stereo/FM stereo w/cassette, seek & scan and		

Code	Description	Base Cost	Sgstd. List
	graphic equalizer with 6 Infinity speakers	182	214
G7	**Seat Trim** — cloth and leather; N/A w/CYE	NC	NC
CYE	**7 Passenger Seating**	NC	NC
CYS	**Quad Command 7 Passenger Seating** — includes 4 bucket seats and 3 passenger rear bench	262	308
PC	**Tires** — P205/70R15 whitewalls	59	69
—	**New York Warranty Enhancement** — required in New York State	106	125

1991 dodge

CARAVAN FRONT WHEEL DRIVE

CARAVAN (4 Cylinder)

Code	Model	Base Cost	Sgstd. List
L52	Base Caravan	11859	13215
H52	Special Edition	12854	14345
P52	Limited Edition	15758	17645
P52 w/ASP	ES	17073	19140

GRAND CARAVAN (6 Cylinder)

Code	Model	Base Cost	Sgstd. List
H53	Special Edition	14394	16095
P53	Limited Edition	17174	19255

Destination Charge: All models 520 520

STANDARD EQUIPMENT:

CARAVAN: Air conditioning (Caravan LE, Grand Caravan LE), power assisted front disc/rear drum brakes, chimes (headlights on, seatbelt and key in ignition), console (front storage/overhead/trip computer) (Caravan LE, Grand Caravan LE), body protect urethane coating, stainless steel exhaust, electric rear window defroster (Caraven LE, Grand Caravan LE), power front and rear door locks (Caravan LE, Grand Caravan LE), 2.5 liter 4 cylinder electronic fuel injection engine (Base Caravan, Caravan SE, Caravan LE), 3.3 liter 6 cylinder multi-point injection engine (Grand Caravan SE, Grand Caravan LE), floor mats (Caravan LE, Grand Caravan LE), remote fuel filler door release (Base Caravan, Caravan LE, Grand Caravan LE), tinted glass, aerostyle halogen headlamps, inside hood release, single not horn (Base Caravan), dual note horn (Caravan SE, Caravan LE, Grand Caravan SE, Grand Caravan LE), special body sound insulation (Base Caravan, Caravan SE, Grand Caravan SE), deluxe body sound insulation (Caravan LE, Grand Caravan LE), power liftgate release (Caravan SE, Caravan LE, Grand Caravan SE, Grand Caravan LE), exterior aero black fold-away power mirrors (Base Caravan, Caravan SE, Grand Caravan SE), exterior fold-away heated aero black power mirrors (Caravan LE, Grand Caravan LE), non-illuminated visor vanity mirrors (Base Caravan, Caravan SE, Grand Caravan SE), illuminated visor vanity mirrors (Caravan LE, Grand Caravan LE), AM mono/FM stereo ETR radio with digital clock, 5 passenger, driver and passenger bucket seats with 3 passenger quick release rear bench seats (Base Caravan), 7 passenger driver and passenger bucket seats with 2 and 3 passenger quick release rear bench seats (Caravan SE, Caravan LE, Grand Caravan SE, Grand Caravan LE), electronic speed control (Caravan LE, Grand Caravan LE), rack and pinion power steering, tilt steering column (Caravan LE, Grand Caravan LE), deluxe steering wheel (Base Caravan, Caravan SE, Grand Caravan SE), sport steering wheel (Caravan LE, Grand Caravan LE), bodyside tape stripe (Caravan SE, Grand Caravan SE), upper and lower tape stripe (Caravan LE, Grand Caravan LE), P195/70R14 SBR-BSW tires (Base Caravan, Caravan SE, Caravan LE), P205/70R15 SBR BSW tires (Grand Caravan SE, Grand Caravan LE), spare compact tire (Base Caravan, Caravan SE, Grand Caravan SE), under body spare tire carrier with cable winch, 3 speed automatic transmission (Base Caravan, Caravan SE, Caravan LE), automatic 4 speed electronic transmission (Grand Caravan SE, Grand

Caravan LE), two tone paint (Caravan LE, Grand Caravan LE), deluxe wheel covers (Base Caravan), sport wheel covers (Caravan SE, Caravan LE, Grand Caravan SE, Grand Caravan LE), styled road wheel (Caravan SE, Caravan LE, Grand Caravan SE, Grand Caravan LE), power quarter vent windows (Caravan LE, Grand Caravan LE), liftgate window wiper/washer with intermittent wipe, deluxe windshield wipers with intermittent wipe.

ACCESSORIES

Code	Description	Base Cost	Sgstd. List
—	**Seating**		
CYD	5-passenger (2 buckets, 3-passenger bench) - L52	STD	STD
CYE	7-passenger (2 buckets, 2 passenger bench and 3-passenger bench) - L52	337	397
CYS	7-passenger, quad command seating (2 buckets, 2 inter buckets and 3-passenger bench) - all except L52	507	597
—	converta bed seating (7-passenger, 2 buckets, 2-passenger bench and 3-passenger bench, converta bed) - H52, H53	470	553
AAB	**Popular Value Discount Package** — (includes light package, deluxe convenience package, floor mats, gauges, dual horns, deluxe sound insulation, power liftgate release, dual illuminated visor vanity mirrors [except L52], power door locks, 7-passenger seating)		
	- L52	1216	1431
	- L52 w/AFW pkg	896	1054
	- H52	900	1059
	- H52 w/AFW pkg	632	743
	- H53	900	1059
	- H53 w/AFW pkg	632	743
AFF	**Luxury Value Discount Package** — (includes popular value discount pkg, storage convenience pkg, overhead console, electric rear window defroster, time delay headlamps, power heated foldaway mirrors, radio [AM stereo and FM stereo cassette, "Infiniti I"], power driver seat [P52, P53 only], power front windows, rear quarter vent windows)		
	- H52	1973	2321
	- H52 w/AFW pkg	1561	1837
	- H53	1973	2321
	- H53 w/AFW pkg	1561	1837
	- P52	197	232
	- P53	197	232
AFW	**Family Value Discount Package** — (includes front air conditioning, electric rear window defroster, dual horns, deluxe sound insulation, power liftgate release, light package)		
	- L52	937	1102
	- L52 w/6 cylinder engine	1192	1402
	- H52	885	1041
	- H53	885	1041
ASP	**ES Decor Package** — (not available w/AHT trailer tow) (includes heavy duty brakes, 3.0L MPI engine, 4-speed automatic ultradrive transmission, bodyside and sill molding, fog lamps, P205/70R15 BSW tires, 15" cast aluminum wheels) - P52	STD	STD
AHT	**Heavy Duty Trailer Tow Package** — (not available with AGA or ASP) (includes 120 amp alternator, 625 amp battery, heavy duty [brakes, flasher, radiator, suspension, transmission, oil cooler], 15" conventional spare tire, P205/70R15 BSW SBR tires, 15" wheel covers, trailer tow wiring harness) - H52	473	557
	- H53	377	443
	- P52	473	557
	- P53	377	443

Mfgs. Code	Description	Base Cost	Sgstd. List
	DODGE		
AFM	**Storage Convenience Package** — (includes forward storage console and storage drawer) - H52, H53	127	149
AJK	**Deluxe Convenience Package** — (included in AAB popular value pkg) (includes electronic speed control, tilt steering column, luxury steering wheel) - L52	343	404
	- H52	343	404
	- H53	343	404
AJP	**Power Convenience Package** — (included in luxury value pkg) (includes power door locks and power windows) - H52	417	490
	- H52 w/AAB	213	250
	- H53	417	490
	- H53 w/AAB	213	250
AGA	**Sport Handling Package** — (not available w/ASP LX Decor or SDB heavy duty suspension) (includes heavy duty brakes, rear sway bar, P205/70R15 BSW SBR tires, 15" luxury wheel covers) - H52	117	138
	- P52	117	138
	- H53	20	24
	- P53	20	24
—	**Light Package** — (included in AAB popular value pkg and AFW family value pkg; not available otherwise) (includes ash receiver, storage drawer [if so equipped], map/reading, glove box, underhood, ignition, illuminated entry, liftgate dual flood, door ajar, low washer fluid warning)		
EDM	**Engine** — 2.5 liter electronic fuel injection - L52, H52, P52	STD	STD
EFA	**Engine** — 3.0 liter MPI - L52, H52, P52	590	694
EGA	**Engine** — 3.3 liter MPI - H52, P52	677	796
DGA	**Transmission** — 3 speed automatic (not available w/3.0L engine on P52) - L52, H52, P52	STD	STD
DGB	**Transmission** — 4 speed automatic - H52, P52	147	173
EL	**Leather Trim** — low back bucket seats (requires AFF) - P52, P53	735	865
HAA	**Air Conditioning** — front; included in AFW - L52, H52, H53	728	857
HBB	**Air Conditioning** — rear; includes deluxe insulation and 120 amp alternator - P53	396	466
HBB	**Air Conditioning** — rear; includes deluxe insulation and 120 amp alternator (requires AFM, GFA, HAA) - H53	485	571
	- with AFW, AAB or AFF on H53 - H53	396	466
	- with AHT on H53 - H53	433	509
	- with AFW, AAB or AFF and AHT on H53 - H53	343	404
BRK	**Brakes** — anti-lock - H53, P53	679	799
	- with AGA, AHT or ASP (requires EGA) - H52, P52	679	799
	- includes 15" tires and wheels (requires EGA) - H52, P52	754	887
MPA	**Applique** — Woodgrain; n/a with ASP - P52, P53	NC	NC
MDA	**Bracket** — front license plate	NC	NC
GFA	**Defroster** — electric rear window (includes power liftgate release); included in AFW - L52	184	217
GFA	**Defroster** — electric rear window; included in AFW and AFF - H52, H53	143	168
JPH	**Door Locks** — Power - speed sensitive actuation; included in AJP, AAB and AFF - L52, H52, H53	204	240
NAE	**Emissions** — California control and testing	87	102
GAE	**Glass** — sunscreen	352	414
MWA	**Luggage Rack**	122	143
P	**Paint** — extra cost	65	77
APB	**Paint** — two tone - H52, H53	252	296
RAS	**Radio** — AM mono/FM stereo w/cassette non seek and scan w/4 speakers; n/a w/AFF	132	155
RAN	**Radio Infinity I** — AM stereo/FM stereo w/cassette and seek and scan; included in AFF - with 6 infinity speakers - H52, P52, H53, P53	392	461
RAY	**Radio Infinity II** — AM stereo/FM stereo w/cassette, seek/scan and graphic		

Mfgs. Code	Description	Base Cost	Sgstd. List
	equalizer (requires AAB or AFF) - with 6 infinity speakers (w/AAB) - H52, P52, H53, P53	574	675
	- with 6 infinity speakers (w/AFF) - H52, P52, H53, P53	182	214
SDB	**Suspension** — heavy duty; in AHT; n/a w/AGA	59	69
—	**Seat** — power left (included in AFF) - P52, P53		
TLB	**Tires** — 205/70R14 SBR WSW (requires AAB on L52/H52) - L52, H52, P52	122	143
TPC	**Tires** — 205/70R15 SBR WSW; (requires AHT or AGA on H52/P52 and AAB on H52/H53) - H52, P52, H53, P53	59	69
TBB	**Tire** — conventional spare 14"; (requires 14" tires and wheel) - L52, H52, P52	93	109
	- conventional spare 15" (requires 15" tires and wheels on L52, H52,P52)	93	109
—	**Windows** — power - front doors; included in AJP and AFF - H52, P52, H53, P53		
WJL	**Wheels** — cast aluminum 15"; included in ASP or requires AGA on 52's - H52, P52, H53, P53	309	363
W49	**Wheel Covers (4)** — wire 14; n/a w/AGA, AHT or ASP) - L52, H52, P52	208	245
MP8	**Woodgrain Delete** — includes bodyside stripe with monotone paint - P52, P53	NC	NC
—	**Warranty Enhancement for New York** — mandatory	106	125

CARAVAN ALL WHEEL DRIVE

CARAVAN ALL WHEEL DRIVE (6 Cylinder)

H52	Special Edition	15401	17240
P52	Limited Edition	18301	20535
P52 w/ASP	LE	18753	21049
H53	Grand Caravan Special Edition	16022	17945
P53	Grand Caravan Limited Edition	18802	21105

Destination Charge: All models 520 520

STANDARD EQUIPMENT:

CARAVAN ALL WHEEL DRIVE: Front air conditioning (LE, Grand Caravan LE), power front disc/rear drum brakes, warning chimes, front storage console (LE, Grand Caravan LE), mini trip computer (LE, Grand Caravan LE), lower body protective urethane coating, rear window defroster (LE, Grand Caravan LE), power door locks (LE, Grand Caravan LE), 3.3 liter 6 cylinder MFI engine, floor mats (LE, Grand Caravan LE), fuel filler door remote release (LE, Grand Caravan LE), tinted glass, aero-style halogen headlamps, inside hood release, dual note horn, tachometer and gauges (LE, Grand Caravan LE), deluxe body sound insulation (LE, Grand Caravan LE), power liftgate release, power foldaway mirrors (heated on LE and Grand Caravan LE), visor vanity mirror (illuminated on LE and Grand Caravan LE), AM mono and FM stereo ETR w/digital clock, electronic speed control (LE, Grand Caravan LE), power steering, tilt steering column (LE, Grand Caravan LE), luxury steering wheel (LE, Grand Caravan LE), bodyside stripe (SE, Grand Caravan SE), P205/70R15 SBR BSW tires, compact spare, automatic 4-speed ultradrive transmission, woodgrain bodyside (LE, Grand Caravan LE), luxury wheel covers, liftgate window wiper/washer.

ACCESSORIES

—	**Seating**		
CYE	7-passenger (2 bucket, 2-passenger bench and 3-passenger bench)	STD	STD
CYS	7-passenger, quad command seating (2 buckets 2 inter buckets and 3-passenger bench)	507	597

Mfgs. Code	Description **DODGE**	Base Cost	Sgstd. List
—	converta bed seating (7-passenger, 2 buckets, 2-passenger bench and 3-passenger bench, converta bed) - H52, H53	470	553
AAB	**Popular Value Discount Package** — (not available w/AFF luxury value package) (includes light package, deluxe convenience package, floor mats, gauges, deluxe sound insulation, dual illuminated visor vanity mirrors, power door locks) - H52	900	1059
	- H52 w/AFW	632	743
	- H53	900	1059
	- H53 w/AFW	632	743
AFF	**Luxury Value Discount Package** — (includes popular value package, storage convenience package, overhead console, electric rear window defroster, headlamps time delay, power dual heated mirrors, AM stereo and FM stereo cassett "Infinity I", power driver seat [P52 and P53 only], power windows, rear quarter vent windows)		
	- H52	1973	2321
	- H52 w/AFW pkg	1561	1837
	- H53	1973	2321
	- H53 w/AFW pkg	1561	1837
	- P52	197	232
	- P53	197	232
AFW	**Family Value Discount Package** — (includes front air conditioning, electric rear window defroster, deluxe sound insulation, light package)		
	- H52	885	1041
	- H53	885	1041
ASP	**ES Decor Package** — (not available w/AHT trailer tow package) (includes bodyside and sill molding, fog lamps, cast aluminum 15" wheels) - P52	STD	STD
AHT	**Heavy Duty Trailer Tow Package** — (includes 120 amp alternator, 625 amp battery, heavy duty [flasher, radiator, transmission oil cooler], trailer tow wiring harness) - H52, H53, P52, P53	225	265
AFM	**Storage Convenience Package** — (includes console and storage drawer) - H52, H53	127	149
AJK	**Deluxe Convenience Package** — (included in AAB popular value package) (includes electronic speed control, tilt steering column, luxury steering wheel) - H52, H53	343	404
AJP	**Power Convenience Package** — (included in AFF luxury value package) (includes power door locks, power windows)		
	- H52	417	490
	- H52 w/AAB	213	250
	- H53	417	490
	- H53 w/AAB	213	150
—	**Light Package** — (included in AAB popular value package and AFW family value package; not available otherwise) (includes lights for ash receiver, storage drawer [if so equipped], map/reading, glove box, underhood, ignition, illuminated entry, liftgate dual flood, door ajar, low washer warning fluid warning)		
EL	**Leather Trim** — low back bucket seats (requires AFF) - P52, P53	735	865
HAA	**Air Conditioning** — front; included in AFW - H52, H53	728	857
MPA	**Applique** — woodgrain; n/a w/ASP - P52, P53	NC	NC
MDA	**Bracket** — front license plate	NC	NC
GFA	**Defroster** — electric rear window; included in AFW and AFF - H52, H53	143	168
JPH	**Door Locks** — power; included in AJP, AAB and AFF - H52, H53	204	240
NAE	**Emissions** — California control and testing	87	102
GAE	**Glass** — sunscreen	352	414
P	**Paint** — extra cost	65	77
APB	**Paint** — two tone - H52, H53	252	296
APB	**Paint** — two tone - P52, P53	NC	NC
RAS	**Radio** — AM mono/FM stereo w/cassette, non seek and scan w/4		

Mfgs. Code	Description	Base Cost	Sgstd. List
	speakers	132	155
RAN	**Radio Infinity I** — AM stereo/FM stereo w/cassette and seek and scan; included in (AFF) - w/6 Infinity speakers	392	461
RAY	**Radio Infinity II** — AM stereo/FM stereo w/cassette and seek/scan and graphic equalizer (requires AAB or AFF) - w/6 Infinity speakers (w/AAB) - w/6 Infinity speakers (w/AFF)	574	675
—	**Seat** — power left; included in AFF - P52, P53		
TPC	**Tires** — 205/70R15 SBR WSW; (requires AAB or AFF on H52/H53)	59	69
—	**Windows** — power - front doors; included in AJP and AFF		
WJL	**Wheels** — cast aluminum 15"; included in ASP	309	363
MP8	**Woodgrain Delete** — includes bodyside stripe with monotone paint - P52, P53	NC	NC
—	**Warranty Enhancement for New York** — mandatory	106	125

COLT

COLT (4 Cylinder)

Code	Model	Base Cost	Sgstd. List
B2DE24	Colt Base	6358	6949
B2DL24	Colt GL	7069	7845
B3DM46	Colt Vista FWD	9300	11941
B3EM46	Colt Vista 4WD	10342	13167
	Destination Charge: All models	328	328

STANDARD EQUIPMENT:

COLT: Assist grip, power assisted front disc/rear drum brakes, 5 mph bumper system, cigarette lighter (Colt GL), console, side window demisters, 1.5 liter 4 cylinder multi-port injection engine, stainless steel exhaust system, remote release fuel filler door (Colt GL), temperature and fuel gauges, flush aerostyle halogen headlights, molded cloth headliner, inside car hood release, dome and ashtray lights, lights (warning, oil pressure, brakes, seatbelts, low fuel), outside left manual mirror (Base Colt), outside dual manual remote mirror (Colt GL), inside day/night mirror, manual rack and pinion type steering, deluxe steering wheel, MacPherson type strut and coil springs suspension, tachometer (Colt GL), P155/80R13 steel belted radial black sidewall tires, 4 speed manual transmission (Base Colt), 5 speed manual transmission (Colt GL), trip odometer, Argent styled steel wheels with center cap, two speed windshield wipers (Base Colt), 2 speed windshield wipers with fixed intermittent wipe (Colt GL).

COLT VISTA: Assist grips, maintenance-free battery, power disc front and drum rear brakes, 5 mph color-keyed bumpers, cigarette lighter, child protection rear door locks, electronic liftgate defroster, side window demisters, 2.0 liter 4 cylinder multi-port injection engine, locking fuel filler door with remote release, temperature and fuel gauges, tinted glass, halogen headlights, molded cloth covered headliner, rear seating area heat ducts, remote hood release, lights (warning - brakes, seatbelts, oil pressure, low fuel, door ajar, battery), day/night mirrors, dual outside manual remote mirrors, front mudguards, rear mudguards (Vista 4WD), speedometer with trip odometer, power rack and pinion steering (Vista 4WD), deluxe color-keyed steering wheel, front MacPherson type struts with coil spring with stabilizer bar suspension, steel radial black sidewall tires with compact spare, P165/80R13 tires (Vista FWD)m P185/70R14 tires (Vista 4WD), 5 speed manual transmission, Argent steel wheels with center cap 13" (Vista FWD), Argent steel wheels with bright center cap 14" (Vista 4WD), 2 speed windshield wipers with variable intermittent wipe.

ACCESSORIES

Code	Description	Base Cost	Sgstd. List
HAA	**Air Conditioning** — Colt Base, Colt GL	625	753

Mfgs. Code	Description	Base Cost	Sgstd. List
	DODGE		
	- Colt Vista Wagon	613	739
CLA	**Carpet Protectors**	23	28
NAE	**California Emission Controls**	NC	NC
WMC	**Wheel Trim Rings** — Colt Base, Colt GL	46	55
RAG	**AM/FM Radio w/2 Speakers** — Colt Base, Colt GL	180	217
KDO	**Bodyside Stripe Set** — Colt Base	82	99
DGA	**Automatic Transmission** — Colt Base	499	601
	- Colt GL, Colt Vista	414	499
—	**Optional Packages — Colt Base**		
1FB	**Pkg B** — (includes rear defroster) - Colt Base	55	66
1FC	**Pkg C** — (includes tinted glass) - Colt Base	52	63
1FD	**Pkg D** — (includes rear defroster and tinted glass) - Colt Base	107	129
—	**Optional Packges — Colt GL**		
1FC	**Pkg C** — (includes rear defroster and tinted glass) - Colt GL	107	129
1fD	**Pkg D** — (includes rear defroster, tinted glass, power steering, fixed intermittent wiper/washer) - Colt GL	345	416
1FE	**Pkg E** — (includes rear defroster, tinted glass, power steering, fixed intermittent wipers, rear wiper/washer and digital clock) - Colt GL	500	603
1FF	**Pkg F** — (includes rear defroster, tinted glass power steering, fixed intermittent wipers, rear wiper/washer, digital clock, 4 aluminum wheels) - Colt GL	724	872
1FG	**Pkg G** — (includes rear defroster, tinted glass, power steering, fixed intermittent wipers, rear wiper/washer, digital clock, 4 aluminum wheels, rear spoiler and tachometer) - Colt GL	878	1058
—	**Optional Packages — Colt Vista Wagon FWD**		
1FA	**Pkg A** — (includes AM/FM ETR radio, rear wiper/washer, power steering) - Colt Vista Wagon FWD	570	687
1FB	**Pkg B** — (includes speed control, AM/FM ETR stereo radio, rear wiper/washer, power steering, power door locks, power windows) - Colt Vista Wagon FWD	1081	1303
1FC	**Pkg C** — (includes AM/FM ETR radio, power steering and custom pkg) - Colt Vista Wagon FWD	789	951
1FD	**Pkg D** — (includes AM/FM ETR cassette radio, speed control, power steering, power door locks, power windows, custom pkg and 13" aluminum wheels) - Colt Vista Wagon FWD	1665	2006
1FE	**Pkg E** — (includes AM/FM ETR radio, speed control, rear wiper/washer, power steering) - Colt Vista Wagon FWD	722	870
—	**Optional Packages — Colt Vista Wagon 4WD**		
1FA	**Pkg A** — (includes AM/FM ETR radio, rear wiper washer) - Colt Vista Wagon 4WD	355	428
1FB	**Pkg B** — (includes AM/FM ETR radio, speed control, rear wiper/washer, power door locks and power windows) - Colt Vista Wagon 4WD	867	1044
1FC	**Pkg C** — (includes AM/FM ETR radio and custom pkg) - Colt Vista Wagon 4WD	508	612
1FD	**Pkg D** — (includes AM/FM ETR cassette radio, speed control, power door locks, power windows and custom pkg) - Colt Vista Wagon 4WD	1150	1386
1FE	**Pkg E** — (includes AM/FM ETR cassette radio, speed control, power door locks, power windows, limited slip differential, custom pkg and 14" aluminum wheels) - Colt Vista Wagon 4WD	1589	1915
1FF	**Pkg F** — (includes AM/FM ETR radio, speed control rear wiper/washer) - Colt Vista Wagon 4WD	507	611
1FG	**Pkg G** — (includes AM/FM ETR radio, limited slip differential and custom pkg) - Colt Vista Wagon 4WD	689	830

Mfgs. Code	Description	DODGE	Base Cost	Sgstd. List

DAYTONA

DAYTONA (4 Cylinder)

VL24	2 Dr Base Hatchback	9461	10450
VH24	2 Dr ES Hatchback	10569	11695

DAYTONA (4 Cylinder Turbo)

VX24	2 Dr Shelby Hatchback	11753	13025

Destination Charge: All models 479 479

STANDARD EQUIPMENT:

DAYTONA: Heel and toe capability accelerator pedal, maintenance-free battery, power assisted front disc/rear drum brakes (Base Daytona, ES), power assisted 4 wheel disc 15" high performance brakes (Shelby), soft fascia bumpers with integral nerf 5 mph protection, chimes (seatbelt warning, key in ignition, headlights "on"), console armrest with storage compartment, lower body protective urethan coating, side window demisters, aluminized steel exhaust system (Base Daytona, ES), aluminized steel performance tuned exhaust system (Shelby), 2.5 liter 4 cylinder electronic fuel injection engine (Base Daytona, ES), 2.5 liter 4 cylinder turbo charged multi-point injection engine (Shelby), fog lights (ES, Shelby), gauges - fuel, temperature, voltage, oil pressure, turbo boost (with turbo engine only), tachometer, trip odometer, tinted glass, ground effects applique on lower sill and fenders and wake modifier (ES, Shelby), concealed halogen headlights with time delay, hood release, sound premium insulation, remote liftgate release, message center, mirrors (outside dual black remote control, vanity right and left side non-illuminated), AM mono/FM stereo radio with digital clock and 4 speakers, passive driver airbag and active 3-point unibelt restraint system, low back front bucket seats with recliners, split back rear fold-down seats, body color rear spoiler, sport suspension (all Daytona suspension components include gas charged struts and shocks), maximum performance Shelby - includes performance tuned shocks, struts, springs and large diameter sway bars (Shelby), power assisted rack and pinion steering with quick ratio, 4-spoke sport steering wheel (Base Daytona, ES), 4-spoke leather-wrapped steering wheel (Shelby), P185/70R14 steel black sidewall all-season tires (Base Daytona), P205/6015 steel black all-season touring tires (ES), P205/55VR16 steel black performance speed rated tires (Shelby), compact spare tire, rear tonneau cover (ES, Shelby), 5 speed manual high capacity VX24 transmission, Venturi wheel cover (Base Daytona), Eurocast aluminum 15" x 6" road wheels (ES), cast aluminum 16" x 6" unidirectional pumper wheels (Shelby), deluxe windshield wiper/washer with intermittent wipe.

ACCESSORIES

AWN **Super Discount Package** — includes air conditioning, front floor mats, lights (glove box, cargo, underhood, dual map/reading), outside dual power remote control mirrors (if GFA is ordered mirrors are heated), tilt steering column, power door locks, electronic speed control, radio (AM mono/FM stereo w/cassette - non-seek & scan) - ES, Base Daytona, total retail price - 1733, discount - 700, net price 878 1033

AAM **Popular Equipment Discount Package** — includes air conditioning, front floor mats, lights (glove box, cargo, underhood, dual map/reading), black outside dual power remote control mirrors (if GFA is ordered mirrors are heated), tilt steering column - Shelby, total retail price - 1124, discount - 150, net price 828 974

AAW **Value Discount Package** — includes power door locks, electronic speed control, radio (AM mono/FM stereo w/cassette - non seek & scan) - Base Daytona, ES, Shelby, total retail price - 609, discount - 220, net price . 331 389

AAN **Popular Equipment - No Air Package** — includes front floor mats, lights (glove box, underhood, dual map/reading), black outside dual power remote control mirrors (if GFA is ordered mirrors are heated), tilt steering

Mfgs. Code	Description **DODGE**	Base Cost	Sgstd. List
	column - Base Daytona, ES	258	303
AGY	**V6 Performance Package** — (requires AWN or AAN pkg) - includes power 4 wheel disc brakes, 3.0 V6 MPI engine w/performance tuned exhaust, leather-wrapped steering wheel (includes leather shift knob on manuals only), performance handling suspension - ES	861	1013
ADK	**Premium Light Package** — (requires AWN, AAM or AAN pkgs; not available with AGS C/S Competition pkg) - includes illuminated entry lighting system and dual illuminated vanity visor mirrors - Base Daytona, ES, Shelby	167	196
AGS	**C/S Competition Package** — includes power 4-wheel disc brakes, 2.5 liter high torque turbo I engine with 5-speed high capacity transmission, rear spoiler, maximum performance Shelby suspension, P205/55 SBR unidirectional tires, turbo accessories (boost gauge, performance tuned exhaust, power bulge hood), cast aluminum 16"x 6" pumper wheels - Base Daytona	1836	2160
AY5	**Steel Wheel Discount Package** — includes P205/60R14 SBR all season touring tires and 14" styled steel wheels - Base Daytona, total retail price - 253, discount - 143, net price	94	110
AY6	**Aluminum Wheel Discount Package** — (requires AWN or AAN Pkgs) - includes P205/60R14 SBR all season touring tires, 14" cast aluminum wheels - Base Daytona, total retail price - 479, discount - 143, net price	286	336
EDM	**Engine** — 2.5 liter electronic fuel injection - Base Daytona, ES	STD	STD
EDT	**Engine** — 2.5 liter multi point fuel injection high torque turbo 1 - Shelby	STD	STD
EFA	**Engine** — 3.0 liter V6 - Base Daytona, ES	590	694
DDM	**Transmission** — 5 speed manual - Base Daytona, ES	STD	STD
DDN	**Transmission** — 5 speed manual - Base Daytona, ES	NC	NC
DDV	**Transmission** — 5 speed manual high capacity - Shelby	STD	STD
DGA	**Transmission** — 3 speed automatic	465	547
DGB	**Transmission** — 4 speed automatic - Base Daytona, ES	544	640
—	**Air Conditioning** — in AAM & AWN package only		
MDA	**Bracket** — front license plate	NC	NC
CUN	**Console** — overhead; includes sunglass and garage door opener storage, compass and outside temperature, dome and map lights; requires AAM, AAN or AWN; n/a w/(GWB) - ES, Shelby	225	265
GFA	**Defroster** — rear window electric; requires AAM, AAN or AWN	169	199
—	**Door Locks** — power, available in AWN and AAW only		
NAE	**Emission** — California control and testing	87	102
—	**Radio** — AM mono/FM stereo cassette, non seek and scan; available in AWN or AAW only		
RAN	**Radio** — AM stereo/FM stereo cassette, seek and scan w/6 Infinity speakers (requires AAM or AAN) - ES, Shelby	419	493
RAN	**Radio** — AM stereo/FM stereo cassette, seek and scan, w/6 Infinity speakers (requires AWN or AAW) - ES, Shelby	287	338
RAY	**Radio** — AM stereo/FM stereo cassette, seek and scan, w/6 Infinity speakers and 5/band graphic equalizer (requires AAM or AAN) - ES, Shelby	600	706
RAY	**Radio** — AM stereo/FM stereo cassette, seek and scan, w/6 Infinity speakers and 5/band graphic equalizer (requires AWN or AAW) - ES, Shelby	468	551
RDP	**Compact Disc Player** — requires RAN or RAY - ES, Shelby	382	449
JPS	**Seat** — power, 6-way (requires AAN or AWN) - Base Daytona, ES	252	296
X7	**Seat** — power, 8-way (requires AWN or AAN and AAW, AGY, JPA on ES); (requires AAM, AAW or JPA on Shelby) - ES, Shelby	638	751
XL	**Seat** — leather trim - ES, Shelby	1192	1402
LSA	**Security Alarm** — includes panel warning light; requires AAN and AAW or AWN on ES (requires AAM and AAW on Shelby) - ES, Shelby	127	149
—	**Speed Control** — electronic; available in AAW and AWN only		

Code	Description	Base Cost	Sgstd. List
—	**Steering Column** — tilt; available in AAM, AAN or AWN only		
MSE	**Sun Louver** — rear window; n/a w/rear window wiper/washer (JHB), (AGS)	182	214
GWB	**Sun Roof Removable** — requires AAM, AAN or AWN; n/a w/(AGS) or (CUN)	344	405
CSC	**Tonneau Cover** — security; n/a w/(AGS) - Base Daytona	63	74
JPA	**Windows** — power (requires AAN and AAW or AWN on Base Daytona/ES); (requires AAM and AAW on Shelby)	221	260
JHB	**Wiper/Washer** — liftgate (requires AAM, AAN or AWN) n/a w/sun louver (MSE) or (AGS)	110	129
—	**Warranty Enhancement for New York** — mandatory	106	125

DYNASTY

DYNASTY (4 Cylinder)

Code	Description	Base Cost	Sgstd. List
DH41	4 Dr Sedan	11808	13645

DYNASTY LE (6 Cylinder)

Code	Description	Base Cost	Sgstd. List
DP41	4 Dr LE Sedan	13032	15085

Destination Charge: All models 545 545

STANDARD EQUIPMENT:

DYNASTY: Power front disc/rear drum brakes, 5 mph protection bumpers, front and rear bumper guards (LE), chimes (warning for key in ignition, headlights and turn signal on, seatbelts), lower body protective urethane coating, electric rear window defroster, 2.5 liter 4 cylinder electronic fuel injection engine (Base Dynasty), 3.0 liter V6 multi-port injection engine (LE), aluminized steel exhaust system, locking glove box, single halogen headlights, tinted glass, inside hood release, instrument panel (mechanical includes speedometer, odometer, trip odometer, gauges for fuel, voltage, oil pressure and temperature), message center, mirrors (visor vanity, black cloth-covered left and right outside dual remote control), black/bright bodyside moldings, AM mono/FM stereo ETR radio with digital clock and four speakers, passive driver air bag and active 3-point unibelt restraint system, power steering, bodyside stripes, P195/75R14 BSW all-season steel belted radial tires with compact spare, automatic 3 speed transmission (Base Dynasty), automatic 4 speed ultradrive transmission (LE), remote release trunk, 14" luxury wheel covers (Base Dynasty), 14" premium wheel covers (LE), deluxe windshield wiper/washer with intermittent wipe.

ACCESSORIES

Code	Description	Base Cost	Sgstd. List
AAB	**Popular Equipment Discount Package** — (includes AJK deluxe convenience on Base Dynasty and LE and AJP power convenience on LE) - includes manual air conditioning, power door locks, 3.3L V6 MPI engine (LE), front and rear floor mats, message center (standard on LE), bodyside stripe (standard on LE), electronic speed control, tilt steering column, undercoating, heated dual power remote control mirrors (LE), power windows (LE), - Base Dynasty, total retail price - 1673, discount - 350, net price	1125	1323
	- LE, total retail price -2008, discount - 450, net price	1324	1558
AFF	**Luxury Equipment Discount Package** — includes AAB popular equipment pkg and AJP power convenience pkg plus illuminated entry, mirrors (automatic day/night rearview and dual illuminated visor vanity), power 6-way driver and passenger seats, leather-wrapped steering wheel, wiring harness, (pre-wired for cellular phone), wire wheel covers - LE, total retail		

Mfgs. Code	Description	DODGE	Base Cost	Sgstd. List
	price - 3382, discount - 600, net price		2365	2782
AJK	**Deluxe Convenience Package —** (included in AAB popular equipment pkg and AFF luxury equipment pkg) - includes electronic speed control, tilt steering column - LE		299	352
AJP	**Power Convenience Package —** (requires AAB popular equipment package) - includes heated dual power remote control mirrors and power windows - Base Dynasty, total retail price - 419, discount - 40, net price		322	379
AJB	**Security Package —** (requires AAB popular equipment package) - includes security alarm, keyless remote entry, illuminated entry, illuminated visor vanity mirrors - Base Dynasty		402	473
	- LE		402	473
	- LE w/AFF pkg		235	277
AJW	**Power Accessories Package —** (requires AFF luxury equipment package) - includes power decklid pull down and power antenna - LE		135	159
—	**Customer Preferred Equipment Packages (includes model plus pkg)**			
	Base Dynasty			
22B	Pkg 22B — includes Base Dynasty with 2.5 liter EFI engine, 3-speed automatic transmission and air conditioning		12489	14446
24B	Pkg 24B — includes Base Dynasty with 3.0 liter V6 EFI engine, 4-speed automatic transmission and air conditioning		13158	15233
26B	Pkg 26B — includes Base Dynasty with 3.3 liter V6 EFI engine, 4-speed automatic transmission and air conditioning		13158	15233
24C	Pkg 24C — includes Base Dynasty with 3.0 liter V6 EFI engine, 4-speed automatic transmission, air conditioning, floor mats, undercoating, speed control and tilt column, power door locks, bodyside tape stripe and message center		13585	15735
26C	Pkg 26C — includes Base Dynasty with 3.3 liter V6 EFI engine, 4-speed automatic transmission, air conditioning, floor mats, undercoating, speed control and tilt column, power door locks, bodyside tape stripe and message center		13585	15735
	LE Dynasty			
24E	Pkg 24E — includes LE Dynasty with 3.0 liter V6 EFI engine, 4-speed automatic transmission and air conditioning		13713	15886
26E	Pkg 26E — includes LE Dynasty with 3.3 liter V6 EFI engine, 4-speed automatic transmission, air conditioning		13713	15886
26F	Pkg 26F — includes LE Dynasty with 3.3 liter V6 EFI engine, 4-speed automatic transmission, air conditioning, floor mats, undercoating, speed control and tilt column, power door locks, power windows, power mirrors		14340	16623
26G	Pkg 26G — includes LE Dynasty with 3.3 liter V6 EFI engine, 4-speed automatic transmission, air conditioning, floor mats, undercoating, speed control and tilt column, power door locks, power windows, power mirrors, automatic adjustable rearview mirror, illuminated entry and vanity mirrors, rear center armrest cupholder, cellular phone pre-wire, leather-wrapped steering wheel, 6-way driver and passenger power seats, wire wheel covers		15380	17847
EDM	**Engine —** 2.5 liter electronic fuel injection; n/a w/(DGB) - Base Dynasty		STD	STD
EFA	**Engine —** 3.0 liter V6 multi point fuel injection - Base Dynasty		590	694
EGA	**Engine —** 3.3 liter V6 multi point fuel injection; in AAB/AFF on LE - Base Dynasty		590	694
EGA	**Engine —** 3.3 liter V6 multi point fuel injection; in AAB/AFF on LE - LE		NC	NC
DGA	**Transmission —** 3-speed automatic with lock-up converter; n/a w/(EFA, EGA) - Base Dynasty		STD	STD
DGB	**Transmission —** electronic 4 speed - Base Dynasty		79	93
HAA	**Air Conditioning —** manual (in AAB and AFF)		698	821
MDA	**Bracket —** front license plate		NC	NC
BRF	**Brakes —** 4 wheel disc anti-lock; requires V6 engine on Base Dynasty		764	899

Mfgs. Code	Description	Base Cost	Sgstd. List

DODGE

Mfgs. Code	Description	Base Cost	Sgstd. List
JPH	**Door Locks** — power; (in AAB and AFF)	277	326
NAE	**Emissions** — California	87	102
P	**Paint** — extra cost pearl coat/clear coat	65	77
RAS	**Radio** — AM mono/FM stereo with cassette (non seek and scan)	132	155
RAY	**Radio** — AM stereo and FM stereo cassette w/seek and scan, graphic equalizer and 4 speaker; (requires AAB or AFF)	364	428
ARB	**Radio** — "Infinity RS"; includes RAY radio and 10 infinity speakers in 6 locations and a trunk mounted amplifier (requires AFF) - LE	690	812
JPP	**Seat** — power 8-way, driver/pass with memory and power recliner (requires AFF) - LE	337	396
JPS	**Seat** — power 6-way, driver only (requires AAB) - LE	252	296
LF	**Seat Trim** — 50/50 front bench - Base Dynasty	316	372
HP	**Seat Trim** — leather 50/50 front bench (requires AFF) - LE	502	590
TBB	**Spare Tire** — conventional	72	85
GWA	**Sunroof** — power (requires AFF) - LE	673	792
SER	**Suspension** — rear automatic load leveling (requires AAB or AFF) - LE	191	225
TKL	**Tires** — P195/75R whitewall all season radial	62	73
W48	**Wheelcovers** — wire; (in AFF) (requires AAB)	194	228
WHE	**Wheels** — cast aluminum (requires AAB) - LE	237	279
	- LE w/AFF	43	50
—	**Warranty Enhancement for New York** — mandatory	106	125

MONACO

MONACO (6 Cylinder)

Code	Description	Base Cost	Sgstd. List
DP41	4 Dr LE Sedan	11861	13695
DS41	4 Dr ES Sedan	14194	16440
	Destination Charge: All models	480	480

STANDARD EQUIPMENT:

MONACO: Air conditioning system (ES), power disc front/rear drum brakes (LE), power four-wheel disc brakes (ES), soft fascia bumper with 5 mph protection, chimes (warning for seatbelt, key in ignition, turn signal cancel), center console with auto transmission, lower body protective urethane coating, electric rear window defrosters, side window demisters, 3.0 liter V6 MPI engine, aluminized steel exhaust system, all glass tinted windows, locking glove box, bright grille (LE), body color grille (ES), cloth covered headliner, dual halogen aerostyle headights, dual electric horn, inside hood release, instrument panel (mechanical cluster includes 100 mph speedometer and trip odometer, gauges for oil pressure, fuel, temperature and digital clock), light group, right and left remote control black mirror (LE), day/night rearview mirror, outside dual remote mirrors (ES), outside dual black power mirror (ES), non-illuminated passenger side visor vanity mirror (LE), bodyside moldings, AM mono/FM stereo radio with four speakers (LE), AM/FM cassette ET stereo radio with four speakers (ES), power rack and pinion type steering, leather-wrapped steering wheel (ES), deluxe steering wheel (LE), bodyside and decklid stripes (LE), lower bodyside and fascia stripes (ES), suspension (independent front and rear, front includes struts and coil springs, rear includes gas shocks and torsion bars) (LE), touring suspension includes above plus stiffer front springs and tuned shocks (ES), P195/70R14 black BSW all-season steel radial tires (LE), P205/7-R14 black BSW steel belted radial performance tires (ES), compact spare tire, 4 speed automatic transmission, deluxe windshield wipers with intermittent wipe, Venturi wheel covers (LE), 14" polycast Eurosport wheels (ES).

Mfgs. Code	Description	Base Cost	Sgstd. List

DODGE

ACCESSORIES

Mfgs. Code	Description	Base Cost	Sgstd. List
HAB	**Air Conditioning** — (automatic) - LE	745	877
JPB	**Power Door Locks**	208	235
BRF	**Anti-Lock Brakes** — power 4-wheel disc	764	899
CLE	**Floor Mats** — front and rear	39	46
MWC	**Luggage Rack Deck Lid** — (bright) - LE	99	117
MWC	**Luggage Rack Deck Lid** — (black) - ES	99	117
JPA	**Power Windows** — requires power door locks	277	326
TBB	**Conventional Spare Tire**	81	95
NAE	**California Emission Controls**	87	102
LAC	**Illuminated Entry System** — requires popular equipment discount pkg and keyless entry system	66	78
GXM	**Keyless Entry System** — requires popular equipment discount pkg and illuminated entry system	109	128
WHG	**Wheels** — (polycast Eurosport 14") - LE	88	104
WJS	**Wheels** — (aluminum lace 15"; includes P205/60R15 SBR all-season tires)		
	- LE w/o popular equipment discount pkg	445	523
	- LE w/popular equipment discount pkg	356	419
WJS	**Wheels** — (aluminum lace 15"; includes P205/60HR15 SBR performance tires) - ES	328	386
RAF	**Radio** — (AM/FM stereo w/cassette) - LE	203	239
ARA	**Radio** — premium AM/FM stereo w/cassette and graphic equalizer, 6 Jensen Accusound speakers and power antenna (LE requires popular equipment discount pkg)	324	381
RBB	**Radio** — (premium AM/FM stereo w/cassette and compact disc player, power antenna, 6 Jensen Accusound speakers) - models w/popular equipment discount pkg	561	660
RBB	**Radio** — (premium AM/FM stereo w/cassette and compact disc player) - models w/luxury equipment discount pkg	237	279
JPS	**Seats** — power 6-way driver	252	296
JA	**Seats** — dual leather 6-way power (requires luxury equipment discount pkg)		
	- LE	844	993
	- ES	757	891
ADC	**Deluxe Convenience Package** — includes tilt steering wheel and cruise control	299	352
ADN	**Electronic Features Package** — includes trip computer and message center (requires popular equipment discount pkg)	260	306
AAY	**Family Value Discount Package** — includes power door locks, power windows, cruise control, air conditioning, tilt steering wheel (net suggested list price includes a discount of $250) - LE	1309	1540
AWC	**Enthusiast Package** — includes touring suspension, P205/60R15 SBR all-season touring tires, power 4-wheel disc brakes, aluminum lace wheels (requires popular equipment discount pkg) - LE	561	660
AFF	**LE Luxury Equipment Discount Package** — includes popular equipment discount pkg plus illuminated entry system, power antenna, keyless entry system, AM/FM premium radio w/cassette, graphic equalizer and 6 speakers, leather-wrapped steering wheel, electronic features pkg, dual illuminated visor vanity mirrors (net suggested list price includes a discount of $500) - LE	2747	3232
AFF	**ES Luxury Equipment Discount Package** — includes popular equipment discount pkg, illuminated entry system, keyless entry system, AM/FM premium radio w/cassette, graphic equalizer and 6 speakers, power antenna (net suggested list price includes a discount of $850) - ES	1510	1777
AAM	**LE Popular Equipment Discount Package** — includes air conditioning, power door locks, power decklid release, tilt steering wheel, power		

Code	Description	Base Cost	Sgstd. List
	windows, 6-way power driver seat, dual power mirrors, cruise control, AM/FM stereo radio w/cassette, floor mats, remote fuel-filler door release, polycast Eurosport wheels (net suggested list price includes a discount of $375) - LE	1943	2286
AAM	**ES Popular Equipment Discount Package** — includes power windows, power door locks, tilt steering wheel, 6-way power driver seat, cruise control, remote fuel-filler door release, power deck lid release, 205/60HR15 SBR performance tires, floor mats, keyless entry system, illuminated entry system, aluminum lace wheels - ES	969	1140

SHADOW

SHADOW (4 Cylinder)

Code	Description	Base Cost	Sgstd. List
DL24	2 Dr America Hatchback	7172	7699
DL44	4 Dr America Hatchback	7447	7995
DH24	2 Dr Highline Hatchback	8149	8899
DH44	4 Dr Highline Hatchback	8419	9199
DS24	2 Dr ES Hatchback	9478	10375
DS44	4 Dr ES Hatchback	9748	10675
DH27	2 Dr Highline Convertible	11836	12995
DS27	2 Dr ES Convertible	12801	14068
	Destination Charge: All models	465	465

STANDARD EQUIPMENT:

SHADOW HATCHBACK: Power front disc and rear drum brakes, black bumpers with 5 mph protection, chimes (headlights on, seatbelts and key in ignition), cigarette lighter, mini console with storage bins, side window demisters, childproof door locks (4-door only), 2.2 liter 4 cylinder electronic fuel injection engine, quiet tuned exhaust system, body color grille, single rectangular halogen aerostyle headlights, cloth covered headliner, hood release, single note horn, instrument panel (mechanical includes 125 mph speedometer on ES, odometer, trip odometer with reset and tachometer, gauges for fuel, voltmeter, and temperature warning, lights for oil pressure, turn signal, high beam, seatbelts, brakes, engine, air bag), hood pad and premium body sound insulation, outside left remote control black mirror, inside day/night rearview mirror, driver and passenger side vanity mirror, narrow bodyside black molding, liftgate, windshield, belt and upper door black molding, AM/FM stereo radio with digital clock and two speakers, passive driver air bag and active 3-point unibelt restraint system, removable shelf panel, 16:1 rack and pinion power steering, luxury steering wheel, P185/70R14 SBR BW tires with compact spare, 5 speed manual transmission, "Venturi" design wheel covers, deluxe windshield wiper/washer with intermittent wipe.

SHADOW CONVERTIBLE: Power front vented disc and rear drum brakes, body colored fascia, nerf strips and 5 mph protection bumpers (Highline), chimes (headlights on, seatbelts, key in ignition), cigarette lighter, full center console with armrest, side window demisters, 2.5 liter 4 cylinder electronic fuel injection engine, quiet tuned exhaust system, body color grille, single rectangular halogen aerostyle headlights, inside hood release, instrument panel (mechanical includes 125 mph speedometer, odometer, trip odometer with reset, oil pressure, turn signal, high beam, seatbelts, brakes, engine, air bag), premium sound insulation, dual outside remote control black mirror, day/night rearview inside mirrors, covered vanity driver and passenger side mirrors, bright bodyside molding, liftgate, windshield, belt and upper door black moldings, AM/FM stereo radio with digital clock and two speakers, passive driver air bag and 3-point unibelt restraint system, removable shelf panel, floor mounted shift lever, 14:1 rack and pinion power steering, luxury steering wheel, precision feel suspension (gas-charged front Iso-struts and rear shock absorbers with front and rear sway bars), P185/70R14 SBR blackwall tires with compact spare, 5 speed manual transmission, sport wheel covers (Highline), cast wheel covers (ES), power windows, deluxe windshield wipers with intermittent wipe.

ACCESSORIES

Mfgs. Code	Description	Base Cost	Sgstd. List
—	**Customer Preferred Equipment Packages (includes model plus pkg)**		
W	**America W Package —** (includes models and specific equipment mentioned) - 2 Dr Hatchback and 5 speed manual transmission	7207	7599
	- 4 Dr Hatchback and 5 speed manual transmission	7393	7799
	- 2 Dr Hatchback and automatic transmission	7672	8146
	- 4 Dr Hatchback and automatic transmission	7858	8346
X	**America X Package —** (includes rear defroster, light package, dual outside remote mirrors, floor mats, AM/FM stereo radio and narrow bodyside moldings) - 2 Dr Hatchback and 5 speed manual transmission	7795	8291
	- 4 Dr Hatchback and 5 speed manual transmission	7991	8503
	- 2 Dr Hatchback and automatic transmission	8260	8838
	- 4 Dr Hatchback and automatic transmission	8456	9050
Y	**America Y Package —** (includes America X Pkg plus air conditioning and tinted glass) - 2 Dr Hatchback and 5 speed manual transmission	8559	9189
	- 4 Dr Hatchback and 5 speed manual transmission	8755	9401
	- 2 Dr Hatchback and automatic transmission	9023	9736
	- 4 Dr Hatchback and automatic transmission	9220	9948
A	**Highline Hatchback A Package —** (includes models and specific equipment mentioned) - 2 Dr Hatchback with 2.2 liter engine and 5 speed manual transmission	8303	9070
	- 4 Dr Hatchback with 2.2 liter engine and 5 speed manual transmission	8483	9270
	- 2 Dr Hatchback with 2.2 liter engine and automatic transmission	8768	9617
	- 4 Dr Hatchback with 2.2 liter engine and automatic transmission	8948	9817
	- 2 Dr Hatchback with 2.5 liter engine and manual transmission	8546	9356
	- 4 Dr Hatchback with 2.5 liter engine and manual transmission	8726	9556
	- 2 Dr Hatchback with 2.5 liter engine and automatic transmission	9011	9903
	- 4 Dr Hatchback with 2.5 liter engine and automatic transmission	9191	10103
B	**Highline Hatchback B Package —** (includes air conditioning, tinted glass, rear defroster and tilt steering wheel) - 2 Dr Hatchback with 2.2 liter engine and 5 speed manual transmission	9131	10044
	- 4 Dr Hatchback with 2.2 liter engine and 5 speed manual transmission	9311	10244
	- 2 Dr Hatchback with 2.2 liter engine and automatic transmission	9596	10591
	- 4 Dr Hatchback with 2.2 liter engine and automatic transmission	9776	10791
	- 2 Dr Hatchback with 2.5 liter engine and 5 speed manual transmission	9374	10330
	- 4 Dr Hatchback with 2.5 liter engine and 5 speed manual transmission	9554	10530
	- 2 Dr Hatchback with 2.5 liter engine and automatic transmission	9839	10877
	- 4 Dr Hatchback with 2.5 liter engine and automatic transmission	10019	11077
C	**Highline Hatchback C Package —** (includes rear defroster, tilt steering wheel, light package, floor console, 4 radio speakers, dual note horn, liftgate release, wide bodyside moldings, bodyside accent stripes, intermittent wipers, tachometer with 125 mph speedometer, manual outside remote mirrors) - 2 Dr Hatchback with 2.5 liter engine and 5 speed manual transmission	9097	10004
	- 4 Dr Hatchback with 2.5 liter engine and 5 speed manual transmission	9287	10216
	- 2 Dr Hatchback with 2.5 liter engine and automatic transmission	9562	10551
	- 4 Dr Hatchback with 2.5 liter engine and automatic transmission	9752	10763
D	**Highline Hatchback D Package —** (includes Highline C Pkg plus air conditioning and tinted glass) - 2 Dr Hatchback with 2.5 liter engine		

Mfgs. Code	Description	Base Cost	Sgstd. List
	and 5 speed manual transmission	9605	10602
	- 4 Dr Hatchback with 2.5 liter engine and 5 speed manual transmission	9795	10814
	- 2 Dr Hatchback with 2.5 liter engine and automatic transmission	10070	11149
	- 4 Dr Hatchback with 2.5 liter engine and automatic transmission	10260	11361
E	**Highline Hatchback E Package —** (includes air conditioning, tinted glass, rear defroster, tilt steering wheel, light package, floor console, 4 radio speakers, liftgate release, dual note horn, wide bodyside moldings, bodyside accent stripes, intermittent wipers, tachometer with 125 mph speedometer, power outside remote mirrors, speed control, power door locks, AM/FM stereo cassette radio, floor mats) -2 Dr Hatchback with 2.5 liter engine and 5 speed manual transmission	10171	11268
	- 4 Dr Hatchback with 2.5 liter engine and 5 speed manual transmission	10396	11521
	- 2 Dr Hatchback with 2.5 liter engine and automatic transmission	10636	11815
	- 4 Dr Hatchback with 2.5 liter engine and automatic transmission	10861	12068
G	**ES Hatchback G Package —** (includes models and specific equipment mentioned) - 2 Dr with 2.5 liter non-turbo engine and 5 speed manual transmission	9631	10545
	- 4 Dr with 2.5 liter non-turbo engine and 5 speed manual transmission	9811	10745
	- 2 Dr with 2.5 liter non-turbo engine and automatic transmission	10095	11092
	- 4 Dr with 2.5 liter non-turbo engine and automatic transmission	10275	11292
	- 2 Dr with 2.5 liter turbo engine and 5 speed manual transmission	10250	11274
	- 4 Dr with 2.5 liter turbo engine and 5 speed manual transmission	10430	11474
	- 2 Dr with 2.5 liter turbo engine and automatic transmission	10715	11821
	- 4 Dr with 2.5 liter turbo engine and automatic transmission	10895	12021
H	**ES Hatchback H Package —** (includes air conditioning, tinted glass, light package, rear defroster, tilt steering wheel, speed control, power door locks, power outside remote mirrors, AM/FM stereo cassette with seek, liftgate release, floor mats, dual note horn) - 2 Dr with 2.5 liter non-turbo engine and 5 speed manual transmission	10969	12120
	- 4 Dr with 2.5 liter non-turbo engine and 5 speed manual transmission	11194	12373
	- 2 Dr with 2.5 liter non-turbo engine and automatic transmission	11434	12667
	- 4 Dr with 2.5 liter non-turbo engine and automatic transmission	11659	12920
	- 2 Dr with 2.5 liter turbo engine and 5 speed manual transmission	11589	12849
	- 4 Dr with 2.5 liter turbo engine and 5 speed manual transmission	11814	13102
	- 2 Dr with 2.5 liter turbo engine and automatic transmission	12054	13396
	- 4 Dr with 2.5 liter turbo engine and automatic transmission	12279	13649
A	**Highline Convertible A Package —** (includes models and specific equipment mentioned) - Convertible with 2.5 liter non-turbo engine and 5 speed manual transmission	11836	12995
	- Convertible with 2.5 liter non-turbo engine and automatic transmission	12300	13542
B	**Highline Convertible B Package —** (includes air conditioning, tinted glass) - Convertible with 2.5 liter non-turbo engine and 5 speed manual transmission	12546	13831
	- Convertible with 2.5 liter non-turbo engine and automatic transmission	13011	14378
C	**Highline Convertible C Package —** (includes tilt steering wheel, light package, 4 stereo speakers, intermittent wipers, dual note horn, bodyside moldings, bodyside accent stripe, tachometer cluster) - Convertible with 2.5 liter non-turbo engine and 5 speed manual transmission	12170	13388
	- Convertible with 2.5 liter non-turbo engine and automatic transmission	12635	13935
D	**Highline Convertible D Package —** (includes Highline Convertible C Pkg plus air conditioning and tinted glass) - Convertible with 2.5 liter non-turbo engine and 5 speed manual transmission	12635	13936
	- Convertible with 2.5 liter non-turbo engine and automatic transmission	13201	14602
E	**Highline Convertible E Package —** (includes Highline Convertible D Pkg		

Mfgs. Code	Description	Base Cost	Sgstd. List
	plus power outside remote mirrors, speed control, power door locks, AM/FM stereo cassette radio, floor mats) - Convertible with 2.5 liter non-turbo engine and 5 speed manual transmission	13201	14602
	- Convertible with 2.5 liter non-turbo engine and automatic transmission	13666	15149
	- Convertible with 2.5 liter turbo engine and 5 speed manual transmission	13847	15362
	- Convertible with 2.5 liter turbo engine and automatic transmission	14312	15909
G	**ES Convertible G Package** — (includes models and specific equipment mentioned) - Convertible with 2.5 liter non-turbo engine and 5 speed manual transmission	12801	14068
	- Convertible with 2.5 liter non-turbo engine and automatic transmission	13266	14615
	- Convertible with 2.5 liter turbo engine and 5 speed manual transmission	13421	14797
	- Convertible with 2.5 liter turbo engine and automatic transmission	13886	15344
H	**ES Convertible H Package** — (includes air conditioning, tinted glass, tilt steering, light package, dual note horn, power outside remote mirrors, speed control, power door locks, Infinity I sound speakers, floor mats) - Convertible with 2.5 liter non-turbo engine and 5 speed manual transmission	13981	15456
	- Convertible with 2.5 liter non-turbo engine and automatic transmission	14446	16003
	- Convertible with 2.5 liter turbo engine and 5 speed manual transmission	14601	16185
	- Convertible with 2.5 liter turbo engine and automatic transmission	15066	16732
HAA	**Air Conditioning** — (includes tinted glass) - America w/W pkg, Highline w/A pkg, ES w/G pkg	672	791
—	**Tinted Glass** — (required with air conditioning) - America w/W pkg, Highline w/A pkg, ES w/G pkg	91	107
MDA	**Bracket** — front license plate (standard where required, no charge otherwise	NC	NC
CUN	**Console Overhead** — includes thermometer, compass, reading lights, and storage bins (n/a with sunroof and convertible) - Highline w/C,D or E pkgs; ES w/G and H pkgs	225	265
GFA	**Defroster** — electric rear window (required in New York State; n/a with Convertible) - America w/W pkg, Highline w/A pkg, ES w/G pkg	139	163
JPB	**Door Locks** — power - 2-door (Highline w/A, B, C, D pkgs; ES w/G pkg)	165	194
	- 4-door (Highline w/A, B, C, D pkgs; ES w/G pkg)	200	235
NAE	**Emissions** — California	87	102
CLE	**Floor Mats** — Front and rear - Highline w/A, B, C, D pkgs; ES w/G pkg	39	46
JHA	**Intermittent Wipers** — Highline w/A, B pkgs	48	56
GTE	**Mirrors** — dual outside remote (standard convertible) - Highline w/A, B pkgs	59	69
GTK	**Mirrors** — dual outside power remote (requires power door locks at extra cost) - Highline w/C, D pkgs; ES w/G pkg	48	57
	- Highline w/A, B pkgs	107	126
P	**Paint** — extra cost	65	77
JPS	**Power Seat** — driver's side (requires power mirrors, power locks and power windows) - Highline w/C, D, E pkgs; ES w/G, H pkgs	252	296
JPA	**Power Windows** — (requires power mirrors and power locks) - 2-door Highline w/C, D, E pkgs; ES w/G, H pkgs	213	250
	- 4-door Highline w/C, D, E pkgs; ES w/G, H pkgs	269	316
RAL	**Radio** — AM/FM stereo with digital clock - America w/W pkg	241	284
RAS	**Radio** — Deluxe AM/FM stereo with cassette and 4 speaker sound system - America w/W pkg	416	489
	- America w/X, Y pkgs; Highline w/A, B pkgs	174	205
RAN	**Radio** — Infinity I sound system - Highline w/E pkg	234	275
	- ES w/G pkg	366	430
NHM	**Speed Control** — electronic (requires SUA tilt steering) - Highline w/A,		

Code	Description	Base Cost	Sgstd. List
	B, C, D pkgs; ES w/G pkg	182	214
GWB	**Sunroof** — flip up (manual) - Highline w/ES pkg	322	379
SUA	**Tilt Steering Column** — Highline w/A pkg; ES w/G pkg	117	138
TBB	**Tire** — conventional spare (n/a Convertible) - America, Highline	72	85
—	**Tire** — conventional spare w/aluminum wheels (n/a Convertible) - ES	181	213
WHK	**Wheels** — Cast Aluminum (4) - Highline	279	328
—	**Warranty Enhancement for New York**	106	125

SPIRIT

Code	Description	Base Cost	Sgstd. List
SPIRIT (2.5 Liter 4 Cylinder)			
DH41	4 Dr Base Spirit Sedan	9784	10925
DP41	4 Dr LE Spirit Sedan	11544	12925
SPIRIT (2.5 Liter 4 Cylinder Turbo)			
DX41	4 Dr ES Spirit Sedan	12234	13709
SPIRIT (2.2 Liter 16 Valve 4 Cylinder Turbo)			
DS41	4 Dr R/T Spirit	15852	17820
Destination Charge:	All models	465	465

STANDARD EQUIPMENT:

SPIRIT SEDAN: Maintenance-free battery, power front/disc rear drum brakes (Base Spirit, LE), four wheel disc brakes (ES), soft fascia bumpers with integral nerf and 5 mph protection, full passenger compartment carpeting, chimes (warning for headlights on, seatbelt and key in ignition), full console with bucket seats and floor shift (Base Spirit), full console with armrest with bucket seats and floor shift (LE, ES), lower body protective urethane coating, electric rear window defroster (LE, ES), side window demisters, 2.5 liter 4 cylinder electronic fuel injection engine (Base Spirit, LE), 2.5 liter 4 cylinder turbo-charged multi-port injection engine (ES), fascia integral fog lamps (LE, ES), remote release fuel filler door, tinted glass rear window (Base Spirit), tinted glass all windows (LE, ES), locking glove box, bright grille (painted on ES), lower sill and fascia chin ground effects (ES), single halogen aerostyled headlights, cloth covered headliner, counter balanced hood, inside hood release, dual electric horn, instrument panel (mechanical cluster includes 120 mph speedometer, odometer, trip odometer, gauges for oil pressure, voltmeter, fuel, temperature, warning lights for high beam, seatbelt, brakes, check engine, check gauges, turn signal, air bag), premium sound insulation (LE, ES), front and rear floor mats (LE, ES), message center (LE, ES), outside dual remote control black mirrors, left vanity visor mirrors, narrow bodyside moldings (Base Spirit), medium width bodyside moldings (LE, ES), AM mono/FM stereo ETR radio with digital clock and two speakers (Base Spirit) AM mono/FM stereo ETR radio with digital clock and four speakers (LE), AM mono/FM stereo radio cassette (non seek and scan), with digital clock and four speakers (ES), passive driver air bag and 3-point unibelt restraint system, electronic speed control (LE, ES), tilt steering column (LE, ES), rack and pinion type power steering, luxury steering wheel (Base Spirit, LE), leather-wrapped luxury steering wheel (ES), bodyside stripe, bodyside and deck stripe (LE, ES), suspension (firm ride and handling includes gas shocks, position sensitive struts, solid front and rear sway bar), P195/70R14 SBR BSW all-season touring tires (Base Spirit, LE), P205/60R15 SBR BSW all-season performance tires (ES), compact spare tire, 5 speed manual transmission with center console (not available with bench seat), 3 speed automatic transmission (LE), trip computer (ES), dress up trunk, remote release trunk, Venturi 14" wheel cover (Base Spirit), Atlas 14" wheel cover (LE), Eurocast aluminum 15" wheel cover (ES), deluxe windshield wiper/washer with intermittent wipe.

SPIRIT RT: Air conditioning, maintenance-free battery, four wheel disc brakes, soft fascia bumpers with integral nerf and 5 mph protection, full passenger compartment, carpeting, chime (warning for headlights on, seatbelt and key in ignition), lower body protective urethane coating, electric rear window defroster, side window demisters, 2.2 liter 16V DOHC turbo-charged MPI engine, fascia integral fog lamps, tinted glass, locking glove box, bright painted grille, lower sill ground effects, single halogen aerostyle headlights, cloth covered headliner, inside hood release, dual electric horn, instrument panel (mechanical cluster includes 120 mph speedometer, odometer, trip odometer, gauges for oil pressure, voltmeter, fuel, temperature, warning lights for high beam, seatbelt, brakes, check engine, check gauges, turn signal, air bag), premium sound insulation, front and rear floor mats, message center (6 functions: low washer fluid, door ajar, deck ajar, headlight out, taillight out, stoplight out), outside dual power control heated black mirror, left visor vanity mirror, medium width bodyside moldings, AM/FM stereo ETR cassette radio (non seek and scan) with digital clock and four speakers, passive driver air bag and 3-point unibelt restraint system, seats (performance buckets - low back with recliner (front), 55/45 split fold-down (rear), electronic speed control, rear deck spoiler, tilt steering column, rack and pinion type power steering, leather-wrapped luxury steering wheel, suspension (firm ride and handling - includes gas shocks, position sensitive struts, solid front and rear sway bar), P205/60R15 SBR BSW all-season performance tires, compact spare tire, 5 speed manual transmission with center console, trip computer, dress up trunk, remote release trunk, Eurocast aluminum 15" wheel, deluxe windshield wiper/washer with intermittent wipe.

ACCESSORIES

Code	Description	Base Cost	Sgstd. List
AWN	**Super Discount A Package —** (includes AAM popular equipment pkg and AJK deluxe convenience pkg; n/a with AWP super discount pkg B) - includes manual air conditioning, electric rear window defroster, front and rear floor mats, tinted glass, 4 speaker system, electronic speed control, tilt steering wheel - Base Spirit, total retail price - 1565, discount - 650, net price	778	915
AWP	**Super Discount B Package —** includes AWN super discount A pkg plus dual power remote heated black mirrors, power windows and power door locks - Base Spirit, total retail price - 2241, discount - 750, net price	1267	1491
AWR	**Super Discount C Package —** includes manual air conditioning, dual power remote heated black mirrors, power windows, power door locks -LE Spirit, total retail price - 1497, discount - 525, net price	826	972
	ES Spirit, total retail price - 1497, discount - 525, net price	826	972
AAC	**Premium Equipment Discount Package —** includes 55/45 split folding rear seats, premium body sound insulation, lights (map, underhood, cigarette lighter), message center - Base Spirit, total retail price - 319, discount - 78, net price	205	241
AJK	**Deluxe Convenience Discount Package —** (in AWN super discount A pkg and AWP super discount B pkg) - includes front and rear floor mats, electronic speed control and tilt steering wheel - Base Spirit, total retail price - 409, discount - 50, net price	305	359
AJP	**Power Equipment Discount Package —** (included in AWP super discount pkg B and AWR super discount pkg C) - includes dual power remote heated black mirrors, power windows and power door locks - R/T Spirit, total retail price - 583, discount - 50, net price	453	533
AFH	**Overhead Convenience Discount Package —** includes overhead console (reading lamps, compass and outside temperature readouts, sunglasses and storage), dual illuminated visor vanity mirrors - LE Spirit - total retail price - 383, discount - 50, net price	283	333
	- ES Spirit, total retail price - 383, discount - 50, net price	283	333
EDM	**Engine —** 2.5 liter electronic fuel injection - Base, LE	STD	STD
EDT	**Engine –** 2.5 liter multi-point fuel injection turbo - LE	590	694
EFA	**Engine —** 3.0 liter multi-point fuel injection V6 - Base, LE	590	694
	- ES	NC	NC
EDS	**Engine —** 2.2 liter multi-point fuel injection 16 valve intercooled turbo - RT	STD	STD
DDM	**Transmission —** 5 speed manual - Base, ES	STD	STD

Mfgs. Code	Description **DODGE**	Base Cost	Sgstd. List
DGA	**Transmission** — 3 speed automatic - Base, ES	465	547
DGB	**Transmission** — 4 speed electronic automatic - Base, ES	544	640
DGB	**Transmission** — 4 speed electronic automatic - LE	79	93
DDV	**Transmission** — 5 speed manual, heavy duty - R/T	STD	STD
HAA	**Air Conditioning** — (in AWN, AWP, AWR); only available in (AWN) or (AWP) on DH41 - LE, ES	698	821
CUA	**Armrest** — center console mounted (with manual transmission only)	69	81
MDA	**Bracket** — front license plate	NC	NC
BRF	**Brakes** — four wheel disc w/anti-lock	764	899
CUF	**Console/Armrest** — center mounted required for floor shift auto trans - Base	132	155
GFA	**Defroster** — electric rear window in (AWN), (AWP); required in New York State - Base	139	163
JPB	**Door Locks** — power (in AWP, AWR, AJP)	208	245
NAE	**Emissions** — California Control and testing	86	102
P	**Paint** — extra cost	65	77
RAS	**Radio** — AM mono/FM stereo w/cassette, digital clock, 4 speakers - Base	174	205
	- w/package (AWN) or (AWP) on Base - Base, LE	132	155
RAN	**Radio** — AM stereo/ FM stereo with cassette, digital clock, seek/scan, 4 Infinity speakers; requires pkg (AWN) or (AWP) on Base - Base, LE	366	430
	- ES, R/T	234	275
RAY	**Radio** — AM stereo/FM stereo w/cassette, digital clock, seek/scan, 4 Infinity speakers, graphic equalizer - LE	548	645
JPS	**Seat** — power driver side; requires (AWN) or (AWP) on Base	252	296
BF	**Seats** — front bench, rear full fixed bench; n/a w/floor shift trans - Base	87	102
N7	**Seats** — front bucket, rear 55/45 split fold down bench; requires (AAC); - Base		
NF	**Seats** — front bench, rear 55/45 split fold down bench; requires (AAC); n/a w/floor shift trans. - Base	52	61
VF	**Seats** — premium front bench, rear 55/45 split fold down bench; n/a with floor shift trans. - LE	52	61
GWB	**Sunroof** — glass, pop-up; includes deflector, removable shade, storage bag, tie down straps - LE, ES	344	405
TKT	**Tires** — P195/70R14 SBR WSW all season touring tread - Base	62	73
TPX	**Tires** — P205/60R15 SBR BSW all season performance tread; requires (WJF) - Base, LE	81	95
TBB	**Tires** — conventional spare 14"; available w/14" tires only - Base, LE	81	95
WJF	**Wheels** — 15" eurocast aluminum road wheel; requires (TPX) tires - Base, LE	279	328
—	**Windows** — power in (AWP), (AWR), (AJP); only available in pkgs (AWP), (AWR) or (AJP)		
—	**Warranty Enhancement for New York** — mandatory	106	125

STEALTH

STEALTH (6 Cylinder)

DL24	Stealth Base	13849	16293
DS24	Stealth ES	15348	18056
DP24	Stealth R/T	20532	24155
DX24	Stealth R/T Turbo All Wheel Drive	24877	29267

Destination Charge: All models ... 328 328

Mfgs. Code	Description	DODGE	Base Cost	Sgstd. List

STANDARD EQUIPMENT:

STEALTH: Air conditioning (R/T, R/T Turbo), power assisted front/rear disc brakes, anti-lock brakes (R/T, R/T Turbo), sport style bumpers (Base Stealth, Sport), black performance bumpers (R/T, R/T Turbo), chimes (door, key, lights), console, rear electric defroster, power door locks (R/T, R/T Turbo), 3.0 liter SOHC 12V V6 engine (Base Stealth), 3.0 liter DOHC 24V V6 engine (Sport, R/T), 3.0 liter DOHC 24V V6 (R/T Turbo), floor mats (R/T, R/T Turbo), fuel door release, tinted glass, pop-up halogen headlamps with automatic off, inside hood release, dual note horn, instrument panel (speedometer, tachometer, analog, trip odometer, indicator lights, gauges for oil pressure, fuel, radiator coolant, temperature, battery voltage, turbo boost), liftgate release, heated mirror (R/T, R/T Turbo), AM/FM MPX radio (ultimate sound - 100 watt AM/FM cassette with six speakers, 6 AM/FM presets, seek/scan tape sensor, auto reverse, 7 band graphic equalizer and CD jack) (R/T, R/T Turbo), driver air bag and 3-point unibelt restraint system, seating (low back bucket with recliners, manually adjustable headrest, rear seats - bench split back, folding type (Sport, R/T, R/T Turbo), rear body color spoiler (R/T, R/T Turbo), leather shift knob, electronic sport suspension with tour and sport settings (Sport, R/T, R/T Turbo), power assisted rack and pinion steering, 4 wheel steering hydraulic control (in-phase steering at speeds above 30 mph) (R/T Turbo), tilt steering column, leather-wrapped steering wheel, P205/65R15 BSW tires (Base Stealth), P215/55R16 BSW tires (Sport, R/T), P245/45XR17 tires (R/T Turbo), compact T125/90D16 spare tire, 5 speed manual transmission, 15" x 6" polycast wheels (Base Stealth), 16" x 8" aluminum wheels (Sport, R/T), 17" x 8" aluminum wheels (R/T Turbo).

ACCESSORIES

Code	Description	Base Cost	Sgstd. List
DGB	**Transmission** — 4-speed automatic electronic (NA on R/T Turbo All Wheel Drive)	675	813
HAA	**Air Conditioning** — manual (NA on R/T or R/T Turbo All Wheel Drive)	702	846
SL/ AL	**Leather Trim**	700	843
NAE	**California Emissions**	NC	NC
CLA	**Carpet Protectors** — Stealth Base	23	28
RAN	**Radio** — (AM/FM cassette) - Stealth Base	150	181
—	**Optional Packages — Stealth Base**		
1FA	**Pkg 1FA** — (includes 15" aluminum wheels) - Stealth Base	215	259
1FB	**Pkg 1FB** — (includes Pkg 1FA plus power windows, power door locks, speed control and carpet protectors) - Stealth Base	694	836
1FC	**Pkg 1FC** — (includes Pkg 1FB plus rear wiper/washer) - Stealth Base	804	969
1FD	**Pkg 1FD** — (includes Pkg 1FC plus radio ultimate sound) - Stealth Base	1199	1445
1FE	**Pkg 1FE** — (includes Pkg 1FC plus anti-lock brakes and security alarm) - Stealth Base	2589	3119
—	**Optional Packages - Stealth ES**		
1FB	**Pkg 1FB** — (includes power windows, power door locks, speed control, carpet protectors, rear wiper/washer, radio w/cassette) - Stealth ES	740	891
1FC	**Pkg 1FC** — (includes power windows, power door locks, speed control, carpet protectors, rear wiper/washer and radio ultimate sound) - Stealth ES	984	1186
1FD	**Pkg 1FD** — (includes power windows, power door locks, speed control, carpet protectors, rear wiper/washer, radio ultimate sound, anti-lock brakes and security alarm) - Stealth ES	2022	2436
1FE	**Pkg 1FE** — (includes power windows, power door locks, speed control, carpet protectors, rear wiper/washer, radio ultimate sound with CD, anti-lock brakes and security alarm) - Stealth ES	2374	2860
1FF	**Pkg 1FF** — (includes Pkg 1FE plus electronic damped suspension) - Stealth ES	2673	3221
—	**Optional Packages — Stealth R/T and R/T Turbo AWD**		
1FB	**Pkg 1FB** — (includes radio ultimate sound w/CD) - Stealth R/T and R/T Turbo AWD	352	424

1991 eagle

PREMIER

		Base Cost	Sgstd. List
PREMIER (6 Cylinder)			
BBXP41	4 Dr LX Sedan	12999	14999
BBXS41	4 Dr ES Sedan	14917	17255
BBXS41 w/AGG	4 Dr ES Limited Sedan	16821	19495
Destination Charge:	All models	480	480

STANDARD EQUIPMENT:
PREMIER: Air conditioning, monochromatic appearance (ES Ltd), wide black bodyside moldings with bright insert (LX), lower bodyside protective cladding (ES), clearcoat paint, digital quartz clock, full-length console with armrest, rear window defroster, rear child-protection type door locks, dual gas strut hood supports, 3.0 liter V6 MPI engine, extra quiet insulation, electronic information package (includes trip computer/vehicle maintenance monitor (ES, ES Ltd), carpeted floor mats, front wheel drive, gauges (analog rally instrumentation (includes speedometer, tachometer, fuel gauge, coolant temperature gauge, odometer, oil pressure gauge, low fuel warning light), halogen quad headlamps, dual note horn, inside hood release, light group (includes dual map light, trunk light, underhood light, dual rear courtesy light, sentinel headlamp), dual heated remote control black mirrors, day/night rearview mirror, dual-illuminated visor vanity mirrors (ES, ES Ltd), bright belt moldings (LX), power antenna (ES Ltd), power four-wheel disc brakes, power rack and pinion steering, power group includes keyless entry system, decklid release, remote fuel door release, illuminated entry (ES Ltd), power windows (ES Ltd), 6-way driver and passenger power seats (ES Ltd), AM/FM ET stereo radio with four speakers (LX), AM/FM cassette ET stereo with four speakers - "Accusound by Jensen" (ES), AM/FM cassette premium audio system (ES Ltd), Gemini/Gibson fabric 45/45 bucket seats (LX), Barton/Gibson fabric 45/45 bucket seats with see-through adjustable headrests (ES), leather 45/45 bucket seats (ES Ltd), rear fold-down 3-passenger center armrest, front and rear stabilizer bars, vinyl steering wheel (LX), perforated leather-wrapped steering wheel (ES, ES Ltd), tinted glass, P195/70R14 black all-season steel radial tires (4) (LX), P205/60R15 black all-season steel radial tires (4) (ES), P205/60HR15 black all-season steel performance radial tires (5) (ES Ltd), spare tire space-saver, T125/70D15 with 15" x 4" wheel (LX, ES), conventional full size on 15" steel rim (ES Ltd), 4-speed overdrive automatic floor shift transmission, 2 speed windshield wipers with intermittent wipe, full Argent 14" wheel covers (LX), polycast Eurosport 15" wheels (4) (ES), aluminum sport style 15" x 6" wheels (4) (ES Ltd).

ACCESSORIES

Code	Description	Base Cost	Sgstd. List
P7	**Bucket Seats** — (45/45) w/fabric (Gemini/Gibson) - LX	STD	STD
S7	**Buckets Seats** — (45/45) w/fabric (Barton/Gibson) - ES	STD	STD
	- ES Limited	(252)	(296)
JL	**Buckets Seats** — (45/45) w/leather facing; includes power seats - driver and passenger (requires AAF) - ES	994	1169
FP	**Engine** — 3.0 liter, V6 MPI (182 CID)	STD	STD
GB	**Transmission** — automatic 4-speed overdrive, floor shift	STD	STD
NAE	**California Emission** — (mandatory in state of California)	87	102
NAF	**High Altitude Emissions**	NC	NC
BRF	**Anti-Lock Brake System** — LX, ES	679	799
MWC	**Luggage Rack** — rear deck lid - bright - LX	99	117
MWG	**Luggage Rack** — rear deck lid - black - ES, ES Limited	99	117
JPB	**Power Door Locks** — LX	200	235

Mfgs. Code	Description	Base Cost	Sgstd. List
	EAGLE		
—	**Warranty Enhancement for New York** — mandatory	106	125
AWF	**Power Group** — includes keyless entry; power rear deck lid release; remote fuel door release; illuminated entry - LX	254	299
JPA	**Power Windows** — (requires power locks) - LX, ES	277	326
JPS	**Power Seat** — driver (6-way w/fabric seat) - LX, ES	252	296
ARA	**Radio, Premium Audio System** — AM/FM cassette ET stereo radio with six "Accusound by Jensen" speakers with graphic equalizer, power amp. and power antenna - LX, ES	324	381
RBB	**Radio, Compact Disc Player System** — includes AM/FM cassette E.T. stereo, remote power amp., six "Accusound by Jensen" speakers and power antenna - (w/AAD or AAE) - LX	561	660
	- (w/AAF) - LX	237	279
	- (w/AAE) - ES	561	660
	- (w/AAF or AGG) - ES, ES Limited	237	279
NHM	**Speed Control** — LX	182	214
SUA	**Tilt Steering Column** — LX	117	138
ADN	**Trip Computer Vehicle Monitor** — LX	260	306
TBB	**Tire, Conventional Spare** — LX	81	95
WJS	**Wheels, Lace Style Cast Aluminum (4)** — 15" x 6"; includes P205/60R15 tires on LX (TPK) - LX	445	523
	- ES	256	301
MDA	**License Plate Bracket** — front (standard in states required)	NC	NC
—	**Discount Packages**		
AAD	**LX Discount Pkg** — (includes speed control, tilt steering column, AM/FM/cassette ET stereo radio) - total package price	502	591
	- discount	85	100
	- net price	417	491
AAE	**LX Discount Pkg** — (includes AAD Pkg plus illuminated dual visor mirrors, power door locks, power windows) - total package price	1080	1270
	- discount	425	500
	- net price	655	770
AAF	**LX Discount Pkg** — (includes speed control, tilt steering column, illuminated dual visor mirrors, power door locks, power windows, power group, power driver's seat, premium audio (includes AM/FM/cassette, ET stereo w/graphic equalizer, power amp, power antenna, 6-speakers), trip computer/vehicle monitor) - total package price	2169	2552
	- discount	616	725
	- net price	1553	1827
AAE	**ES Discount Pkg** — includes power group (keyless entry, power decklid release, remote fuel release, illuminated entry), power windows		
	- w/o JPS power driver seat		
	- total package price	531	625
	- discount	85	100
	- net price	446	525
	- w/JPS power driver seat		
	- total package price	783	921
	- discount	(638)	(750)
	- net price	145	171
AAF	**ES Discount Pkg** — includes power group (keyless entry, power decklid release, remote fuel release, illuminated entry), premium audio system (AM/FM/cassette E.T. stereo w/graphic equalizer, power amp, power antenna, 6-speakers)		
	- w/o JPS power driver seat or JL leather seats		
	- total package price	855	1006
	- discount	170	200
	- net price	685	806

Mfgs. Code	Description	Base Cost	Sgstd. List
	- w/JPS power driver seat		
	- total package price	1107	1302
	- discount	723	850
	- net price	384	452
	- w/JL leather seats		
	- total package price	1849	2175
	- discount	723	850
	- net price	1126	1325

SUMMIT

Mfgs. Code	Description	Base Cost	Sgstd. List
SUMMIT (4 Cylinder)			
B2XE24	3 Dr Base Hatchback	6358	6949
B2XL24	3 Dr ES Hatchback	7068	7845
B2XM41	4 Dr Base Sedan	7765	8618
B2XP41	4 Dr ES Sedan	8613	9623
Destination Charge:	49 States	328	328
	: Alaska	455	455

STANDARD EQUIPMENT:

SUMMIT: Maintenance-free battery, power assisted front disc/rear drum brakes, 5 mph bumpers, carpeting, cigar lighter (except Base Hatchback), electronic digital clock (ES Sedan), center console with storage bin, remote control decklid release (ES Sedan), rear window defroster (ES Sedan), side window demister, 1.5 liter 4 cylinder MPI engine, front wheel drive, locking fuel filler door, remote control fuel filler door release (ES Sedan), 13.2 gallon fuel tank, tachometer (ES Sedan), tinted glass (Sedans), quad halogen headlights, inside hood release, single note horn (dual note horn on ES Sedan), black left manual exterior mirror (Base Hatchback), black dual remote control mirrors (ES Hatchback, Base Hatchback), color-keyed dual electric mirrors (ES Sedan), inside day/night rearview mirror, passenger and driver visor vanity mirrors (ES Sedan), rear heater ducts (ES Sedan), all vinyl bucket seats (Base Hatchback), full face fabric low back bucket seats (ES Hatchback, Base Sedan), full face velour luxury bucket seats with driver side height control (ES Sedan), split folding rear seat (Hatchbacks, ES Sedan), manual rack-and-pinion steering, (power rack-and-pinion steering on ES Sedan), deluxe steering wheel (sport steering wheel on ES Sedan), adjustable tilt steering wheel (ES Sedan), P155/80R13 black all-season steel belted radial tires (Base Models), P175/70R13 black all-season steel belted radial tires (ES Models), compact spare tire, 4-speed manual transmission (Base Hatchback), 5-speed manual overdrive transmission (ES Hatchback, Sedans), trip odometer, styled steel wheels (Base Models), full wheel covers (ES Models),intermittent windshield wipers (ES Sedan).

ACCESSORIES

Mfgs. Code	Description	Base Cost	Sgstd. List
—	**Engine/Transmission**		
JBCB	1.5 liter I-4 MPI/4-speed manual - Base Summit	STD	STD
JBDR	1.5 liter I-4/5-speed manual - ES Summit	STD	STD
JBGA	1.5 liter I-4 MPI/3-speed automatic - Base Summit	499	601
	- ES Summit	414	499
NAE	**California Emission Controls**	NC	NC
HAA	**Air Conditioning**	625	753
CLA	**Floor Mats** — carpeted	23	28
RAG	**AM/FM Radio w/2 Speakers**	180	217
WMC	**Wheel Trim Rings** — Base Summit	46	55

EAGLE

Mfgs. Code	Description	Base Cost	Sgstd. List
—	**Quick Order Groups**		
	Base Summit Hatchback		
1FA	Package 1FA — Base	NC	NC
1FB	Package 1FB — (includes rear window defroster) - Base	55	66
1FC	Package 1FC — (includes tinted glass) — Base	52	63
1FD	Package 1FD — (includes tinted glass and rear window defroster) - Base	107	129
	ES Summit Hatchback		
1FC	Package 1FC — (includes rear window defroster and tinted glass) - ES	107	129
1FD	Package 1FD — (includes 1FC Pkg plus power steering and fixed intermittent wipers) - ES	345	416
1FE	Package 1FE — (includes 1FD Pkg plus rear wiper/washer and digital clock - ES	500	603
1FF	Package 1FF — (includes 1FE Pkg plus aluminum wheel) - ES	724	872
1FG	Package 1FG — (includes 1FF Pkg plus rear spoiler and tachometer) - ES	878	1058
—	**Customer Preferred Packages**		
	Base Summit Sedan		
21A	Package 21A — (includes model and standard equipment) - Base and 5-speed transmission	7764	8618
	- Base and auto transmission	8323	9291
21B	Package 21B — (includes fuel door and trunk release, trunk trim, dual visor vanity mirrors, fixed intermittent wipers, rear window defroster)		
	- Base and 5-speed transmission	7883	8760
	- Base and automatic transmission	8441	9433
21C	Package 21C — (includes 21B Pkg plus digital clock, power steering, AM/FM E.T. stereo w/6 speakers - Base and 5-speed transmission	8391	9373
	- Base and auto transmission	8950	10046
21D	Package 21D — (includes 21C Pkg plus AM/FM cassette E.T. stereo w/6 speakers [upgraded]) - Base and 5-speed transmission	8570	9588
	- Base and automatic transmission	9129	10261
	ES Summit Sedan		
21E	Package 21E — (includes model and standard equipment) - ES and 5 -speed transmission	8613	9623
	- ES and auto transmission	9171	10296
21F	Package 21F — (includes AM/FM E.T. stereo w/6 speakers, speed control and variable intermittent wipers) - ES and 5-speed transmission	9034	10131
	- ES and auto transmission	9593	10804
21G	Package 21G — (includes AM/FM casette E.T. stereo w/6 speakers, speed control and variable intermittent wipers) - ES and 5-speed transmission	9173	10298
	- ES and automatic transmission	10092	11406
21J	Package 21J — (includes 21H Pkg plus 4 13" x 5" aluminum wheels)		
	- ES and 5-speed transmission	9762	11008
	- ES and automatic transmission	10321	11681

TALON

Description	Base Cost	Sgstd. List
TALON (4 Cylinder)		
BDXH24 Base Coupe (5-speed)	11911	12990
BDXP24 TSi Front Wheel Drive Coupe (5-speed)	13368	14609
BDXP24 TSi Front Wheel Drive Coupe (auto)	14068	15432
BDFP24 TSi All Wheel Drive Coupe (5-speed)	15082	16513
BDFP24 TSi All Wheel Drive Coupe (auto)	15781	17336
Destination Charge: All models	328	328

Mfgs. Code	Description	EAGLE	Base Cost	Sgstd. List

STANDARD EQUIPMENT:

TALON: Performance fascias and lower bodyside aero effects (TSi FWD, TSi AWD), maintenance-free battery, 5 mph impact resistant bumpers, clearcoat paint, digital clock, center console with integral armrest/storage, rear window defroster, driver's footrest, front lower fascia mounted driving lamps (TSi FWD, TSi AWD), 2.0 liter I-4 MPI DOHC 16-valve engine (Base FWD), 2.0 liter MPI DOHC 16-valve intercooled turbo engine (TSi FWD, TSi AWD), exhaust system (stainless steel with chrome tips, sport tuned), front carpeted, color-keyed floor mats, full-tinted glass with windshield sun-shade band, locking glove box, retractable halogen-type headlamps with automatic "off" feature, dual note horn, sport instrumentation (full analog gauges including 7000 RPM tachometer), turbo boost gauge (TSi FWD, TSi AWD), leather-wrap sport steering wheel and gear shift handle (TSi FWD, TSi AWD), cigarette lighter, dual map overhead lighting, courtesy lights, mirrors (day/night, rearview, dual visor vanity), black dual power remote control mirrors, bodyside molding (protective wrap around style; color keyed), four wheel disc power brakes, variable assist rack and pinion power steering, AM/FM ET stereo radio with cassette player and four speakers, fuel filler door and liftgate remote releases, front automatic passive restraint seatbelts, front highback bucket seats with recliners and driver's lumbar adjustment (Base FWD), performance bucket seats with driver's thigh, side and lumbar adjustments (TSi FWD, TSi AWD), two passenger rear seats with split folding seatback (Base FWD, TSi FWD), black rear spoiler, tilting steering column, front suspension (independent struts with stabilizer bar, sport tuned), rear suspension (struts with trailing beam, stabilizer bar, sport tuned) (Base FWD, TSi FWD), enthusiast suspension, upgraded springs, struts and stabilizer bars and independent double wishbone rear design (TSi AWD), P205/55HR16 speed rated all-season BSW radial tires (Base FWD), P205/55VR16 high speed rated all-weather radial tires (TSi FWD, TSi AWD), P125/70D15 minispare tire, removable cargo tonneau security cover, 5 speed manual overdrive transmission, four 16" polycast sport-styled light quartz wheels (Base FWD, TSi FWD), four 16" alloy wheels (TSi AWD), 2-speed windshield wipers with variable intermittent wipe.

ACCESSORIES

Code	Description	Base Cost	Sgstd. List
BRF	**Anti-Locking Brake System** — Base Talon, TSi Front Wheel Drive	786	925
	- TSi All Wheel Drive	579	681
GWB	**Sunroof** — (pop-up)	311	366
WNB	**16" Alloy Wheels (4)** — Base Talon, TSi Front Wheel Drive	236	278
NAE	**California Emission Controls**	NC	NC
LSA	**Security Alarm System** — TSi	139	163
PJFV	**Leather Bucket Seats** — TSi	363	427
—	**Warranty Enhancement for New York** — mandatory	106	125
RDP	**Radio** — (compact disc player) - TSi Front Wheel Drive	329	387
	- TSi All Wheel Drive	534	628
RAY	**Radio** — (premium audio system) - TSi All Wheel Drive	205	241
—	**Preferred Equipment Packages (includes model plus pkg)**		
23B	**Base Talon Package 23B** — (includes air conditioning) - models w/5 speed transmission	12600	13801
	- models w/automatic transmission	13185	14489
23C	**Base Talon Package 23C** — (includes air conditioning, speed control, liftgate wiper/washer, power windows/door locks) - models w/5 speed transmission	13261	14578
	- models w/automatic transmission	13846	15266
23D	**Base Talon Package 23D** — (includes Base Talon Pkg 23C plus premium audio system [AM/FM cassette], 16" alloy wheels) - models w/5 speed transmission	13702	15097
	- models w/automatic transmission	14287	15785
25F	**TSi (Front Wheel) Package 25F** — (includes air conditioning, speed control, liftgate wiper/washer, power windows/door locks) - models w/5 speed transmission	14718	16197
	- models w/automatic transmission	15417	17020
25G	**TSi (Front Wheel) Package 25G** — (includes TSi (front wheel) pkg 25F		

	plus premium audio system [AM/FM/cassette], 16" alloy wheels)		
	- models w/5 speed transmission	15159	16716
	- models w/automatic transmission	15859	17539
25J	**TSi (All Wheel Drive) Package 25J** — (includes air conditioning, speed control, liftgate wiper/washer, power windows/door locks) - models w/5 speed transmission	16432	18101
	- models w/automatic transmission	17131	18924

1991 ford

AEROSTAR WAGON

AEROSTAR WAGONS (6 Cylinder)

Code	Description	Base Cost	Sgstd. List
A11	XL 2WD Regular Length	11780	13131
A31	XL 2WD Extended Length	12570	14028
A21	XL E-4WD Regular Length	13891	15529
A41	XL E-4WD Extended Length	14699	16448
A11	XLT 2WD Regular Length	14008	15662
A31	XLT 2WD Extended Length	14798	16560
A21	XLT E-4WD Regular Length	16119	18061
A41	XLT E-4WD Extended Length	16927	18980
A11	EB 2WD Regular Length	16749	18778
A31	EB 2WD Extended Length	17539	19675
A21	EB E-4WD Regular Length	18860	21176
A41	EB E-4WD Extended Length	19669	22095
	Destination Charge: All models	525	525

STANDARD EQUIPMENT:

AEROSTAR WAGON: Tinted glass, luggage rack (Eddie Bauer), fold-away aero mirrors, forged aluminum wheels (Eddie Bauer), front air conditioning (XLT), front and rear air conditioning with auxiliary heater (Eddie Bauer), electric rear window defroster (Eddie Bauer), electronics group (Eddie Bauer), electron AM/FM stereo radio with digital clock (XL, XLT), super sound system (Eddie Bauer), dual captain's chairs (XLT, Eddie Bauer), interval windshield wipers, rear window wiper/washer, convenience group, 3.0L EFI V6 engine (2WD), 4.0L EFI V6 engine (4WD), 5-speed manual transmission (2WD), 4-speed automatic overdrive transmission (4WD).

ACCESSORIES

Code	Description	Base Cost	Sgstd. List
99U	**3.0L EFI V6 Engine** — 2WD	STD	STD
99X	**4.0L EFI V6 Engine** — 2WD	255	300
99U	**4.0L EFI V6 Engine** — E-4WD	STD	STD
44M	**Transmission** — 5-speed manual overdrive (2WD only)	STD	STD
44T	**Transmission** — automatic overdrive (standard on E4WD)	568	668
—	**Limited Slip Axle**	215	252
—	**Optional Axle Ratio (Upgraded)**	32	38
422	**California Emissions System**	85	100
428	**High Altitude Principal Use Emissions**	NC	NC
—	**Tires**		
T85	P215/70Rx14SL steel radial BSW all season	STD	STD
T8E	P215/70Rx14SL steel radial WSW all season	72	84
T86	P215/75Rx14SL steel radial BSW all season (except regular length 2WD)	NC	NC

Mfgs. Code	Description	Base Cost	Sgstd. List
	FORD		
T8F	P215/75Rx14SL steel radial WSW all season (except regular length 2WD)	72	84
—	**Optional Seating**		
21A	7-passenger w/bucket seats	252	296
214	5-passenger w/dual captain's chairs	624	734
21D	7-passenger w/dual captian's chairs and 2 & 3 passenger seat/bed - use with package 400	1379	1622
	- use with package 401 or 403	458	539
21B	7-passenger w/dual captain's chairs	920	1083
21E	7-passenger w/quad captain's chairs	498	585
21F	7-passenger w/quad captain's chairs and 3-passenger seat/bed - use with package 403	518	610
	- use with package 405	NC	NC
572	**Air Conditioning**	719	846
574	**Air Conditioning, High Capacity, and Auxiliary Heater** — use with package 400	1209	1422
	- use with all other packages	489	576
414	**Console, Floor**	148	174
—	**Console, Floor, Not Included**	(52)	(61)
57Q	**Defroster, Electric Rear Window**	141	166
151	**Electronics Group**		
	- use with package 400 or 401	712	838
	- use with package 403	633	745
558	**Exterior Appearance Group**		
	- use with package 400	518	610
	- use with package 401	180	212
	- use with package 403	79	93
	- use w/XLT trim w/o privacy glass and power convenience group	432	509
41H	**Heater, Engine Block**	28	33
153	**License Plate Bracket**	NC	NC
593	**Light Group**	135	159
615	**Luggage Rack**	120	141
542	**Mirrors, Swing Lock "A" Pillar**	45	52
963	**Molding, Bodyside Protection**	54	63
—	**Paint, Clearcoat**	NC	NC
—	**Paint, Stripe, Deluxe (credit)**	(25)	(29)
—	**Power Convenience Group**		
	- use with exterior appearance group	381	449
	- use with all other packages	426	501
51A	**Spare Tire, Conventional**	90	106
514	**Spare Tires** — underbody space saver not included (spare tire mounted inside vehicle)	(19)	(22)
52N	**Speed Control/Tilt Steering Wheel**	294	346
535	**Trailer Towing Package**	239	282
434	**Underseat Stowage Bin (RH)**	31	37
646	**Wheels, Forged Aluminum**		
	- use with XL trim	300	352
	- use with XLT or exterior appearance group	266	313
—	**Radio Systems**		
589	electronic AM/FM stereo with cassette/clock	87	102
58Y	radio credit option	(155)	(183)
—	**Preferred Equipment Packages**		
400A	XL Base Pkg	NC	NC
401A	XL Plus Pkg		
	- total package price	2318	2727
	- discount	723	850
	- net price	1595	1877
403A	XLT Regular Length		

Mfgs. Code	Description	Base Cost	Sgstd. List
	- total package price	1001	1178
	- discount	595	700
	- net price	406	478
403A	XLT Extended Length		
	- total package price	1001	1178
	- discount	765	900
	- net price	236	278
405A	Eddie Bauer		
	- total package price	922	1084
	- discount	595	700
	- net price	327	384

ESCORT

ESCORT (4 Cylinder)

Mfgs. Code	Description	Base Cost	Sgstd. List
P10	Pony 2 Dr Hatchback	7393	7976
P11	LX 2 Dr Hatchback	7849	8667
P12	GT 2 Dr Hatchback	10356	11484
P14	LX 4 Dr Hatchback	8230	9095
P15	LX 4 Dr Wagon	8750	9680

Destination Charge: All Models 365 365

STANDARD EQUIPMENT:

ESCORT: Aerodynamic single rectangular halogen headlamps, fog lamps (GT), black remote-control driver's side breakaway mirror (Pony, LX), black dual electric remote-control breakaway mirrors (GT), dark or medium titanium bodyside protection moldings (LX), color-keyed bodyside protection molding (GT), rear reflex applique (GT), rocker panel cladding (GT), rear spoiler (GT), 13" x 5" semi-styled steel wheels with center cap (Pony), 13" x 5" semi-styled steel wheels with full luxury wheel cover (LX), 15" x 5½" styled aluminum wheels (GT), rear ashtrays (LX, GT), motorized front shoulder belt restraint system with manual lap belts, cargo area cover, cigarette lighter, center console with forward bin and cup holders (Pony, LX), center console with bin and removable tray with cup holders (GT), vinyl door trim with armrest and integral map pocket/speaker grille (Pony), cloth door trim with armrest, integral map pocket/speaker grille and carpet lower (LX, GT), light group (GT), non-illuminated passenger visor mirror (Pony, LX), illuminated driver/passenger visor mirrors (GT), low-back cloth and vinyl reclining bucket seats (Pony), upgraded low-back cloth and vinyl reclining bucket seats with luxury trim (LX), sport performance cloth reclining bucket seats (GT), full-fold bench-type rear seat with dual release handles (Pony), split-fold 60/40 rear seat with dual release handles (LX, GT), integral rear seat headrests (GT), two-spoke soft black steering wheel (Pony, LX), two-spoke sport black steering wheel with hand grips (GT), maintenance-free battery, power front disc/rear drum brakes (Pony, LX), front disc/rear disc power brakes (GT), side window demisters, 1.9 liter SEFI I-4 engine (Pony, LX), 1.8 liter DOHC 16-valve EFI I-4 engine (GT), engine fuel cutout light, engine malfunction indicator light, engine low-coolant warning light, front wheel drive, remote control fuel door release (GT), tinted glass, inside hood release, remote control liftgate release (GT), radio prep package including antenna (A-pillar mount), wiring and speaker grille (Pony), electronic AM/FM stereo radio with integral clock (LX), electronic AM/FM stereo radio with cassette and clock (GT), rear seat heat ducts, front and rear stabilizer bars, manual rack-and-pinion steering (Pony, LX), power rack-and-pinion steering (GT), four wheel independent suspension, sport handling (GT), tachometer (GT), temperature gauge, P175/70R13 BSW tires (Pony, LX), P185/60HR15 BSW tires (GT), trip odometer, 5-speed manual transaxle, 2-speed windshield wipers with fixed interval feature (Pony, LX), 2-speed windshield wipers with variable interval feature (GT).

Mfgs. Code	Description	Base Cost	Sgstd. List

FORD

ACCESSORIES

Mfgs. Code	Description	Base Cost	Sgstd. List
99J	**Engine** — 1.9L SEFI (standard on Pony and LXI)		
998	**Engine** — 1.8L DOHC (standard on GT)		
445	**Transaxle** — 5-speed manual	STD	STD
44T	**Transaxle** — 4-speed overdrive automatic	622	732
422	**California Emissions System**	59	70
428	**High Altitude Emissions System**	NC	NC
—	**Tires**		
T15	P175/70Rx13 BSW — Pony and LX	STD	STD
T39	P185/60HRx15 BSW — GT	STD	STD
—	**Seats**		
R	cloth and vinyl low back buckets - Pony	STD	STD
U	upgraded cloth and vinyl low back bucket - LX	STD	STD
T	cloth sport performance bucket - GT	STD	STD
572	**Air Conditioning** — LX and GT only	632	744
57Q	**Defroster, Rear Window**	136	160
60A	**Light/Convenience Group** — LX	246	290
68A	**Light Group/Removable Cupholder Tray**	100	118
54J	**Dual Electric Remote Control Mirrors**	83	98
68B	**Remote Fuel Door/Liftgate Releases**	63	74
60B	**Luxury Convenience Group** — 2-Door LX Hatchback	213	251
	- 4-door LX Hatchback and Wagon	284	334
	- GT	286	336
13B	**Moonroof, Power** — LX Hatchback and GT only	466	549
—	**Paint, Clearcoat**	78	91
—	**Radio Systems**		
587	Radio, AM/FM stereo (Pony)	208	245
589	Radio, AM/FM cassette - Pony	340	400
	- LX	132	155
913	sound system, premium	117	138
58Y	radio credit option - LX	(208)	(245)
	- GT	(340)	(400)
52H	**Steering, Power** — LX and GT only	200	235
60W	**Wagon Group**	204	241
153	**Front License Plate Bracket**	NC	NC
—	**Mandatory Warranty Enhancement** — required on all vehicles registered or sold in New York State	95	110
—	**Preferred Equipment Packages**		
320A	**LX Preferred Equipment Package** — includes power steering, light/convenience group (light group/removable cupholder tray, dual electric remote control mirrors, remote fuel door/liftgate release), rear window defroster - total package price	582	685
	- discount	(425)	(500)
	- net price	(157)	(185)
330A	**GT Preferred Equipment Package** — includes manual air conditioning and luxury convenience group (tilt steering column, speed control, tachometer and power door locks) - total package price	1054	1240
	- discount	(632)	(744)
	- net price	422	496
320F	**LX Preferred Equipment Package** — includes automatic transaxle, manual air conditioning and power steering - total package price	1454	1711
	- discount	(259)	(305)
	- net price	1195	1406

Mfgs. Code	Description	FORD	Base Cost	Sgstd. List

FESTIVA

FESTIVA (4 Cylinder)

		Base Cost	Sgstd. List
T05	L Hatchback	6259	6620
T06	GL Hatchback	7040	7460

Destination Charge: All models 285 285

STANDARD EQUIPMENT:

FESTIVA: Grey front and rear bumpers with side extension (L), color-keyed bumpers with side extension (GL), locking fuel filler door with screw-on tethered gas cap, body color grille, aerodynamic halogen headlamps, LH non-remote mirror, RH non-remote mirror (GL), narrow bodyside protection moldings (L), color-keyed narrow bodyside protection moldings (GL), monochromatic paint, black trim (windshield wipers, windshield molding and door handles), semi-styled 12" x 4" steel wheels (L), painted semi-styled 12" x 4½" steel wheels (GL), opening rear quarter windows, front and rear ashtrays, automatic shoulder restraint belt system (front), manual 3-point shoulder harness (rear), cargo cover (GL), color-keyed floor and luggage compartment carpet, cigarette lighter, integral electronic clock with radio (GL), rear coat hooks, consolette, color-keyed door trim with integral armrests (L), full door trim with color inserts and map pockets (GL), fuel and water temperature gauges, glove box, inside hood release, courtesy lamps, color-keyed luggage compartment with molded side trim, inside day/night rearview mirror, cloth and vinyl front high-back reclining bucket seats, flip-fold rear seat, soft-feel shift knob, maintenance-free battery, front disc/rear drum power brakes, side window demisters, 1.3 liter EFI SOHC I-4 engine, front wheel drive, electronic AM/FM stereo radio with four speakers and integral clock (GL), manual rack-and-pinion steering, independent MacPherson strut front suspension with stabilizer, rear torsion (beam "semi-independent" suspension), 145/SR12 BSW all-season tires (L), 165/70SR12 BSW all-season tires (GL), mini spare tire, 5 speed manual overdrive transaxle, two speed windshield wipers, rear window wiper/washer.

ACCESSORIES

		Base Cost	Sgstd. List
99H	**Engine —** 1.3 liter EFI	STD	STD
445	**Transaxle —** 5-speed manual overdrive	STD	STD
440	**Transaxle —** (4-speed automatic) - GL	437	515
422	**California Emission System**	59	70
428	**High Altitude Emission System**	NC	NC
T11	**Tires —** (145/SR 12 BSW) - L	STD	STD
T16	**Tires —** (165/70SR 12 BSW) - GL	STD	STD
A	**Seats —** (cloth & vinyl high back buckets) - L	STD	STD
B	**Seats —** (cloth & vinyl high back buckets) - GL	STD	STD
572	**Air Conditioning —** (manual) - GL	721	849
57Q	**Rear Window Defroster**	136	160
587	**Radio —** (electronic AM/FM stereo w/digital clock) - L	208	245
589	**Radio —** (electronic AM/FM stereo cassette w/digital clock) - L	340	400
	- GL	132	155
21A/ 367	**Roof —** (flip-up open air)	206	243
21B/ 366	**Sports Appearance Pkg**	270	317
52H	**Power Steering —** GL	220	259
173	**Rear Window Wiper/Washer —** L	107	126

LTD CROWN VICTORIA

LTD CROWN VICTORIA (8 Cylinder)

P73	4 Dr Standard Sedan	15724	18227
P74	4 Dr LX Sedan	16265	18863
P76	4 Dr Standard Wagon	15601	18083
P77	4 Dr LX Wagon	16239	18833
P78	4 Dr Standard Country Squire Wagon	15816	18335
P79	4 Dr LX Country Squire Wagon	16454	19085

Destination Charge: All Models 535 535

STANDARD EQUIPMENT:
LTD CROWN VICTORIA: 5 mph front and rear bumpers (Sedans), 5 mph front and rear bumpers with rear bumper step pad (Wagons), bumper rub strips, quad rectangular halogen headlamps, lower bodyside urethane coating, deluxe luggage rack (Wagons), dual electric remote-control mirrors, bright rocker panel molding (Crown Victoria S Sedan, Wagons), black rocker panel molding (Crown Victoria Sedan, Crown Victoria LX Sedan), bright wheellip (Sedans, Crown Victoria Wagon, Crown Victoria LX Wagon), bright hood rear edge molding and door window frame moldings (Crown Victoria, Crown Victoria LX, Country Squire, Country Squire LX), protective bodyside moldings (Crown Victoria, Crown Victoria LX), dual accent stripes on bodysides (Crown Victoria, Crown Victoria LX), simulated woodgrain paneling on bodyside/doorgate with rails (Country Squire, Country Squire LX), padded vinyl rear half-roof (Crown Victoria Sedan, Crown Victoria LX Sedan), deluxe wheel covers, 15" x 6" wheels (Sedans), 15" x 6½" wheels (Wagons), driver's side air bag supplemental restraint system, color-keyed 18 oz. cut-pile carpet, color-keyed removable load floor carpet (Wagons), cigarette lighter in front instrument panel ashtray, cigarette lighter in each door armrest, electronic digital clock, luxury door trim with assist straps and woodtone appliques, front door curb lights, front and rear armrests with integral door pull handles, lockable glove box, "headlamps on" reminder chime, light group (Crown Victoria LX, Country Squire LX), dual illuminated visor mirrors (Crown Victoria LX, Country Squire LX), split bench seats with dual recliners, cloth covered headrests, dual front center armrests and cloth seat trim (Crown Victoria S Sedan, Crown Victoria Sedan), split bench seats with dual recliners, vinyl covered headrests, dual front center armrests and all-vinyl seat trim (Crown Victoria Wagon, Country Squire), split bench seats with dual recliners, seatback map pockets, luxury seat trim, front and (except Wagons), rear center armrests (Crown Victoria LX, Country Squire LX), dual facing rear seats with safety belt retractors (Crown Victoria LX Wagon, Country Squire LX), color-keyed 4-spoke tilt steering wheel, manual temperature control air conditioning, low fuel alert light, autolamp system, maintenance-free battery, power front disc/rear drum brakes (Sedans), power front disc/heavy duty rear drum brakes (Wagons), coolant recovery system, three-way doorgate with power window (Wagons), 5.0 liter SEFI V8 engine, engine emission malfunction indicator light, tinted glass, inside hood release, dual note horn, automatic parking brake release, electronic AM/FM stereo search radio with four speakers, super luxury level sound insulation package (all except Crown Victoria S Sedan), power steering, P215/70R15 WSW all-season tires, mini-spare tire, 4-speed automatic overdrive transmission, trip odometer, deep-well trunk with low liftover height (Sedans), power side windows, interval windshield wipers.

ACCESSORIES

99F	**Engine — 5.0L**	STD	STD
44T	**Transaxle —** automatic overdrive	STD	STD
422	**California Emissions System**	85	100
428	**High Altitude Emissions System**	NC	NC
T3P	**P215/70Rx15 WSW Tires**	STD	STD
—	**Seats**		
A	cloth split bench - Sedans	STD	STD
B	all vinyl split bench (standard on non-LX Wagons)	31	37
E	upgraded cloth split bench (standard on LX)	STD	STD

Mfgs. Code	Description	Base Cost	Sgstd. List
	FORD		
F	leather seating surfaces split bench	416	489
G	duraweave split bench - Wagons	82	96
573	**Air Conditioning** — automatic climate control (n/a on standard)		
	- with package 113B	56	66
	- with all other models	192	225
45A	**Axle, Traction-Lok**	85	100
586	**Audio System, High-Level** — with package 113B	285	335
	- all other models	417	490
631	**Battery, Heavy-Duty** — (72 AMP)	23	27
153	**Bracket, Front License Plate**	NC	NC
—	**Brougham Half Roof Treatment**	617	726
763	**Bumper Guards** — front and rear	53	62
51Q	**Cornering Lamps** — front (n/a on standard)	58	68
57Q	**Defroster, Rear Window**	136	160
12H	**Floor Mats** — front, color-keyed carpet	22	26
12Q	**Floor Mats** — rear, color-keyed carpet	15	17
41H	**Heater, Engine Block Immersion**	17	20
47J	**Illuminated Entry System** — (n/a on standard)	69	82
943	**Light Group**	50	59
903	**Lock Group, Power** — Sedans	234	276
	- Wagons	248	291
961	**Moldings** — vinyl insert bodyside	56	66
—	**Paint, Clearcoat**	196	230
58H	**Radio** — electronic AM/FM stereo cassette	132	155
91H	**Radio Antenna** — power (n/a on standard)	69	82
58Y	**Radio Credit Option**	(175)	(206)
216	**Seats** — dual facing rear	182	215
21A	**Seat** — 6-way power driver's	247	290
21J	**Seats** — 6-way power - dual control (n/a on standard)		
	- with package 113B	247	290
	- all other models	494	580
913	**Sound System** — premium (n/a on standard)	143	168
525	**Speed Control**	178	210
524	**Steering Wheel, Leather-Wrapped**	54	63
66Z	**Suspension** — automatic load-leveling	213	250
662	**Suspension** — heavy-duty handling	22	26
535	**Trailer Towing Package** — heavy-duty w/pkg 121A	321	378
	- all other models	344	405
—	**Vinyl Roof Delete**	(170)	(200)
64L	**Wheels** — four cast aluminum (sparkle) (n/a on standard)	374	440
646	**Wheel Covers** — locking wire style	194	228
924	**Windshield-Insta-Clear** — (n/a on standard)	259	305
—	**Mandatory Warranty Enhancement** — required on all vehicles registered and sold in New York State	95	110
—	**Preferred Equipment Packages**		
110A	**Standard Preferred Equipment Package** — total package price	NC	NC
	- discount	0	0
	- net price	NC	NC
113B	**LX Sedan Preferred Equipment Package** — includes front and rear bumper guards, rear window defroster, front and rear floor mats, power lock group, electronic AM/FM stereo cassette radio, 6-way power driver's seat, speed control, leather-wrapped steering wheel, cornering lamps, illuminated entry system, four cast aluminum (sparkle) wheels		
	- total package price	1572	1849
	- discount	723	850
	- net price	849	999
114B	**LX Sedan Preferred Equipment Package** — includes front and rear		

	bumper guards, front and rear floor mats, power lock group, speed control, leather-wrapped steering wheel, cornering lamps, illuminated entry system, four cast aluminum (sparkle) wheels, hi-level audio system, automatic climate control air conditioning, power radio antenna, 6-way dual control power seat		
	- total package price	2229	2622
	- discount	850	1000
	- net price	1379	1622
113B	**LX Wagon Preferred Equipment Package** — includes all items in 113B LX Sedan Preferred Equipment Pkg		
	- total package price	1586	1864
	- discount	850	1000
	- net price	736	864
114B	**LX Wagon Preferred Equipment Package** — includes all items in 114B LX Sedan Preferred Equipment Package		
	- total package price	2243	2637
	- discount	1190	1400
	- net price	1053	1237

MUSTANG

MUSTANG (4 Cylinder)

P40	2 Dr LX Sedan	9223	10157
P41	2 Dr LX Hatchback	9673	10663
P44	2 Dr LX Convertible	14621	16222

MUSTANG (8 Cylinder)

P40	2 Dr LX 5.0L Sedan	11993	13270
P41	2 Dr LX 5.0L Hatchback	12692	14055
P44	2 Dr LX 5.0L Convertible	17308	19242
P42	2 Dr GT Hatchback	13563	15034
P45	2 Dr GT Convertible	17862	19864

Destination Charge: All Models 430 430

STANDARD EQUIPMENT:

MUSTANG: Integral air dam with front fascia (GT), urethane lower bodyside protection, front and rear body color fascias with black rub strips and Mustang nomenclature (LX, LX 5.0L), front and rear body color or titanium fascias and rub strips with GT nomenclature molded into rear fascia (GT), color-keyed convertible top cover (Convertible), aerodynamic halogen headlamps, round Hella® fog lamps (GT), luggage rack with high-mount stop lamp (Convertible), dual remote control mirrors - RH convex (Sedan & Hatchback), dual electric remote control mirrors - RH convex (Convertible), black bodyside protection molding (LX, LX5.0L), body-color bodyside protection molding (GT), flared rocker moldings with integral spats (GT), color coordinated bodyside paint stripe (LX, LX 5.0L), single-wing rear spoiler with stop lamp (Hatchback), finned wheel covers (LX), 16" x 7" 5-spoke cast aluminum wheels with locking lug nuts (LX 5.0L, GT), driver's side supplemental air bag restraint system, front and rear ashtrays, front and rear safety belts with shoulder harness, cargo area cover (Hatchback), 16 oz. carpeting, cigarette lighter, integral electronic clock with radio, console with armrest, driver's footrest, glove box, tachometer, trip odometer, voltmeter, temperature, fuel and oil pressure gauges, alert lights for check oil, low coolant, low fuel, and low washer fluid (LX 5.0L, GT), 140 mph speedometer (LX 5.0L, GT), light group, pivoting map light, dual visor mirrors with covers, low-back reclining cloth bucket seats (LX, LX 5.0L), articulated sport seats with cloth trim , cloth headrests and power lumbar support (LX 5.0L, GT), split/fold-down rear seatbacks (Hatchbacks), leather-wrapped steering wheel (LX 5.0L, GT), color-keyed cloth headliner (Sedans & Hatchback), color-keyed sun visors (Sedans &

Hatchbacks), color-keyed vinyl sun visors (Convertibles), traction-lok axle (LX 5.0L, GT), heavy duty maintenance-free battery, power front disc/rear drum brakes, power retractable convertible top (Convertible), side window demisters, 2.3 liter EFI OHC I-4 (LX), 5.0 liter EFI HO (High Output), V8 engine (LX 5.0L, GT), dual exhaust system (LX 5.0L, GT), stainless steel tailpipe terminations (LX 5.0L), tinted glass, dual-note horn, power lock group (Convertible), electronic AM/FM stereo radio with seek and integral clock and four speakers, luxury sound insulation package, variable power rack-and-pinion steering (LX), 14.7:1 constant ratio power rack-and-pinion steering with increased effort (LX 5.0L, GT), handling suspension package with variable rate coil springs and quadra-shock rear suspension (LX 5.0L, GT), 195/75R14 BSW all-season tires (LX), P225/55R16 BSW all-season performance tires (LX 5.0L), P225/55ZR16 BSW performance tires (GT), mini spare tire, 5-speed manual overdrive transmission, power side and quarter windows and glass backlight (Convertible), interval windshield wipers.

ACCESSORIES

Code	Description	Base Cost	Sgstd. List
99M	**Engine** — 2.3L EFI (LX only)	STD	STD
99E	**Engine** — 5.0L EFI HO (LX 5.0L and GT only)	STD	STD
445	**Transaxle** — 5-speed manual	STD	STD
44L	**Transaxle** — 4-speed automatic overdrive (LX only)	506	595
44T	**Transaxle** — 4-speed automatic overdrive (LX 5.0L and GT only)	506	595
422	**California Emissions System**	85	100
428	**High Altitude Emissions System**	NC	NC
—	**Tires**		
T79	P195/75Rx14 BSW - LX	STD	STD
—	P205/65Rx15 BSW (included w/cast aluminum wheels - LX		
T27	P225/55ZRx16 BSW all-season performance - LX 5.0L	STD	STD
T26	P225/55ZRx16 BSW Performance - LX 5.0L	NC	NC
T27	P225/55ZRx16 BSW all-season performance - GT	NC	NC
T26	P225/55ZRx16 BSW performance - GT	STD	STD
—	**Seats**		
F	cloth low back - LX	STD	STD
B	vinyl low back - LX	31	37
D	cloth and vinyl articulated sport - LX 5.0L and GT	STD	STD
C	leather seating surfaces articulated sport - LX 5.0L and GT	416	489
45C	**Axle, Optional Ratio** — (n/a on LX)	NC	NC
18C	**Cargo Tie-Down Net**	56	66
60A	**Custom Equipment Group** — LX Sedan/Hatchback	780	917
	-all other models	595	817
57Q	**Defroster, Rear Window** — (n/a on convertibles)	136	160
12H	**Floor Mats, Front**	28	33
915	**Graphic Equalizer (includes Premium Sound)**		
	- with premium sound 913	118	139
	- without premium sound 913	251	307
—	**Paint, Clearcoat**	78	91
61A	**Power Equipment Group** — (standard on Convertible)	480	565
913	**Sound System, Premium**	143	168
589	**Radio** — electronic AM/FM with cassette	132	155
58Y	**Radio Credit Option** — with package 240A	(340)	(400)
	- with package 245A or 249A	(483)	(568)
	- all other models	(208)	(245)
13C	**Roof** — flip-up open air (Hatchback models only)	302	355
525	**Speed Control**	178	210
954	**Titanium Lower Bodyside Accent Treatment** — GT only	135	159
644	**Wheel Covers** — wire style (LX only) - with package 240A	NC	NC
	- all other models	164	193
64W	**Wheels, Cast Aluminum with Upsize P205/65Rx15 BSW Tires** — (LX		

Mfgs. Code	Description	Base Cost	Sgstd. List
	only) - with package 240A	142	167
	- all other models	306	360
64J	**Wheels, Styled Road** — LX only	164	193
153	**Bracket, Front License Plate**	NC	NC
41H	**Heater, Engine Block Immersion**	17	20
—	**Mandatory Warranty Enhancement** — required on all vehicles registered or sold in New York State	95	110
—	**Preferred Equipment Packages**		
240A	**LX Sedan, Hatchback Preferred Equipment Package** — includes power equipment group (dual electric remote control mirrors, power side windows, power lock group), cargo tie-down net, front floor mats, speed control, electronic AM/FM radio with cassette player and clock, styled road wheels - total package price	1038	1222
	- discount	850	1000
	- net price	188	222
240A	**LX Convertible Preferred Equipment Package** — includes same items in LX Sedan/Hatchback Preferred Equipment Package 240A		
	- total package price	558	657
	- discount	383	450
	- net price	175	207
245A	**LX 5.0L Sedan/Hatchback Preferred Equipment Package** — includes LX Sedan/Hatchback Preferred Equipment Pkg 240A items plus premium sound system and custom equipment group (manual air conditioning and dual illuminated visor mirrors) (styled road wheels deleted)		
	- total package price	1712	2014
	- discount	595	700
	- net price	1117	1314
245A	**LX 5.0L Convertible Preferred Equipment Package** — includes LX Sedan/Hatchback Preferred Equipment Pkg 240A items plus premium sound system and manual air conditioning (styled road wheels deleted)		
	- total package price	1232	1449
	- discount	595	700
	- net price	637	749
249A	**GT Hatchback Preferred Equipment Package** — includes LX Sedan/Hatchback Preferred Equipment Pkg 240A items plus premium sound system and custom equipment group (manual air conditioning, dual illuminated visor mirrors) (styled road wheels deleted)		
	- total package price	1712	2014
	- discount	595	700
	- net price	1117	1314
249A	**GT Convertible Preferred Equipment Package** — includes LX Sedan/Hatchback Preferred Equipment Pkg 240A items plus premium sound system and manual air conditioning (styled road wheels deleted)		
	- total package price	1232	1449
	- discount	595	700
	- net price	637	749

PROBE

PROBE (4 Cylinder)

Mfgs. Code	Description	Base Cost	Sgstd. List
T20	2 Dr GL Hatchback	10594	11691
T22	2 Dr GT Turbo Hatchback	13507	14964

PROBE (6 Cylinder)

Mfgs. Code	Description	Base Cost	Sgstd. List
T21	2 Dr LX Hatchback	11963	13229

Mfgs. Code	Description	FORD	Base Cost	Sgstd. List

Destination Charge: All Models 320 320

STANDARD EQUIPMENT:

PROBE: Front and rear integrated bumper system with full fascias, tinted backlight and quarter window glass, complete tinted glass (LX, GT), front fascia with fog lamps and rear fascia with spoiler and taillamp treatment (GT), concealed headlamps, RH convex and LH remote sail mounted manual, adjustable mirrors (GL), sail mounted dual electric remote control mirrors (LX, GT), protective bodyside moldings (GL, GT), protective bodyside molding with red accent stripe (LX), aero design rocker cladding (GT), black colored molding, monotone rear spoiler (GT), full wheel covers (GL), luxury wheel covers (LX), 15" aluminum wheels (GT), depressed park wipers, automatic shoulder belt restraint system, manual rear seat lap/shoulder belts, 12 oz. color-keyed carpet (GL), 16 oz. color-keyed carpet (LX, GT), integral electronic digital clock with radio, center console with rear ashtray (GL), full center console with folding armrest, storage and rear footwell illumination/overhead console with map light (LX, GT), side window demisters, all vinyl door trim (GL), door trim with cloth inserts and map pockets (LX), door trim with carpeted lower and map pockets (GT), locking glove box, instrument performance cluster [analog cluster with speedometer, odometer, trip odometer, tachometer, fuel gauge, water temperature gauge, low oil light (LX & GT only) and ammeter], turbo boost gauge (GT), warning lights for brakes/seat belts/parking brake/engine check, light group (LX, GT), cargo compartment dome light, flash to pass, front footwell illumination (LX, GT), map light in overhead console (LX, GT), day/night inside rearview mirror, electronic AM/FM stereo radio/clock with four speakers, front bucket seats with dual recliners, cloth headrest and driver seat vertical height adjustment, 50/50 fold-down rear seat, manual adjustable driver seat for tilt, lumbar support and side bolsters (LX, GT), front passenger seat lumbar support and underseat stowage (LX, GT), standard cloth seat trim (GL), luxury cloth seat trim (LX), sport cloth seat trim (GT), floor mounted transaxle shift, leather-wrapped shift knob (LX, GT), soft-feel steering wheel (GL), leather-wrapped steering wheel (LX, GT), cloth covered sun visor with LH storage band and RH vanity mirror (GL), cloth covered sun visor with LH and RH vanity mirrors with covers (LX, GT), heavy duty maintenance-free battery, power front disc/rear drum brakes (GL), power four-wheel disc brakes (LX, GT), rear window defroster (LX, GT), 2.2 liter SOHC/12-valve EFI engine (GL), 3.0 liter EFI V6 engine (LX), 2.2 liter SOHC/12-valve EFI turbocharged/intercooled engine (GT), fog lamps (GT), fuel filler door release (LX, GT), inside hood release, dual-note horn, remote control liftgate release (LX, GT), upgraded sound insulation package (LX, GT), constant ratio power rack-and-pinion steering (GL, LX), variable assist speed sensitive power rack-and-pinion steering (GT), MacPherson strut front suspension, automatic adjusting suspension (GT), handling suspension package (GT), tilt cluster and steering column (LX, GT), P185/70R14 BSW all-season tires (GL), P195/70R14 BSW all-season tires (LX), P205/60VR15 BSW Goodyear Eagle performance tires (GT), 5-speed manual transaxle, 2-speed windshield wipers (GL), interval windshield wipers (LX, GT).

ACCESSORIES

Code	Description	Base Cost	Sgstd. List
99C	**Engine** — 2.2L SOHC (GL only)	STD	STD
99U	**Engine** — 3.0L EFI V6 (LX only)	STD	STD
99L	**Engine** — 2.2L SOHC Turbo (GL only)	STD	STD
445	**Transaxle** — 5-speed manual	STD	STD
44T	**Transaxle** — 4-speed automatic overdrive	622	732
422	**California Emissions System**	59	70
—	**Tires**		
T72	P185/70Rx14 BSW - GL	STD	STD
—	P195/70HRx14 BSW (included w/aluminum wheels) - GL		
T82	P195/70Rx14 BSW - LX	STD	STD
—	P205/60HRx15 BSW (included w/aluminum wheels) - LX		
T63	P205/60VRx15 BSW performance - GT	STD	STD
—	**Seats**		
A	cloth and vinyl buckets - GL	STD	STD

Mfgs. Code	Description **FORD**	Base Cost	Sgstd. List
B	cloth buckets - LX	STD	STD
C	cloth buckets - GT	STD	STD
D	leather seating surfaces buckets - LX, GT	416	489
—	**Mandatory Warranty Enhancement** — required on all vehicles registered or sold in New York State	95	110
572	**Air Conditioning** — manual (includes tinted glass) - GL w/o tinted glass	796	937
	- all other models	695	817
573	**Air Conditioning** — electronic (LX & GT only)		
	- w/o manual air conditioning	850	1000
	- w/manual air conditioning	155	183
552	**Anti-lock Brakes** — LX and GT only	786	924
94H	**Convenience Group 1** — (standard on LX and GT)	173	204
94F	**Convenience Group 2** — (LX and GT only)	181	213
57Q	**Defroster Rear Window** — (standard on LX and GT)	136	160
60A	**Electronics Group** — LX	69	82
	- GT	154	182
155	**Electronic Instrument Cluster** — LX only	337	396
923	**Glass, Tinted** — (standard on LX & GT)	102	120
902	**Locks, Power Door**	166	195
21A	**Power Driver's Seat** — (LX and GT only)	247	290
43R	**Power Windows** — (LX and GT only)	221	260
588	**Radio** — AM/FM cassette with premium sound/power antenna	313	368
584	**Radio** — AM/FM electronic cassette with premium sound/compact disc player/power antenna - without package 253A or 261A	915	1077
	- with package 253A or 261A	602	709
58Y	**Radio Credit Option** — (GL only)	(208)	(245)
13C	**Roof** — flip-up open air (LX and GT only)	302	355
52Q	**Steering Column and Cluster/Tilt** — standard on LX and GT	166	195
525	**Speed Control**	178	210
136	**Trip Computer** — LX and GT only	182	215
146	**Vehicle Maintenance Monitor** — GT only	67	79
—	**Wheels, Aluminum**		
64X	- with P195/70HR14 BSW tires (GL only)	266	313
64V	- with P205/60HR15 BSW tires (LX only)	319	376
153	**Bracket, Front License Plate**	NC	NC
13H	**Heater, Engine Block**	17	20
—	**Preferred Equipment Packages**		
251A	**GL Preferred Equipment Package** — includes rear window defroster, tinted glass, tilt steering column and cluster and convenience group 1 (dual electric remote mirrors, interval windshield wipers, light group)		
	- total package price	577	679
	- discount	425	500
	- net price	152	179
253A	**LX Preferred Equipment Package** — includes convenience group II (walk-in passenger seat, rear washer/wiper, cargo tie down net), electronics group (illuminated visor vanity mirror), manual air conditioning, power windows, speed control, power door locks, AM/FM radio with electronic cassette with premium sound/power antenna		
	- total package price	1823	2145
	- discount	510	600
	- net price	1313	1545
261A	**GT Preferred Equipment Package** — includes convenience group II (walk-in passenger seat, rear washer/wiper, cargo tie down net), electronic group (illuminated entry system, illuminated visor vanity mirror), manual air conditioning, power windows, speed control, power door locks, AM/FM radio with electronic cassette with premium sound/power antenna		
	- total package price	1908	2245

		Base Cost	Sgstd. List
	- discount	510	600
	- net price	1398	1645

TAURUS

Mfgs. Code	Description	Base Cost	Sgstd. List
TAURUS (4 Cylinder)			
P50	4 Dr L Sedan	11548	13352
P52	4 Dr GL Sedan	11742	13582
TAURUS (6 Cylinder)			
P53	4 Dr LX Sedan	14965	17373
P54	4 Dr SHO Sedan	18958	22071
P55	4 Dr L Wagon	12765	14784
P57	4 Dr GL Wagon	12940	14990
P58	4 Dr LX Wagon	16317	18963
	Destination Charge: All Models	480	480

STANDARD EQUIPMENT:
TAURUS: Color-coordinated bumpers, exterior accent group, body-color grille, single halogen headlamps, cornering lamps (LX, SHO), fog lamps (SHO), lower bodyside urethane protection coating (L, GL, SHO), color-coordinated protective cladding (LX, SHO), luggage rack (Wagons), dual electric remote-control sail-mounted mirrors, color-coordinated rocker panel moldings (LX), wheel covers (L, GL), finned wheels (LX), sparkle spoke cast aluminum wheels (SHO), driver air bag supplemental restraint system, front center armrest, rear seat center armrest (GL & LX Sedans, SHO), cargo tie-down net (except L), cigarette lighter, electronic digital clock, console (SHO), convenience kit (LX, SHO), illuminated locking glove box, front and rear grab handles (SHO, Wagons), light group (LX, SHO), day/night rearview mirrors, dual illuminated visor mirrors (LX, SHO), electronic AM/FM stereo search radio (except SHO), electronic AM/FM stereo search radio with cassette player (SHO), split bench seats with dual recliners (L, GL, LX), power driver's seat (LX, SHO), bucket seats with dual recliners (SHO), 60/40 split/fold-down second seat (Wagons), tilt steering column, leather-wrapped steering wheel (SHO), air conditioning (LX, SHO), power front disc/rear drum brakes (except SHO), 4 wheel disc brakes/anti-lock braking system (SHO), rear window defroster (SHO), side window demisters, power door locks (LX, SHO), dual exhaust system (SHO), 2.5 liter sequential EFI 4 cylinder engine (L & GL Sedans), 3.0 liter sequential EFI V6 engine (L Sedan, L & GL Wagons), 3.0 liter DOHC SEFI 24-valve engine (SHO), 3.8 liter sequential EFI V6 engine (LX Wagon), remote fuel door and decklid release (LX), extended range fuel tank (SHO), tinted glass, tachometer/diagnostic alert lights (LX, SHO), luxury sound insulation package (LX), automatic parking brake release (LX), speed control (SHO), power rack and pinion steering, handling suspension (SHO), P215/60R16 94V BSW high performance tires (SHO), P205/70R14 BSW tires with mini-spare tire (all except SHO), 5-speed manual transaxle (SHO), 4-speed automatic overdrive transaxle (all except SHO), power side windows (LX, SHO), interval windshield wipers.

ACCESSORIES

Code	Description	Base Cost	Sgstd. List
99N	**Engine** — 2.5L (standard on L and GL Sedans)	STD	STD
99U	**Engine** — 3.0L (standard on LX Sedan and L/GL Wagons)	443	521
994	**Engine** — 3.8L (standard on LX Wagon) - L/GL Sedans	914	1076
	- all other	472	555
99Y	**Engine** — 3.0L DOHC (standard on SHO)	STD	STD
445	**Transaxle** — 5-speed manual (standard on SHO)	STD	STD
440	**Transaxle** — automatic overdrive (standard on L, GL and LX)	STD	STD
422	**California Emissions System**	85	100

Mfgs. Code	Description **FORD**	Base Cost	Sgstd. List
428	**High Altitude Emissions System**	NC	NC
—	**Tires**		
T78	P205/70Rx14 BSW - L, GL, LX	STD	STD
T7G	P205/70Rx14 WSW - L, GL, LX - package 207A or 208A	15	17
	- all others	69	82
T28	P215/60Rx16 94V BSW high performance - SHO	STD	STD
508	**Conventional Spare Tire** — L, GL, LX	62	73
—	**Seats**		
A,B	cloth split bench - L, GL	STD	STD
B	cloth split bench - L, L Plus, GL	STD	STD
U	vinyl split bench - L, GL	44	51
F	cloth bucket/console - L Plus, GL	NC	NC
X	cloth split bench - LX	STD	STD
Y	cloth bucket/console - LX	NC	NC
H	leather bucket/console - GL	504	593
H	leather bucket/console - LX	416	489
E	leather split bench - LX	416	489
S	cloth and leather buckets - SHO	STD	STD
T	leather buckets - SHO	416	489
573	**Air Conditioning** — electronic climate control (n/a on L)		
	- LX, SHO or Package 204A	155	183
	- GL	850	1000
572	**Air Conditioning, Manual** — (L and GL only)	695	817
552	**Anti-Lock Braking System**	838	985
586	**Audio System, High Level** — (n/a on L standard)		
	- L Plus, GL, LX or package 208A	417	490
	- package 204A or SHO	285	335
	- package 207A	142	167
917	**Audio Digital Disc** — (n/a on L standard)	418	491
473	**Autolamp System** — (LX and SHO only)	62	73
631	**Battery, Heavy-Duty** — (84 amp) (n/a on SHO)	23	27
475	**Cargo Area Cover** — (Wagon only)	56	66
53B	**Convenience Group** — (L and GL only)	706	830
51Q	**Cornering Lamps** — (n/a on L standard)	58	68
57Q	**Defroster, Rear Window**	136	160
41H	**Engine Block Immersion Heater**	17	20
65Z	**Fuel Tank, Extended Range**	39	46
613	**Fuel Door and Decklid Releases** — remote (Sedans only)	78	91
18K	**Fuel Door Release, Remote** — (Wagons only)	35	41
12Y	**Floor Mats, Front and Rear**	36	43
916	**Ford JBL, Audio System** — (n/a on L Standard)	447	526
47J	**Illuminated Entry System** — (n/a on L)	69	82
155	**Instrument Cluster, Electronic** — (n/a on L and SHO) - GL	299	351
	- LX	203	239
144	**Keyless Entry System** — (n/a on L)		
	- GL or LX	186	218
	- package 208A or 211A	116	137
943	**Light Group** — (L and GL only)	50	59
596	**Load Floor Extension** — "Picnic Table" (Wagons only)	77	90
902	**Locks, Power Door** — (L Plus only)	192	226
677	**Mirrors** — dual illuminated visor (n/a on L standard)	85	100
96P	**Moldings** — rocker panel (L Plus and GL only)	47	55
13B	**Moonroof** — Power (GL, LX and SHO only)	659	776
—	**Paint, Clearcoat**	160	188
67R	**Parking Brake Release** — automatic (n/a on SHO)	10	12
58H	**Radio** — electronic AM/FM stereo cassette	132	155
91H	**Radio Antenna, Power** — (n/a on L standard)	69	82

Mfgs. Code	Description FORD	Base Cost	Sgstd. List
58Y	**Radio Credit Option** — (n/a on package 208A, SHO)		
	- AM/FM radio credit (L)	(175)	(206)
	- package 204A radio credit	(307)	(361)
	- package 207A radio credit	(450)	(529)
214	**Seat, Rear Facing, Third** — (Wagons only)	132	155
21J	**Seats, 6-way Power Dual Control** — (n/a on L) - LX, SHO and with package 204A	247	290
	- all other	493	580
913	**Sound System, Premium** — (L Plus, GL and LX only)	143	168
525	**Speed Control**	178	210
52A	**Speed Sensitive Steering Variable Power Assist** — (n/a on SHO)	88	104
524	**Steering Wheel, Leather-Wrapped**	54	63
972	**Stripe, Paint** — (NA on L standard, SHO)	52	61
662	**Suspension, Heavy Duty** — (load carrying) (NA on SHO)	22	26
173	**Washer/Wiper, Rear Window** — (Wagons only)	107	126
64J	**Wheels, Styled Road** — (n/a on L standard SHO) - GL, L Plus	164	193
	- LX (2)	109	128
642	**Wheel Covers, Finned** — (n/a on SHO)	55	65
64K	**Wheels, Cast Aluminum/P205 15 Tires** — (n/a on L Standard)		
	- GL, L Plus	292	344
	- LX	237	279
924	**Windshield, Insta-Clear** — (n/a on L and SHO)	259	305
153	**Bracket, Front License Plate**	NC	NC
127	**Floor Covering, Heavy-Duty Rubber** — (L standard only)	23	27
52Z	**Steering Column, Tilt-Delete** — (n/a on SHO)	(64)	(76)
—	**Mandatory Warranty Enhancement** — required on all models registered and sold in New York State	95	110
—	**Preferred Equipment Packages**		
201A	**L Standard Preferred Equipment Package**	NC	NC
203A	**L Plus Preferred Equipment Package** — includes power door locks, manual air conditioning, rear window defroster, paint stripe		
	- total package price	1075	1264
	- discount	255	300
	- net price	820	964
204A	**GL Sedan Preferred Equipment Package** — includes power convenience group (power door locks, power side windows, 6-way power driver's seat), manual air conditioning, rear window defroster, paint stripe, remote decklid and fuel door releases, light group, rocker panel moldings, electronic AM/FM stereo cassette radio, speed control, finned wheel covers		
	- total package price	2129	2504
	- discount	595	700
	- net price	1534	1804
204A	**GL Wagon Preferred Equipment Package** — includes items in 204A GL Sedan Preferred Equipment Pkg except for decklid release which is deleted		
	- total package price	2086	2454
	- discount	595	700
	- net price	1491	1754
207A	**LX Preferred Equipment Package** — includes rear window defroster, paint stripes, electronic AM/FM stereo cassette radio, speed control, cast aluminum wheels (styled road wheels may be substituted), P205 15" tires, autolamp system, front and rear floor mats, leather-wrapped steering wheel, illuminated entry system, premium sound system		
	- total package price	1099	1295
	- discount	425	500
	- net price	674	795
208A	**LX Sedan Preferred Equipment Package** — includes rear window		

		Base Cost	Sgstd. List
	defroster, paint stripes, speed control, cast aluminum wheels (styled road wheels may be substituted), P205 15" tires, autolamp system, front and rear floor mats, leather-wrapped steering wheel, anti-lock braking system, electronic climate control, high level audio system, keyless entry system, power radio antenna, 6-way power dual control seats, electronic instrument cluster, speed sensitive variable power assist steering		
	- total package price	2593	3050
	- discount	595	700
	- net price	1998	2350
208A	**LX Wagon Preferred Equipment Package** — includes items included in 208A LX Sedan Preferred Equipment Pkg		
	- total package price	2121	2495
	- discount	595	700
	- net price	1526	1795
211A	**SHO Preferred Equipment Package** — includes autolamp system, front and rear floor mats, electronic climate control air conditioning, high-level audio system, keyless entry system, power radio antenna, 6-way power dual control seats		
	- total package price	1040	1224
	- discount	425	500
	- net price	615	724

TEMPO

TEMPO (4 Cylinder)

Code	Description	Base Cost	Sgstd. List
P31	2 Dr GL Sedan	8634	9541
P36	4 Dr GL Sedan	8768	9691
P33	2 Dr GLS Sedan	9362	10358
P38	4 Dr GLS Sedan	9493	10506
P37	4 Dr LX Sedan	9633	10663
P39	4 Dr All Wheel Drive Sedan	10280	11390
Destination Charge:	All Models	455	455

STANDARD EQUIPMENT:

TEMPO: Black upper bumpers with color-keyed lower and bright insert, bright grille with titanium grille texture (GL, LX, 4WD), blackout grille design (GLS), headlamps-on alert chimes, aerodynamic halogen headlamps, lower accent treatment (GLS), black LH sail-mounted manual mirror (GL), black dual electric remote-control outside rearview mirrors (GLS, LX, 4WD), dual "halo" full surround greenhouse molding system, bodyside moldings, rear decklid spoiler (GLS 2-door), dual hood stripes (LX), dual upper bodyside and decklid wraparound stripes (LX, 4WD), deluxe 14" wheel covers (GL), 14" polycast wheels (LX, 4WD), 14" 7-spoke aluminum wheels with locking lug nuts (GLS), cloth fold-down center armrest (GLS, LX), front and rear ashtrays, automatic shoulder belt restraint system, cargo tie-down net (all except GL), deluxe carpet (GL, GLS), luxury carpet (LX, 4WD), cigarette lighter, integral electronic digital clock with radio, consolette, front and rear floor mats (all except GL), lockable glove box, two passenger assist handles (all 4-doors except GL), footwell illumination and luggage compartment light, light group (all except GL), day/night windshield mounted rearview mirror, dual visor mirrors with covers, on/off four wheel drive selector switch located on overhead map light with four wheel drive nomenclature (4WD), low-back front bucket seats with cloth seat trim (GL), upgraded cloth seat trim with seatback pockets (LX, 4WD), sport performance bucket seats with power lumbar feature (GLS), color-keyed steering wheel (all except GLS), black leather-wrapped steering wheel (GLS), trip odometer (all except GL), heavy-duty maintenance-free battery, power front disc/rear drum split diagonal brake system, coolant recovery system, side window demisters, 2.3 liter HSC I-4 engine with multi-port electronic fuel injection (GL, LX), 2.3 liter HSO I-4 engine with multi-port electronic fuel injection (GLS, 4WD), engine malfunction warning light, front wheel drive, tinted glass, inside hood release, dual note horn, illuminated entry system (LX), sport instrumentation cluster includes tachometer, trip odometer, door ajar light, decklid ajar light (all except GL), power lock group includes power door locks, remote fuel filler door and remote decklid release (LX), electronic AM/FM stereo radio and clock (all except GLS), electronic AM/FM stereo radio with cassette player and clock (GLS), luxury sound insulation package, power rack-and-pinion steering, tilt steering wheel [NA with Air Bag SRS] (LX), touring suspension (all except GL), P185/70R14 BSW performance/all-season tires (all except GL), P185/70R14 BSW all-season tires (GL), mini-spare tire, 5-speed manual transaxle (all except 4WD), 3-speed FLC automatic transaxle (4WD), interval windshield wipers with cowl-mounted fluidic washer jets.

ACCESSORIES

Code	Description	Base Cost	Sgstd. List
99X	**Engine** — 2.3L HSC (standard on GL and LX)	STD	STD
99S	**Engine** — 2.3L HSO (standard on GLS and four-wheel drive)	STD	STD
445	**Transaxle** — 5-speed manual	STD	STD
440	**Transaxle** — 3-speed automatic (standard on four-wheel drive)	479	563
422	**California Emissions System**	85	100
428	**High Altitude Emissions System**	NC	NC
—	**Tires**		
T72	P185/70Rx14 BSW - GL	STD	STD
T7K	P185/70Rx14 WSW - GL	69	82
T73	P185/70Rx14 BSW performance - GLS, LX, four WD	STD	STD
T7J	P185/70Rx14 WSW performance - GLS, LX, four WD	69	82
—	**Seats**		
P	cloth low back buckets - GL	STD	STD
S	cloth sport: performance buckets - GLS	STD	STD
R	upgraded cloth low back buckets - LX, four WD	STD	STD
572	**Air Conditioning, Manual**	595	817
594	**Armrest** — front center (n/a on four WD)	47	55
57Q	**Defroster, Rear Window**	136	160
12Y	**Floor Mats** — front and rear	28	33
156	**Instrument Cluster, Sport** — (n/a with package 224A)	74	87
943	**Light Group**	32	38
903	**Lock Group, Power** — 2-door	234	276
	- 4-door	271	318
548	**Luggage Rack, Decklid** — (n/a on 2-door GLS)	97	115
54J	**Mirrors, Dual Electric Remote Control**	103	121
—	**Paint, Clearcoat**	78	91
589	**Radio** — with cassette player and clock, electronic AM/FM stereo	132	155
58Y	**Radio Credit Option** — GL, LX or four WD	(208)	(245)
	- GLS	(340)	(400)
21A	**Seat, Power Driver's** — (n/a with package 224A)	247	290
913	**Sound System, Premium** — (n/a with package 224A)	117	138
525	**Speed Control** — (n/a with SRS air bag)	178	210
52Q	**Steering Wheel, Tilt** — (n/a with SRS air bag)	115	135
59H	**Supplemental Air Bag Restraint System** — (driver only) - SRS - GL	692	815
	- LX	587	690
64J	**Wheels, Polycast**	164	193
43R	**Windows, Power Side** — (4-door only)	267	315
153	**Bracket, Front License Plate**	NC	NC
41H	**Engine Block Immersion Heater**	17	20
648	**Wheels/Trim Rings Styled Steel** — GL only	NC	NC
—	**Mandatory Warranty Enhancement** — required on all models registered and sold in New York State	95	110
—	**Preferred Equipment Packages**		
224A	**GL Preferred Equipment Package**	NC	NC

Mfgs. Code	Description	Base Cost	Sgstd. List
225B	**GL Preferred Equipment Package** — includes manual air conditioning, light group, dual electric remote control mirrors, tilt steering wheel		
	- total package price	945	1111
	- discount	695	817
	- net price	250	294
226A	**GL 2 Door Preferred Equipment Package** — includes items in 22B GL Preferred Equipment Pkg plus front center armrest, rear window defroster, front and rear floor mats, power lock group, AM/FM stereo radio with cassette player and clock, automatic transaxle, polycast wheels		
	- total package price	2165	2546
	- discount	1020	1200
	- net price	1145	1346
226A	**GL 4 Door Preferred Equipment Package** — includes items in 226A GL 2 Door Preferred Equipment Pkg		
	- total package price	2202	2588
	- discount	1020	1200
	- net price	1182	1388
227A	**GL SRS Preferred Equipment Package** — (available only on 4 door models) - includes manual air conditioning, light group, dual electric remote control mirrors, front center armrest, rear window defroster, front and rear floor mats, power lock group, automatic transaxle, supplemental air bag restraint system (SRS)		
	- total package price	2408	2832
	- discount	1237	1455
	- net price	1171	1377
229A	**GLS 2 Door Preferred Equipment Package** — includes manual air conditioning, tilt steering wheel, power lock group, speed control, power driver's seat, premium sound system		
	- total package price	1586	1866
	- discount	425	500
	- net price	1161	1366
229A	**GLS 4 Door Preferred Equipment Package** — includes items in 229A GLS 2 Door Preferred Equipment Pkg		
	- total package price	1623	1908
	- discount	425	500
	- net price	1198	1408
233A	**LX Preferred Equipment Package** — includes manual air conditioning, rear window defroster, AM/FM stereo radio with cassette player and clock, automatic transaxle, decklid luggage rack (may be deleted)		
	- total package price	1539	1810
	- discount	638	750
	- net price	901	1060
232A	**Four Wheel Drive Preferred Equipment Package** — includes tilt steering wheel, rear window defroster, power lock group, AM/FM stereo radio with cassette player and clock, power side windows		
	- total package price	921	1083
	- discount	468	550
	- net price	453	533

THUNDERBIRD

THUNDERBIRD (6 Cylinder)

Mfgs. Code	Description	Base Cost	Sgstd. List
P60	Thunderbird Standard	13258	15318
P62	Thunderbird LX	15311	17734
P64	Thunderbird Super Coupe	18086	20999

Mfgs. Code	Description	FORD	Base Cost	Sgstd. List

Destination Charge: All Models 485 485

STANDARD EQUIPMENT:
THUNDERBIRD: Soft color-keyed front and rear 5 mph bumpers, black bumper rub strips with bright insert (Standard, LX), black bumper rub strips (Super Coupe), lower bodyside cladding (Super Coupe), aerodynamic halogen headlamps, integral fog lamps in front fascia (Super Coupe), black LH remote-control mirror (Standard), black dual electric remote-control mirrors (LX), color-keyed dual electric remote-control mirrors (Super Coupe), black windshield/door/quarter window/backlight moldings (Standard, Super Coupe), black windshield/backlight moldings (Standard, LX), bright door/quarter window moldings (LX), wide black bodyside protection molding with bright insert (Standard, LX), narrow black bodyside protection molding (Super Coupe), deluxe wheel covers (Standard), styled road wheel covers (LX), 16" x 7" cast aluminum wheels with locking lug nuts (Super Coupe), 16 oz. cut-pile carpet (Standard), 24 oz. cut-pile carpet (LX, Super Coupe), full-length console with floor mounted shift, all-vinyl door trim with hand grip handles and storage bins (Standard), luxury-level door trim with woodgrain and courtesy lights (LX), luxury-level door trim with courtesy lights (Super Coupe), driver's footrest (Super Coupe), driver's side footwell lights, illuminated entry system (LX), light convenience group (LX), dual visor mirrors covered with headliner pocket, illuminated visor mirrors (LX), reclining bucket seats with cloth trim and inertia seatback releases (Standard), luxury cloth/leather/vinyl bucket seats with driver's six-way power (LX), articulated sport seats with cloth trim, power adjustable lumbar support, power adjustable seatback side bolsters, seatback map pocket and 4-way headrest (Super Coupe), rear seat center headrest (LX, Super Coupe), side window defoggers, speed control (LX), luxury steering wheel (Standard), luxury leather-wrapped steering wheel (LX), sport soft-feel steering wheel (Super Coupe), tilt steering wheel (LX), manual air conditioning, automatic ride control adjustable suspension (Super Coupe), traction-lok axle (Super Coupe), maintenance-free battery, power front disc/rear drum brakes (Standard, LX), anti-lock braking system (ABS) with four-wheel disc brakes (Super Coupe), integral digital clock with radio, 3.8 liter V6 engine with multi-port sequential EFI (Standard, LX), 3.8 liter V6 engine with multi-port sequential/supercharged/ intercooled with dual exhaust (Super Coupe), tinted glass, dual note horn, analog instrument cluster with trip odometer, low engine oil indicator light/fuel gauge/temperature gauge (Standard), performance analog cluster, adds analog tachometer (LX), and adjustable suspension "firm ride" indicator light and supercharger boost gauge (Super Coupe), power lock group (LX), electronic AM/FM stereo search radio with clock and four speakers (Standard and Super Coupe), electronic AM/FM stereo search radio with cassette tape player and clock (LX), rack-and-pinion power steering (Standard), speed sensitive rack-and-pinion power steering (LX, Super Coupe), special handling package (Super Coupe), P205/70R15 BSW all-season tires (Standard, LX), P225/60R16 97V BSW performance tires (Super Coupe), mini-spare tire, 4-speed automatic overdrive transmission (Standard, LX), 5-speed manual overdrive transmission (Super Coupe), power side windows, interval windshield wipers.

ACCESSORIES

Code	Description	Base Cost	Sgstd. List
994	**Engine** — 3.8L (standard on LX and Standard)	STD	STD
99R	**Engine** — 3.8L EFI super charged (standard on Super Coupe)	STD	STD
99T	**Engine** — 5.0L HO (LX and Standard only)	918	1080
445	**Transaxle** — 5-speed manual (standard on Super Coupe)	STD	STD
44T	**Transaxle** — 4-speed automatic overdrive (standard on LX and Standard)	506	595
422	**California Emissions System**	85	100
428	**High Altitude Emissions System**	NC	NC
—	**Tires**		
T33	P205/70R15 BSW (standard on LX and Standard)	STD	STD
T3F	P205/70R15 WSW - LX and Standard	62	73
T22	P225/60R16 97V BSW performance (standard on Super Coupe)	STD	STD
T23	P225/60R16 97V BSW Eagle GT +4 all-season performance - Super Coupe	62	73
508	**Spare Tire, Conventional** — LX and Standard	62	73

Mfgs. Code	Description	Base Cost	Sgstd. List
	FORD		
—	**Seats**		
W	cloth and vinyl bucket seats	STD	STD
5	luxury cloth/leather/vinyl bucket seats - LX	STD	STD
4	leather seating surfaces bucket seats - LX	416	489
3	cloth articulated bucket seats - Super Coupe	STD	STD
U	leather seating surfaces bucket seats - Super Coupe	529	622
552	**Anti-Lock Braking System** — (includes traction-lok axle)	923	1085
18A	**Anti-Theft System**	208	245
474	**Autolamp Group**	149	176
45A	**Axle, Traction-Lok** — (LX and Standard only)	85	100
917	**Compact Disc Player**	418	491
51Q	**Cornering Lamps**	58	68
57Q	**Defroster, Rear Window**	136	160
573	**Electronic Automatic Temperature Control** - (LX and Super Coupe only)	138	162
155	**Electronic Instrument Cluster** — (LX only)	229	270
588	**Electronic Premium Cassette Radio with Premium Sound**		
	- standard without Package 151A or Super Coupe without Package 157A	391	460
	- standard with Package 151A or Super Coupe with Package 157A	259	305
916	**Ford JBL Audio System**	447	526
12H	**Front Floor Mats**	28	33
47J	**Illuminated Entry**	69	82
144	**Keyless Entry** — Standard or Super Coupe without illuminated entry	185	219
	- LX, Standard or Super Coupe with illuminated entry	116	137
59R	**Light Convenience Group** — Standard	124	146
	- Super Coupe	85	100
903	**Lock Group, Power**	208	245
65B	**Luxury Group** — standard with package 151A	534	627
	- standard with Super Coupe	293	345
13B	**Moonroof, Power** — Standard or Super Coupe without light convenience Group	744	876
	- LX, Standard or Super Coupe with light convenience group	659	776
91H	**Power Antenna**	69	82
589	**Radio** — electronic AM/FM stereo with cassette player/clock	132	155
58Y	**Radio Credit Option**	(208)	(245)
21A	**Seat** — 6-way power driver's	247	290
21J	**Seat** — 6-way power passenger	247	290
52N	**Speed Control and Tilt Steering Wheel**	293	345
146	**Vehicle Maintenance Monitor**	76	89
646	**Wheel Covers, Locking Wire Style** — standard with LX	121	143
	- standard without package 151A	194	228
64M	**Wheels, Cast Aluminum with Upsize BSW Tires**		
	- Standard with Package 151A, LX with package 155A	181	214
	- Standard without package 151A	254	299
153	**Bracket, Front License Plate**	NC	NC
632	**Cold Weather Group** — standard without 151A, LX without 155A, Super Coupe with manual transmission without 157A	174	205
	- Super Coupe with auto transmission without 157A	152	178
	- package 151A, 155A or Super Coupe with manual transmission and 157A	38	45
	- Super Coupe with auto transmission and 157A	16	18
—	**Mandatory Warranty Enhancement** — required on all vehicles registered or sold in New York State	95	110
—	**Preferred Equipment Packages**		
151A	**Standard Preferred Equipment Package** — includes 6-way power driver's seat, electronic AM/FM stereo radio with cassette player/clock, rear		

	window defroster, luxury group, P215/70R15 tires, cast aluminum wheels		
	- total package price	1230	1446
	- discount	553	650
	- net price	677	796
155A	**LX Preferred Equipment Package** — includes rear window defroster, luxury group, P215/70R15 BSW tires, cast aluminum wheels, electronic automatic temperature control, electronic premium cassette radio with premium sound, power antenna, autolamp group, cornering lamps, front floor mats, keyless entry 6-way power passenger seat		
	- total package price	1381	1627
	- discount	553	650
	- net price	828	977
157A	**Super Coupe Preferred Equipment Package** — includes 6-way power driver's seat, electronic AM/FM stereo with cassette player/clock, rear window defroster, luxury group, power lock group, electronic temperature control, power antenna		
	- total package price	1223	1439
	- discount	595	700
	- net price	628	739

1991 geo

METRO

METRO (3 Cylinder)

Code	Description	Base Cost	Sgstd. List
1MS08	3 Dr XFi Hatchback Coupe	6251	6795
1MR08	3 Dr Hatchback Coupe	6251	6795
1MR68	5 Dr Hatchback Sedan	6435	6995
1MR08/B4M	3 Dr LSi Hatchback Coupe	7171	7795
1MR68/B4M	5 Dr LSi Hatchback Sedan	7355	7995
1MR67	3 Dr LSi Convertible	8961	9740

Destination Charge: Coupe and Sedan	265	265
: Convertible	255	255

STANDARD EQUIPMENT:
METRO: 1.0 liter 3 cylinder engine with electronic fuel injection, 5-speed manual transmission with overdrive, power front disc/rear drum brakes, front wheel drive, 5-mph bumpers, independent strut front and rear suspension, base-coat/clear-coat paint, chip-resistant lower body protection, composite halogen headlamps (LSi), dual outside rearview mirrors with LH remote (all except XFi), body-color body-side moldings (LSi), black body-side moldings (Base 3 Dr and 5 Dr Hatchbacks), swing-out rear quarter windows (3 Dr Hatchbacks), warning tones for key-in-ignition and headlamps-on, molded driver's door storage pocket (dual door storage pockets on LSi), full folding rear seat-back (XFi, Base 3 Dr and 5 Dr Hatchbacks), split-folding rear seat-back (LSi Hatchbacks), driver's-side air bag (LSi Convertible), dual front radio speakers, full floor and luggage area carpeting, trip odometer (LSi), steel-belted P145/80R-12 all-season blackwall radial tires (all except LSi Convertible), P165/R-13 all-season blackwall radial tires (LSi Convertible), full wheel covers (all models except XFi), remote hatch release (LSi Hatchbacks), rear window-defogger (LSi Hatchbacks), intermittent wiper system (all models except XFi), rack-and-pinion steering.

ACCESSORIES

— **Metro XFi Base Equipment Group 1** — 1MS08 only; (included with model)

Mfgs. Code	Description GEO	Base Cost	Sgstd. List
	standard equipment	NC	NC
—	**Metro XFi Preferred Equipment Group 2** — 1MS08 only; (includes: standard equipment; radio, electronically tuned AM/FM stereo radio with seek and scan and digital clock)	265	301
UM6	- with UM6 radio, add	123	140
—	**Metro Base Equipment Group 1** — 1MR08 and 1MR68 only; (included with model) standard equipment	NC	NC
—	**Metro Preferred Equipment Group 2** — 1MR08 and 1MR68 only; (includes: standard equipment; radio electronically tuned AM/FM stereo radio with seek and scan and digital clock)	265	301
UM6	- with UM6 radio, add	123	140
—	**Metro Preferred Equipment Group 3** — 1MR08 and 1MR68 only; (includes: standard equipment; radio, electronically tuned AM/FM stereo radio with seek and scan and digital clock and air conditioning)	854	971
UM6	- with UM6 radio, add	123	140
—	**Metro LSi Base Equipment Group 1** — 1MR08/B4M and 1MR68 only; (included with model:) LSi equipment	NC	NC
—	**Metro LSi Preferred Equipment Group 2** — 1MR08/B4M and 1MR68/B4m only; (includes: LSi equipment; radio, electronically tuned AM/FM stereo radio with seek and scan and digital clock)	265	301
UM6	- with UM6 radio, add	123	140
—	**Metro LSi Preferred Equipment Group 3** — 1MR08/B4M and 1MR68/B4M only; (includes: LSi equipment; radio, electronically tuned AM/FM stereo radio with seek and scan and digital clock and air conditioning	854	971
UM6	- with UM6 radio, add	123	140
—	**Metro LSi Convertible Preferred Equipment Group 1** — 1MR67; (included with model:) 5-speed manual transmission	NC	NC
UM7	- with UM7 radio, add	265	301
UM6	- with UM6 radio, add	388	441
—	**Metro LSi Convertible Preferred Equipment Group 2** — 1MR67; (includes: 3-speed automatic transmission)	409	465
UM7	- with UM7 radio, add	265	301
UM6	- with UM6 radio, add	388	441
	Interior Trim		
H2	cloth/vinyl bucket seats with cloth facings (standard on Metro and Metro XFi)	NC	NC
F2	sport cloth bucket seats (standard on Metro LSi)	NC	NC
C2	sport cloth bucket seats (standard on Metro LSi Convertible)	NC	NC
—	**Exterior Color** — paint, solid	NC	NC
LP2	**1.0 Liter SOHC EFI L3 Engine**	NC	NC
C60	**Air Conditioning**	590	670
C49	**Defogger, Rear Window Electric** — standard on Metro LSi	132	150
YF5	**California Emission Requirements** — includes all testing, equipment and/or certification necessary for registration in State of California	NC	NC
NA5	**Standard Emission Equipment**	NC	NC
—	**Floor Coverings** — mats, color-keyed		
B37	front and rear	22	25
B32	front	13	15
D35	**Mirrors, Sport** — LH remote and RH manual black (standard on Metro and LSi models)	18	20
B85	**Moldings, Body Side** — standard on Metro and LSi models	44	50
—	**Radio Equipment** — (includes dual front and rear speakers) for specific radio pricing, please refer to radio information included with each preferred equipment group.		
UM7	electronically tuned AM/FM stereo radio with seek and scan, stereo cassette tape and digital clock		
UM6	radio, electronically tuned AM/FM stereo radio with seek and scan, stereo		

	cassette tape and digital clock		
D85	**Sport Stripe** — excluding XFi and LSi models	44	50
—	**Transmissions**		
MM5	5-speed manual	NC	NC
MX1	3-speed automatic	409	465
C25	**Wiper/Washer, Rear Window**	110	125

PRIZM

PRIZM (4 Cylinder)		
1SK19 4 Dr Notchback Sedan	8906	9680
1SK68 5 Dr Hatchback Sedan	9471	10295
1SL19 4 Dr GSi Notchback Sedan	11219	12195
1SL68 5 Dr GSi Hatchback Sedan	11679	12695
Destination Charge: All Models	345	345

STANDARD EQUIPMENT:

PRIZM: 1.6 liter 4 cylinder 12-valve engine with multi-port fuel injection (all models except GSi), 1.6 liter 4 cylinder 16-valve dual overhead cam engine with multi-port fuel injection (GSi), independent front and rear suspension, 5-speed manual transmission with overdrive, power front disc/rear drum brakes (all models except GSi), power 4-wheel disc brakes (GSi), rack-and-pinion steering (all models except GSi), 5-mph front and rear bumpers, P175/70R-13 all-weather steel-belted radial tires (Prizm 5 Dr Hatchback, Prizm LSi Notchback), P185/60R-14 steel-belted radial tires (GSi), composite halogen headlamps, tinted glass, black body-side moldings (Base Models), chrome and black body-side moldings (LSi), color-keyed body-side moldings (GSi), black reveal window moldings, full wheel covers (LSi), alloy wheels (GSi), center console, radio - AM/FM stereo with seek-scan, digital clock and 4 speakers (GSi), electronic rear window defogger (LSi, GSi), split-folding rear seat-back (Prizm Base Hatchback, LSi, GSi Hatchback), luggage area lamp (LSi, GSi), remote fuel filler door, base-coat/clear-coat paint, rear compartment security cover (Hatchbacks), rear stabilizer bar (all models except Base Notchback), Scotchguard™ fabric protector, cloth and vinyl seats, front wheel drive, stainless steel exhaust system, stone damage protection on rocker panels, underbody protective coating.

ACCESSORIES

—	**Prizm Base Equipment Group** — 1SK19 and 1SK68; (included with model) 5-speed manual transmission	NC	NC
—	**Prizm Preferred Equipment Group 1** — 1SK19 only; (includes: 5 speed manual transmission; P175/70R13 blackwall tires with rear stabilizer bar; defogger, rear window: electric; radio, electronically tuned AM/FM stereo with seek and scan and digital clock; power steering; wheel covers, full; mirrors: outside, LH remote and RH manual)	714	840
UM6	- with UM6 radio, add	119	140
—	**Prizm Preferred Equipment Group 2** — 1SK19 only; (includes: 3-speed automatic transmission; P175/70R13 blackwall tires with rear stabilizer bar; defogger, rear window: electric; radio, electronically tuned AM/FM stereo with seek and scan and digital clock; power steering; wheel covers, full; mirrors: outside, LH remote and RH manual)	1109	1305
UM6	- with UM6 radio, add	119	140
—	**Prizm Preferred Equipment Group 3** — 1SK19 only; (includes: air conditioning; 5-speed manual transmission; P175/70R13 blackwall tires with rear stabilizer bar; defogger, rear window: electric; radio, electronically tuned AM/FM stereo with seek and scan and digital clock; power steering;		

Mfgs. Code	Description	Base Cost	Sgstd. List
	power door lock system; wheel covers, full; remote trunk release; mirrors: outside, LH remote and RH manual)	1517	1785
UM6	- with UM6 radio, add	119	140
—	**Prizm Preferred Equipment Group 4** — 1SK19 only; (includes: air conditioning; 3-speed automatic transmission; P175/70R13 blackwall tires with rear stabilizer bar; defogger, rear window: electric; radio, electronically tuned AM/FM stereo with seek and scan and digital clock; power steering; power door lock system; wheel covers, full; remote trunk release; mirrors: outside, LH remote and RH manual)	1913	2250
UM6	- with UM6 radio, add	119	140
—	**Prizm Preferred Equipment Group 1** — 1SK68 only; (includes: 5-speed manual transmission; defogger, rear window: electric; radio, electronically tuned AM/FM stereo with seek and scan and digital clock; power steering; mirrors, outside, LH remote and RH manual)	563	662
UM6	- with UM6 radio, add	119	140
—	**Prizm Preferred Equipment Group 2** — 1SK68 only; (includes: 3-speed automatic transmission; defogger, rear window: electric; radio, electronically tuned AM/FM stereo with seek and scan and digital clock; power steering mirrors: outside, LH remote and RH manual)	958	1127
UM6	- with UM6 radio, add	119	140
—	**Prizm Preferred Equipment Group 3** — 1SK68 only; (includes: air conditioning; 5-speed manual transmission; defogger, rear window: electric; radio, electronically tuned AM/FM stereo with seek and scan and digital clock; power steering; power door lock system; remote hatch release; mirrors: outside, LH remote and RH manual)	1366	1607
UM6	- with UM6 radio, add	119	140
—	**Prizm Preferred Equipment Group 4** — 1SK68 only; (includes: air conditioning; 3-speed automatic transmission; defogger, rear window: electric; radio, electronically tuned AM/FM stereo with seek and scan and digital clock; power steering; power door lock system; remote hatch release; mirrors: outside, LH remote and RH manual)	1761	2072
UM6	- with UM6 radio, add	119	140
—	**Prizm LSi Preferred Equipment Group 1** — 1SK19 (includes: air conditioning; LSi equipment; 5-speed manual transmission; radio, electronically tuned AM/FM stereo with seek and scan and digital clock; power steering; power door lock system; steering wheel, tilt; remote trunk release)	2127	2502
UM6	- with UM6 radio, add	119	140
—	**Prizm LSi Preferred Equipment Group 2** — 1SK19 (includes: air conditioning; LSi equipment; 3-speed automatic transmission; radio, electronically tuned AM/FM stereo with seek and scan and digital clock; power steering; power door lock system; steering wheel, tilt; remote trunk release)	2522	2967
UM6	- with UM6 radio, add	119	140
—	**Prizm LSi Preferred Equipment Group 3** — 1SK19 (includes: air conditioning; LSi equipment; 3-speed automatic transmission; radio, electronically tuned AM/FM stereo with seek and scan and digital clock; power steering; power windows; power door lock system; speed control, electronic: with resume speed; steering wheel, tilt; windshield wiper system, intermittent; remote trunk release)	2947	3467
UM6	- with UM6 radio, add	119	140
—	**Prizm GSi Base Equipment Group 1** — 1SL19 and 1SL68; (included with model) 5 speed manual transmission	NC	NC
UM6	- with UM6 radio, add	119	140
—	**Prizm GSi Preferred Equipment Group 1** — 1SL19 and 1SL68; (includes: air conditioning; 5-speed manual transmission; seat, split folding rear, standard on GSi Hatchback; steering wheel, tilt; remote trunk/hatch		

Mfgs. Code	Description	Base Cost	Sgstd. List
	release; floor mats, color-keyed front and rear; mirrors, dual visor vanity)		
	- GSi Notchback	900	1059
	- GSi Hatchback	773	909
UM6	- with UM6 radio, add	119	140
—	**Prizm GSi Preferred Equipment Group 2** — 1SL19 and 1SL68; (includes: air conditioning; 4-speed automatic transmission (electronically controlled); seat, split folding rear, standard on GSi Hatchback; steering wheel, tilt; remote trunk/hatch release; floor mats, color-keyed front and rear; mirrors, dual visor vanity - GSi Notchback	1559	1834
	- GSi Hatchback	1431	1684
UM6	- with UM6 radio, add	119	140
—	**Prizm GSi Preferred Equipment Group 3** — 1SL19 and 1SL68; (includes: air conditioning; 5-speed manual transmission; power windows; power door locks; speed control, electronic: with resume speed; seat, split folding rear, standard on GSi Hatchback; steering wheel, tilt; windshield wiper system, intermittent; remote trunk/hatch release; floor mats, color-keyed front and rear; mirrors, dual visor vanity) - GSi Notchback	2158	2539
	- GSi Hatchback	2031	2389
UM6	- with UM6, add	119	140
—	**Interior Trim**		
A2	cloth/vinyl bucket seats	NC	NC
B2	custom cloth bucket seats (included with LSi Equipment Pkg)	NC	NC
C2	custom sport cloth bucket seats (standard on GSi models)	NC	NC
—	**Exterior Color** — paint, solid	NC	NC
—	**Engines**		
L01	1.6 liter DOHC MFI L4 engine	NC	NC
LWO	1.6 liter DOHC MFI L4 engine (standard on GSi)	NC	NC
C60	**Air Conditioning**	587	690
C49	**Defogger, Rear Window Electric**	89	105
B37	**Floor Covering** — mats, color-keyed, front and rear	34	40
YF5	**California Emission Requirements** — includes all testing, equipment and/or certification necessary for registration in State of California	60	70
NA5	**Standard Emission Equipment**	NC	NC
UM6	**Radio Equipment** — electronically tuned AM/FM stereo radio with seek and scan, stereo casette tape and digital clock (includes dual front and rear) (for specific radio pricing, refer to radio information included with each preferred equipment group.		
CA1	**Sun Roof, Electric** — includes map light	451	530
V16	**Tachometer** — 1SK19 LSi only	51	60

STORM

STORM (4 Cylinder)

Code	Description	Base Cost	Sgstd. List
1RF77	3 Dr 2 + 2 Sport Coupe	9603	10670
1RT77	3 Dr 2 + 2 GSi Sport Coupe	11156	12395
	Destination Charge: All Models	325	325

STANDARD EQUIPMENT:

STORM: 1.6 liter 4 cylinder overhead cam 12-valve engine with multi-port fuel injection (Hatchback Coupe, 2+2 Coupe), 1.6 liter 4 cylinder double overhead cam 16-valve engine with multi-port fuel injection (GSi 2+2 Coupe), 5-speed manual transmission, quad rectangular halogen headlamps, pop-up headlamp covers, integral front air dam, body-color body-side moldings, tinted glass, modular instrument cluster with back lighting, tachometer and gages, 4-spoke sport steering wheel, high-back reclining front bucket seats with integral restraints (Hatchback Coupe, 2+2 Coupe), molded sport-style low-back front bucket seats with see-through head restraints (GSi 2+2 Coupe), fully trimmed door panels with armrests, integral door bins, front stereo speakers, floor console with convenience trays, side window defoggers, loadspace security cover (GSi 2+2 Coupe), one-piece opening rear hatch, remote hatch opener, luggage compartment lamp, P185/60HR-14 all-season steel belted radial ply tires (Hatchback Coupe, 2+2 Coupe), full wheel covers (Hatchback Coupe, 2+2 Coupe), stone damage protection on rocker panels, P205/50VR-15 tires (GSi, 2+2 Coupe), Scotchguard™ fabric protector, removable rear quarter windows (Hatchback Coupe), electric rear window defogger, MacPherson strut 4-wheel independent suspension with front stabilizer bar, power assisted constant ratio rack-and-pinion steering, power front disc/rear drum brakes, driver's side airbag, fold-down rear seat dual outside rear view mirrors.

ACCESSORIES

Code	Description	Base Cost	Sgstd. List
—	**Storm Base Equipment Group 1** — 1RF11 only; (included with model)		
	5-speed manual transmission	NC	NC
UM6	- with UM6 radio, add	119	140
—	**Storm Preferred Equipment Group 2** — 1RF77 only; (includes: 3-speed automatic transmission)	463	545
UM6	- with UM6 radio, add	119	140
—	**Storm GSi Base Equipment Group 1** — 1RT77 only; (included with model)		
	5-speed manual transmission	NC	NC
UM6	- with UM6 radio, add	119	140
—	**Storm GSi Preferred Equipment Group 2** — 1RT77 only; (includes: 4-speed automatic transmission)	633	745
UM6	- with UM6 radio, add	119	140
—	**Interior Trim**		
F2	cloth bucket seats	NC	NC
C2	sport cloth bucket seats	NC	NC
—	**Exterior Color** — paint, solid	NC	NC
—	**Engines**		
LO1	1.6 liter SOHC L4 MFI	NC	NC
LWO	1.6 liter DOHC L4 MFI	NC	NC
C6O	**Air Conditioning**	587	690
D42	**Cover, Cargo Security** — standard on 1RT77 model	43	50
YF5	**California Emission Requirements** — includes all testing, equipment and/or certification necessary for registration in State of California	60	70
NA5	**Standard Emission Equipment**	NC	NC
B37	**Floor Covering** — mats, color-keyed, front and rear	26	30
DE1	**Louvers, Rear Window** — 1RF77 only	179	210
UM6	**Radio Equipment** — (includes dual front and rear speakers) electronically tuned AM/FM stereo radio with seek and scan, stereo cassette tape and digital clock (for specific radio pricing, refer to radio information included with each preferred equipment group).		

TRACKER

TRACKER (4 Cylinder)

Code	Description	Base Cost	Sgstd. List
CJ10316	2 Dr	10608	11285
CJ10316/B2Z	2 Dr LSi	11830	12585
CJ10367	2 Dr Convertible	10232	10885
CJ10367/B2Z	2 Dr LSi Convertible	11275	11995
CE10367	2 Dr 2WD Convertible	8459	8999

Destination Charge: All Models 280 280

STANDARD EQUIPMENT:

TRACKER: 1.6 liter 4 cylinder overhead cam engine with electronic fuel injection, 5-speed manual transmission with overdrive, manual locking front hubs (Base 4WD Models), automatic locking hubs (LSi), halogen headlamps, dual block sport mirrors (all except LSi), dual body-color mirrors (LSi), upper band tinted windshield (LSi), swing-out rear side glass (4WD Hardtop, LSi Hardtop), nonremovable plastic side windows (Convertibles), electric rear window defogger (4WD Hardtop, LSi Hardtop), zip-out clear plastic rear window (Convertibles), full-size lockable spare tire, spare tire cover (LSi), high-back reclining front bucket seats (all except LSi), reclining front bucket seats with "see through" adjustable head restraints (LSi), individual rear bucket seats (LSi), vinyl door trim with armrest and storage pocket (all except LSi), full-cover molded door trim with armrest and storage (LSi), instrument panel gage cluster with tachometer and trip odometer (all except 2WD Base Convertible), AM/FM stereo radio with seek-scan (LSi), front and rear tow hooks, swing-open locking hinged tailgate, canvas top with fold and stow feature (Convertibles), P205/75R-15 on-/off road type tires (all except 2WD Base Convertible), P195/75R-15 all-season steel belted radial tires (2WD Base Convertible), front and rear floor mats (LSi), custom cloth interior (LSi), intermittent windshield wipers (LSi), power front disc/rear drum brakes.

ACCESSORIES

Mfgs. Code	Description	Base Cost	Sgstd. List
—	**Tracker and Tracker Convertible Base Equipment Group 1 —** CJ10316 and CJ10367; (included with model) standard equipment	NC	NC
—	**Tracker and Tracker Convertible Preferred Equipment Group 2 —** CJ10316 and CJ10367; (includes: standard equipment; radio, electronically tuned AM/FM stereo radio with seek and scan and digital clock)	266	302
UM6	- with UM6 radio, add	122	139
—	**Tracker and Tracker Convertible Preferred Equipment Group 3 —** CJ10367; (includes: standard equipment; radio, electronically tuned AM/FM stereo radio with seek and scan and digital clock; air conditioning)	877	997
UM6	- with UM6 radio, add	122	139
—	**Tracker LSi and LSi Convertible Base Equipment Group 1 —** CJ10316/B2Z and CJ10367/B2Z; (included with model) LSi equipment	NC	NC
—	**Tracker LSi and LSi Convertible Preferred Equipment Group 2 —** CJ10316/B2Z and CJ10367/B2Z; (includes: LSi equipment; radio, electronically tuned AM/FM stereo radio with seek and scan, stereo cassette tape and digital clock)	122	139
—	**Tracker LSi and LSi Convertible Preferred Equipment Group 3 —** CJ10316/B2Z and CJ10367/B2Z; (includes: LSi equipment; radio, electronically tuned AM/FM stereo radio with seek and scan, stereo cassette tape and digital clock; air conditioning)	734	834
—	**Tracker 2WD Convertible Preferred Equipment Group 1 —** CE10367; (includes: standard equipment)	NC	NC
—	**Tracker 2WD Convertible Preferred Equipment Group 2 —** CE10367; (includes: standard equipment; radio, electronically tuned AM/FM stereo radio with seek and scan and digital clock)	266	302
UM6	- with UM6 radio, add	122	139
—	**Tracker 2WD Convertible Preferred Equipment Group 3 —** CE10367; (includes: standard equipment; radio, electronically tuned AM/FM stereo radio with seek and scan and digital clock; air conditioning)	877	997
UM6	- with UM6 radio, add	122	139
—	**Interior Trim**		

Mfgs. Code	Description	Base Cost	Sgstd. List
H2	cloth bucket seats (standard on Tracker 2-door and Convertible)	NC	NC
C2	custom cloth bucket seats (standard on Tracker LSi and Tracker LSi Convertible	NC	NC
—	**Exterior Color** — paint, solid	NC	NC
LS5	**1.6 Liter EFI Engine**	NC	NC
C60	**Air Conditioning**	612	695
P17	**Cover, Spare Tire** — standard on Tracker LSi and Tracker LSi Convertible	29	33
YF5	**California Emission Requirements** — includes all testing, equipment and/or certification necessary for registration in State of California	NC	NC
NA5	**Standard Emission Equipment**	NC	NC
—	**Seating**		
AP8	rear seat not desired CE10367 models only	NC	NC
AM7	rear seat CE10367 model only, standard on 4WD Tracker models	392	445
B37	**Floor Coverings** — mats, color-keyed, front and rear (standard on LSi models)	25	28
B84	**Moldings: Body Side** — CJ10316 models (standard on Tracker LSi)	52	59
	- Convertible models (include rocker panel molding) standard on LSi Convertible	75	85
—	**Radio Equipment** — radio, electronically tuned AM/FM stereo radio with seek and scan, stereo cassette tape and digital clock. (Includes dual front and rear speakers) (for specific radio pricing refer to radio information included with each preferred equipment group).		
NY7	**Shield, Transfer Case**	66	75
N40	**Steering, Power**	242	275
Z72	**Trailering Special Equipment** — includes wiring harness and trailering hitch	96	109
QA4	**Wheels, Alloy**	286	325
—	**Transmissions**		
MM5	5-speed manual	NC	NC
MX1	3-speed automatic	497	565

1991 lincoln

CONTINENTAL

CONTINENTAL (6 Cylinder)

M97	Continental Executive Series	25763	30211
M98	Continental Signature Series	27367	32120

Destination Charge: All Models 580 580

STANDARD EQUIPMENT:

CONTINENTAL: Body-color bumpers, bright grille, halogen headlamps, cornering lights, body-color dual power remote-control heated mirrors, moldings (belt, wheellip and rocker panel), vinyl bodyside molding, bodyside accent stripes (Signature Series), full wheel covers (Executive Series), styled aluminum wheels (Signature Series), rear quarter windows, driver's side air bag supplemental restraint system, dual front seat fold-down armrests, rear seat folding center armrest, electronic digital clock, overhead console with courtesy/reading lamps, front floor mats (front and rear on Signature Series), illuminated glove box, roof rail assist handles, 4-way articulated front seat, electronic instrumentation - digital speedometer, multi-function gauge (temperature, oil, battery charge), digital and analog fuel gauges and tripminder computer, rear seat reading lights, map pockets, day/night rearview mirror, dual illuminated visor mirrors (Signature Series), radio (electronic

AM/FM stereo search with cassette tape player, 4 speakers and premium sound system), leather seat trim, 6-way twin-comfort driver's seat with power driver and manual passenger recliners (Executive Series), 6-way/6-way twin-comfort seats with dual power recliners (Signature Series), color-keyed tilt steering wheel (leather-wrapped on Signature Series), dual sun visors, electronic automatic climate control air conditioning with sunload sensor, automatic power antenna, maintenance-free battery, power 4-wheel disc brakes with anti-lock brake system (ABS), coolant recovery system, power decklid pulldown (Signature Series), remote decklid release, defroster group (heated rear window and outside rearview mirrors), power door locks, 3.8 liter V6 EFI engine, dual exhaust system, front wheel drive, remote fuel filler door, tinted glass, headlamp convenience group (Signature Series), dual note horn, illuminated entry system (Signature Series), keyless entry system (Signature Series), engine compartment light, automatic parking brake release, speed control, front and rear stabilizer bars, power rack-and-pinion steering, vehicle level control suspension, P205/70R15 BSW tires, 4-speed electronic automatic overdrive transaxle, power side windows, interval windshield wipers.

ACCESSORIES

Code	Description	Base Cost	Sgstd. List
994	**Engine —** 3.8 liter EFI V6	STD	STD
44T	**Transaxle —** 4-speed electronic automatic overdrive	STD	STD
422	**California Emissions System**	84	100
428	**High Altitude Principal Use Emissions System**	NC	NC
T33	**Tires —** P205/70R15 BSW	STD	STD
—	**Wheels**		
—	Standard Wheel Cover (Executive)	STD	STD
64Q	Styled Aluminum Wheels (Executive)	467	556
64Q	Styled Aluminum Wheels (Signature)	STD	STD
64N	Geometric Spoke Aluminum Wheels (Executive)	467	556
64N	Geometric Spoke Aluminum Wheels (Signature)	NC	NC
—	**Seats**		
88I	Leather Twin Comfort Lounge (Executive)	STD	STD
88J	Leather Twin Comfort Lounge (Signature)	STD	STD
88M	Cloth Twin Comfort Lounge (Executive)	NC	NC
88L	Cloth Twin Comfort Lounge (Signature)	NC	NC
18A	**Anti-Theft Alarm System**	248	295
94H	**Comfort/Convenience Group**	696	828
945	**Console Group, Overhead**	209	249
144	**Keyless Illuminated Entry System**	189	225
46A	**Memory Seat With Power Lumbar**	253	301
13B	**Moonroof, Power**	1293	1540
917	**Digital Audio Disc Player**	519	617
916	**Ford JBL Audio System**	483	575
524	**Steering Wheel, Leather-Wrapped**	101	120
515	**Telephone, Cellular**	671	799
924	**Insta-Clear Windshield**	259	309
41H	**Engine Block Immersion Heater**	22	26
153	**Front License Plate Bracket**	NC	NC
—	**Mandatory New York Warranty Enhancement**	95	110

MARK VII

MARK VII (8 Cylinder)

Code	Description	Base Cost	Sgstd. List
M93	Mark VII LSC Series	25781	30238
M92	Mark VII Bill Blass Designer Series	25885	30362

	Base Cost	Sgstd. List
Destination Charge: All Models	580	580

Mfgs. Code	Description	LINCOLN	Base Cost	Sgstd. List

STANDARD EQUIPMENT:

MARK VII: Front and rear bumper rub strips (charcoal with argent accent stripe), front cornering lamps, fog lamps (LSC), bright grille, halogen headlamps, dual fold-away heated power remote-control mirrors, moldings (wheellip, belt), lower bodyside molding, color-keyed bodyside protection, lower bodyside paint in dark charcoal (LSC), two-color bodyside and decklid paint stripes (Blass), 16" x 7" BBS aluminum road wheels with exposed lug nuts, rear seat fold-down center armrest, electronic alert chimes, floor console, overhead console, front and rear floor mats, 2-way articulated front seat headrests, analog instrumentation including tachometer, message center, quarter-mounted dual-intensity courtesy/reading lights, front seat back map pockets, day/night rearview mirror, dual illuminated visor mirrors, radio (electronic AM stereo/FM stereo search with cassette tape player, four coaxial speakers and premium sound system), front seat back robe records (Blass), leather seat trim (LSC), leather or cloth seat trim (Blass), articulated sport seats with dual power recliners and power lumbar support with seat bolster (LSC), individual luxury seats with dual power recliners (LSC), 6-way/6-way driver and passenger power seats, color-keyed leather-wrapped steering wheel with air bag, electronic automatic climate control air conditioning, power antenna, maintenance-free battery, power 4-wheel disc brakes with anti-lock brake system (ABS), coolant recovery system, compass/thermometer group, power decklid pulldown, remote-control decklid release, side window defoggers, rear window defroster, power door locks, 5.0 liter high output V8 MPI engine, dual exhaust, remote-control fuel filler door release, tinted glass, headlamp convenience group, dual note horn, illuminated entry system, keyless entry system, low engine oil alert light, automatic parking brake release, speed control, front and rear stabilizer bars, power rack-and-pinion steering (quick ratio), tilt steering wheel, handling suspension, electronic air suspension with automatic level control, P225/60R16 BSW performance tires, automatic overdrive transmission, power windows, interval windshield wipers.

ACCESSORIES

Code	Description	Base Cost	Sgstd. List
99E	**Engine** — 5.0 liter high output EFI V8	STD	STD
44T	**Transaxle** — 4-Speed Overdrive Automatic	STD	STD
422	**California Emissions System**	84	100
428	**High Altitude Principal Use Emission System**	NC	NC
T21	**Tires** — P225/60R16 BSW	STD	STD
—	**Wheels** — BBS Handling road wheel	STD	STD
—	**Seats**		
88S	Articulated Sport Seats, Leather (LSC)	STD	STD
88T	Articulated Sport Seats, Cloth & Leather (LSC)	NC	NC
88R	Individual Luxury Seats, Leather (LSC)	NC	NC
88P	Individual Luxury Seats, Leather (Bill Blass)	STD	STD
88M	Individual Luxury Seats, Cloth (Bill Blass)	NC	NC
18A	**Anti-Theft Alarm System**	248	295
45A	**Axle, Traction-lok**	85	101
61A	**Mirror, Electrochromic Automatic Dimming**	93	111
13B	**Moonroof, Power**	1293	1540
585	**AM/FM Stereo Radio w/Digital Disc Player**	251	299
916	**Ford JBL Audio System**	483	575
413	**Special Edition Audio**	571	680
515	**Telephone, Cellular**	671	799
41H	**Engine Block Immersion Heater**	22	26
153	**Front License Plate Bracket**	NC	NC
—	**Mandatory New York Warranty Enhancement**	95	110

Mfgs. Code	Description	Base Cost	Sgstd. List

LINCOLN

TOWN CAR

	TOWN CAR (8 Cylinder)		
M81	Town Car Standard Series	25127	29458
M82	Town Car Signature Series	27611	32416
M83	Town Car Cartier Designer Series	29365	34504
	Destination Charge: All Models	580	580

STANDARD EQUIPMENT:

TOWN CAR: Color-coordinated bumpers, halogen headlamps, dual power remote-control heated mirrors, bodyside moldings, dual shade paint (Signature Series, Cartier Designer), upper bodyside accent paint stripe, deluxe wheel covers (Executive Series), turbine spoke aluminum wheels (Signature Series), geometric spoke aluminum wheels (Cartier Designer), driver side air bag supplemental restraint system, rear seat center fold-down armrest, dual front seat fold-down armrests, electronic alert chimes, electronic digital clock, front floor mats (front and rear on Signature Series and Cartier Designer), lockable glove box, roof rail assist handles, analog instrument cluster (electronic with message center on Signature Series and Cartier Designer), rear compartment reading lamp, dual floor well lights (Signature Series, Cartier Designer), map pockets (Signature Series, Cartier Designer), day/night inside rearview mirror, illuminated passenger-side visor mirror (dual illuminated mirrors on Signature Series and Cartier Designer), radio-electronic AM stereo/FM stereo search with cassette tape player, six speakers and premium sound system (Executive Series, Signature Series), Ford JBL audio system (Cartier Designer), cloth seat trim (cloth and supple leather trim on Cartier Designer), seats-twin comfort lounge with 6-way power driver's side with dual manual recliners and 2-way front seat headrests (Signature Series), seats-twin comfort lounge with 6-way/6-way power and 2-way front seat headrests (Executive Series), seats - twin comfort lounge with 6-way/6-way power with dual recliners, memory seat, power lumbar support and 2-way front seat headrests (Cartier Designer), color-keyed luxury steering wheel with supplemental driver air bag (leather-wrapped wheel on Signature Series and Cartier Designer), door pull straps, automatic temperature control air conditioning, automatic power antenna, heavy duty battery, power 4-wheel disc brakes, coolant recovery system, remote-control decklid release, power decklid pulldown (Signature Series, Cartier Designer), rear window defroster, power door locks, 4.6 liter V8 EFI engine, engine temperature gauge, dual exhaust (Cartier Designer), remote fuel filler door release, tinted glass, headlamps convenience system (Signature Series, Cartier Designer), dual note horn, keyless entry system (Signature Series, Cartier Designer), cornering lamps, engine compartment light, low engine oil alert light, automatic parking brake release, speed control, power steering, tilt steering wheel, P215/70R15 steel-belted radial WSW tires, automatic overdrive transmission, power side windows, interval windshield wipers.

ACCESSORIES

99W	**Engine** — 4.6 Liter EFI V8	STD	STD
44T	**Transaxle** — 4-speed overdrive automatic	STD	STD
422	**California Emissions System**	84	100
428	**High Altitude Principal Use**	NC	NC
—	**Tires**		
T3P	P215/70R15 WSW Tires	STD	STD
T31	P215/70R15 BSW Tires	NC	NC
—	**Wheels**		
649	Deluxe Wheel Covers (Executive)	STD	STD
64H	Turbine Spoke Aluminum Wheels (Executive)	467	556
64H	Turbine Spoke Aluminum Wheels (Signature)	STD	STD
64H	Turbine Spoke Aluminum Wheels (Cartier)	STD	STD
64P	Geometric Spoke Aluminum Wheels (Executive)	467	556
64P	Geometric Spoke Aluminum Wheels (Signature)	NC	NC
64P	Geometric Spoke Aluminum Wheels (Cartier)	STD	STD
—	**Seats**		

Mfgs. Code	Description **MERCURY**	Base Cost	Sgstd. List
88A	Cloth Twin Comfort Lounge (Executive)	STD	STD
88C	Cloth Twin Comfort Lounge (Signature)	STD	STD
88H	Cloth & Leather Twin Comfort Lounge (Cartier)	NC	NC
88B	Leather Twin Comfort Lounge (Executive)	479	570
88D	Leather Twin Comfort Lounge (Signature)	479	570
88F	Leather Twin Comfort Lounge (Cartier)	NC	NC
18A	**Anti-Theft Alarm System**	248	295
552	**Anti-Lock Brake System, 4-Wheel**	STD	STD
62D	**Anti-Lock Brake System, 4-Wheel Delete**	(786)	(936)
553	**Traction Assist**	187	222
94H	**Comfort/Convenience Group**	625	744
155	**Instrumentation, Electronic**	209	249
46E	**Memory Seat, Programmable**	422	502
61A	**Mirror, Electrochromic Automatic Dimming**	93	111
13B	**Moonroof, Power**	1293	1540
958	**Paint Treatment, Monotone —** Signature	NC	NC
585	**AM/FM Stereo Radio w/Digital Disc Player**	251	299
916	**Ford JBL Audio System**	483	575
515	**Telephone, Cellular**	671	799
—	**Vinyl Roof, Full Padded**	1008	1200
924	**Windshield, Insta-Clear**	259	309
153	**Front License Plate Bracket**	NC	NC
41H	**Engine Block Immersion Heater**	22	26
418	**Heavy-Duty Package (High Altitude)**	459	547
418	**Heavy-Duty Package (Other)**	529	630
464	**Dual Exhaust System (w/High Altitude)**	NC	NC
464	**Dual Exhaust System (Other)**	69	83
535	**Trailer Tow III Package (High Altitude)**	281	335
535	**Trailer Tow III Packager (Other)**	351	417
54B	**Livery Package (High Altitude)**	281	335
54B	**Livery Package (Other)**	351	417
—	**Mandatory New York Warranty Enhancement**	95	110

1991 mercury

CAPRI

CAPRI (4 Cylinder)

T01	Standard Convertible	11746	12990
T03	XR2 Convertible	14354	15920

Destination Charge: All Models 355 355

STANDARD EQUIPMENT:

CAPRI: Front and rear bumper rub strip, front and rear body-color bumpers, concealed fog lamps (XR2), body-color grille, halogen pop-up retractable headlamps, black dual power mirrors, rear decklid spoiler (XR2), styled steel wheels (Base Capri), aluminum wheels (XR2), driver's side air bag supplemental restraint system, digital clock, full console, locking glove box, rear heat ducts, footwell courtesy lights, day/night rearview mirror, mud guards, electronic AM/FM stereo radio (Base Capri), electronic AM/FM stereo with cassette tape player (XR2), cloth individual dual reclining front sport bucket seats, 4-spoke leather-wrapped wheel, air conditioner (XR2), 4-wheel power disc brakes, 1.6 liter DOHC 16-valve MPI engine (Capri), 1.6 liter DOHC 16-valve turbocharged/intercooler MPI engine (XR2), tinted glass, power door locks (XR2), speed control

(XR2), front and rear stabilizer bars, power rack-and-pinion steering, sport tuned suspension (XR2), mini-spare tire, P185/60R14 BSW tires, 5-speed manual transaxle with 5th gear overdrive (Base Capri), 5-speed manual transaxle with 4th and 5th gear overdrive (XR2), lower bodyside urethane protection, power side windows, intermittent windshield wipers.

ACCESSORIES

Code	Description	Base Cost	Sgstd. List
—	**Engines**		
99Z	1.6L EFI DOHC (Capri Standard)	STD	STD
996	1.6L EFI DOHC Turbo (Capri XR2)	STD	STD
—	**Transaxles**		
445	5-speed manual	STD	STD
44T	4-speed overdrive automatic (not available on XR2)	622	732
422	**California Emissions System**	85	100
428	**High Altitude Emission System**	NC	NC
T76	**P185/60R14 BSW Tires**	STD	STD
572	**Air Conditioner, Manual** — std on XR2	695	817
902	**Door Locks, Power** — std on XR2	149	176
13T	**Hardtop** — includes carrier cover, dome light and rear window defroster	1094	1287
476	**Tonneau Cover**	166	195
64A	**Wheels, Aluminum**-std on XR2	293	345
—	**Radio Systems**		
58H	AM/FM stereo/cassette (std on XR2)	132	155
586	AM/FM stereo/cassette, premium (Standard)	370	435
586	AM/FM stereo/cassette, premium (XR2)	238	280
58Y	AM/FM stereo delete credit (Standard)	(208)	(245)
58Y	AM/FM stereo/cassette delete credit (XR2)	(340)	(400)
153	**Front License Plate Bracket**	NC	NC
—	**Mandatory New York Warranty Enhancement** — required on vehicles sold and registered in New York State	95	110
651A	**Preferred Equipment Package 651A** — (includes manual air conditioner, aluminum wheels and power door locks) - XR2,- total package price	1137	1338
	- discount	425	500
	- net price	712	838

COUGAR

COUGAR (6 Cylinder)

Code	Description	Base Cost	Sgstd. List
M60	LS	13497	15629

COUGAR (8 Cylinder)

Code	Description	Base Cost	Sgstd. List
M62	XR7	17981	20905

Destination Charge: All Models 485 485

STANDARD EQUIPMENT:

COUGAR: Bumper rub strips, soft fascia front and rear bumpers (body-color on XR7), bright grille (body-color on XR7), low-profile halogen headlamps, fog lamps (XR7), dual black power remote-control mirrors (body-color on XR7), black bodyside moldings (body-color on XR7), luxury wheel covers (LS), 7-spoke 16" x 7" cast aluminum wheels (XR7), deluxe carpeting (luxury on XR7), full-length floor console, driver's left-foot footrest (XR7), locking glove box, performance instrument cluster with tachometer (XR7), side window demisters, day/night rearview mirror, concealed driver and unconcealed passenger visor mirrors, electronic AM/FM stereo radio with 4 speakers and digital clock, deluxe color-keyed safety belts, reclining individual bucket seats with luxury cloth and two-way adjustable headrests (LS), sport seats with power lumbar supports and four-way adjustable headrests (XR7), seatback map pockets (XR7), rear seat fold-down armrest, integral rear seat headrests (XR7), luxury steering wheel (LS), sport steering wheel (XR7), air conditioning, traction-lok axle (XR7), maintenance-free battery, power front disc/rear drum brakes (LS), power 4-wheel disc brakes with anti-lock brake system (XR7), coolant recovery system, 3.8 liter SEFI V6 engine (LS), 5.0 liter HO SEFI V8 engine (XR7), dual exhaust (XR7), stainless steel exhaust, tinted glass, dual note horn, lower bodyside protection, power rack-and-pinion steering (LS), electronic speed sensitive variable assist power steering (XR7), handling suspension (XR7), P205/70R15 BSW tires (LS), P225/60R16/97V BSW performance tires (XR7), mini-spare tire, automatic overdrive transmission, power side windows, interval windshield wipers.

ACCESSORIES

Code	Description	Base Cost	Sgstd. List
—	**Engines**		
994	3.8L SEFI V6 (std LS)	STD	STD
99T	5.0L HO SEFI V8 (std XR7)	STD	STD
99T	5.0L HO SEFI V8 (LS-requires 414)	1007	1184
44T	**Transaxle** — automatic 4-speed overdrive	STD	STD
422	**California Emissions System**	85	100
428	**High Altitude Emissions System**	NC	NC
—	**Tires**		
T33	P205/70R15 BSW (LS)	STD	STD
T3F	P205/70R15 WSW (LS)	62	73
T37	P215/70R15 BSW (LS) available only in pkg 262A or 263A		
508	conventional spare tire (LS)	62	73
45A	**Axle, Traction-Lok**-LS	85	100
552	**Anti-Lock Brake System**-LS	838	985
18A	**Anti-Theft Alarm System**	208	245
632	**Cold Weather Group** — LS w/o 261, 262, 263	174	205
632	**Cold Weather Group** — XR7 w/o 265, 266	152	178
632	**Cold Weather Group** — LS w/261, 262, 263	38	45
632	**Cold Weather Group** — XR7 w/265, 266	16	18
51Q	**Lamps, Front Cornering**	58	68
57Q	**Defroster, Rear Window**	136	160
146	**Diagnostic Maintenance Monitor**	76	89
12H	**Floor Mats, Front Carpet**	28	33
474	**Headlamp Convenience Group**	149	176
47J	**Illuminated Entry System**	69	82
155	**Instrument Cluster, Electronic**	229	270
144	**Keyless Entry System**	185	219
144	**Keyless Entry System** — w/262	116	137
60B	**Lamp Group, Luxury**	207	244
943	**Light Group**	39	46
903	**Lock Group, Power**	234	276
414	**Luxury Trim Option**	573	674
677	**Mirrors, Dual Illuminated Visor**	85	100
13B	**Moonroof, Power**	659	776
—	**Radio Systems**		
589	electronic AM/FM stereo/cassette w/clock	132	155
58Y	electronic AM/FM stereo w/clock delete credit	(208)	(245)
588	high-level AM/FM cassette w/clock (w/263, 266 pkgs)	391	460
	high-level AM/FM cassette w/clock (w/262,265 pkgs)	259	305
—	JBL sound system	447	526
917	compact disc player	418	491
91H	**Antenna, Power**	69	82
21A	**Seat, 6-way Power Driver's**	247	290
21J	**Seats, Dual 6-way Power** — in pkgs w/21A	247	290

Mfgs. Code	Description	Base Cost	Sgstd. List
21J	**Seats, Dual 6-way Power**	494	580
219	**Seat, Split Fold-Down Rear**	113	133
889	**Seat Trim, Leather** — LS	416	489
881	**Seat Trim, Leather** — XR7	416	489
525	**Speed Control, Finger Tip**	178	210
524	**Steering Wheel, Leather-Wrapped**	54	63
573	**Temperature Control, Electronic Automatic**	138	162
52Q	**Steering Wheel, Tilt**	115	135
645	**Wheel Covers, Styled Sport**	73	85
646	**Wheel Covers, Locking Radial Spoke** — LS w/o 261 pkg	194	228
646	**Wheel Covers, Locking Radial Spoke** — LS w/261 pkg	121	143
64M	**Wheels, 15" Cast Aluminum** — LS w/o 261 pkg	254	299
153	**Front License Plate Bracket**	NC	NC
—	**Mandatory New York Warranty Enhancement** — required on vehicles sold and registered in New York	95	110
—	**Preferred Equipment Packages**		
	LS		
261A	preferred equipment pkg 261A - (includes tilt steering wheel, fingertip speed control, electric rear window defroster and styled sport wheel covers)		
	- total package price	502	590
	- discount	111	130
	- net price	391	460
262A	preferred equipment pkg 262A - (includes tilt steering wheel, fingertip speed control, electric rear window defroster, front carpet floor mats, 6-way power driver's seat, luxury trim option, illuminated entry system, leather-wrapped steering wheel, electronic AM/FM stereo cassette radio, cast aluminum wheels, P215/70R15 BSW tires, dual illuminated visor mirrors, power lock group and light group) - total package price	2144	2523
	- discount	723	850
	- net price	1421	1673
263A	preferred equipment pkg 263A - (includes tilt steering wheel, fingertip speed control, electric rear window defroster, front carpet floor mats, luxury trim option, leather-wrapped steering wheel, cast aluminum wheels, P215/70R15 BSW tires, dual illuminated visor mirrors, power lock group, light group, keyless entry system, diagnostic maintenance monitor, 6-way dual power seats, high level electronic AM/FM stereo cassette radio, luxury lamp group, power antenna) - total package price	3118	3670
	- discount	763	898
	- net price	2355	2772
	XR7		
265A	preferred equipment pkg 265A - (includes 6-way power driver's seat, tilt steering wheel, fingertip speed control, electric rear window defroster, electronic AM/FM stereo cassette radio, power lock group) - total package price	1042	1226
	- discount	1042	1226
	- net price	NC	NC
266A	preferred equipment pkg 266A - (includes 6-way power driver's seat, tilt steering wheel, fingertip speed control, electric rear window defroster, power lock group, front carpet floor mats, keyless entry system, diagnostic maintenance monitor, high level electronic AM/FM stereo cassette radio, luxury lamp group, dual illuminated visor mirrors, power antenna and light group) - total package price	1990	2344
	- discount	1037	1220
	- net price	953	1124

Mfgs. Code	Description	MERCURY	Base Cost	Sgstd. List

GRAND MARQUIS, COLONY PARK

GRAND MARQUIS (8 Cylinder)

Code	Description	Base Cost	Sgstd. List
M74	4 Dr GS Sedan	16183	18741
M75	4 Dr LS Sedan	16608	19241
M78	4 Dr Colony Park GS Wagon	16334	18918
M79	4 Dr Colony Park LS Wagon	16820	19490
	Destination Charge: All Models	525	525

STANDARD EQUIPMENT:

GRAND MARQUIS/COLONY PARK: Front and rear bumper guards (Colony Park), front and rear bumper rub strips, dual rectangular halogen headlamps, deluxe luggage rack (Colony Park), dual remote-control power mirrors, bright wheellip moldings (Grand Marquis), wide black/bright lower bodyside moldings (Grand Marquis), bright rocker panel molding, dual accent bodyside stripes (Grand Marquis), padded rear half vinyl roof (Grand Marquis), full wheel covers, cigarette lighter, electronic digital clock, locking glove box, light group (LS), inside day/night rearview mirror, electronic AM/FM stereo radio with four speakers, fold-down rear seat center armrest (Grand Marquis LS), map pockets (LS), fold-down rear seat (Colony Park), cloth seat trim (vinyl on Colony Park GS), seats - twin-comfort lounge with dual recliners and two-way headrests (GS), seats - luxury twin-comfort lounge with dual recliners and two-way headrests (LS), tilt steering column, color-keyed 4-spoke steering wheel with driver side air bag supplemental restraint system, lockable side and underfloor stowage compartment (Colony Park), trip odometer, air conditioning, autolamp on/off delay system, maintenance-free battery, power front disc/rear drum brakes, reminder chimes, coolant recovery system, 5.0 liter EFI V8 engine with sequential multi-port fuel injection, inside hood release, dual note horn, automatic parking brake release, luxury sound insulation package, mini-spare tire, power steering, power three-way tailgate (Colony Park), P215/70R15 WSW all-season steel-belted radial tires, automatic overdrive transmission, power side windows, concealed windshield wipers with interval feature.

ACCESSORIES

Code	Description	Base Cost	Sgstd. List
99F	**5.0L EFI V8 Engine**	STD	STD
44T	**Automatic Overdrive Transmission**	STD	STD
422	**California Emission System**	85	100
428	**High Altitude Control Emissions**	NC	NC
T3P	**P215/70R15 All-Season WSW Radial Tires**	STD	STD
—	**Seats**		
88J	cloth seat trim (GS Wagon only)	46	54
88K	vinyl seat trim (GS Sedan only)	31	37
88M	leather trim option (LS Sedan and Wagon only)	416	489
573	**Air Conditioner, Automatic Climate Control**	192	226
573	**Air Conditioner, Automatic Climate Control** — when ordered w/packages 192A, 193A, 172A, 156A or 157A which include rear defroster	56	66
45A	**Axle, Traction-Lok**	85	100
631	**Battery, Heavy Duty** — included with Trailer Tow III	23	27
153	**Front License Plate Bracket**	NC	NC
761	**Bumper Guards, Front**	32	38
762	**Bumper Guards, Rear**	21	24
508	**Tire, Convention Spare**	73	85
51Q	**Front Cornering Lamps**	58	68
613	**Decklid Release, Power** — included in power lock group	43	50
57Q	**Defroster, Electric Rear Window**	136	160
12H	**Floor Mats, Front Carpet**	22	26
12Q	**Floor Mats, Rear Carpet**	15	17

Mfgs. Code	Description	Base Cost	Sgstd. List
	MERCURY		
152	**Frames, License Plate**	7	9
41H	**Heater, Engine Block Emmersion**	17	20
47J	**Illuminated Entry System**	69	82
943	**Light Group**	39	46
903	**Lock Group, Power** — (Sedans) includes electric decklid release	234	276
903	**Lock Group, Power** — (Wagons) includes electric tailgate lock	248	291
677	**Mirrors, Dual Illuminated Visor**	92	109
961	**Molding, Bodyside Protection** — n/a on Sedans	56	66
CLR	**Paint, Clearcoat**	196	230
—	**Radio Systems**		
58H	electronic AM/FM stereo cassette radio	132	155
58Y	radio credit option	(175)	(206)
586	audio system, high level	417	490
586	audio system, high level when ordered with pkgs 157A, 172A or 173A	285	335
586	audio system, high level when ordered with pkg 193A	142	167
913	sound system, premium	143	168
91H	antenna, power	69	82
86E	**Roof, Formal Coach Vinyl**	617	726
86C	**Roof, Full Cloth Carriage**	1306	1537
86H	**Roof, Full Vinyl Carriage**	1306	1537
216	**Seats, Dual Inboard Facing Rear**	182	215
21A	**Seat, 6-Way Power Driver**	247	290
21J	**Seats, 6-Way Power-Dual Control**	494	580
21J	**Seats, 6-Way Power-Dual Control** — when ordered with packages containing 6-way power driver's seat	247	290
525	**Speed Control, Fingertip**	178	210
524	**Steering Wheel, Leather-Wrapped**	54	63
66Z	**Suspension, Automatic Load Leveling**	213	250
662	**Suspension, Handling/Heavy Duty**	22	26
535	**Trailer Tow III Package**	344	405
646	**Wheel Covers, Locking Wire-Styled**	194	228
64L	**Wheel, Turbine Spoke Aluminum**	374	440
64L	**Wheels, Turbine Spoke Aluminun Upgrade**	180	212
924	**Windshield, Insta-Clear**	259	305
—	**Mandatory New York Warranty Enhancement** — required on all vehicles registered and sold in New York State	95	110
—	**Preferred Equipment Packages**		
	GS Sedan		
156A	preferred equipment pkg 156A - (includes front carpet floor mats, rear carpet floor mats, 6-way power driver seat, illuminated entry system, fingertip speed control, electric rear window defroster, locking wire wheel covers, front bumper guards, rear bumper guards, power lock group and light group) - total package price	1187	1397
	- discount	255	300
	- net price	932	1097
157A	preferred equipment pkg 157A - (includes items in preferred equipment package 156A plus electronic AM/FM stereo cassette radio, turbine spoke aluminum wheels, dual illuminated visor mirrors) - total package price	1591	1873
	- discount	425	500
	- net price	1166	1373
157A	preferred equipment pkg 157A - (includes items in preferred equipment package 156A plus electronic AM/FM stereo cassette radio, locking wire-style wheel covers and dual illuminated visor mirrors) - total package price	1411	1661
	- discount	435	500
	-net price	986	1161
	LS Sedan		

Mfgs. Code	Description	Base Cost	Sgstd. List
172A	preferred equipment pkg 172A - (includes front carpet floor mats, rear carpet floor mats, license plate frames, 6-way power driver seat, illuminated entry system, front cornering lamps, leather-wrapped steering wheel, fingertip speed control, electric rear window defroster, electronic AM/FM stereo cassette radio, turbine spoke aluminum wheels, dual illuminated visor mirrors, front bumper guards, rear bumper guards, power lock group and power radio antenna) - total package price	1740	2049
	- discount price	553	650
	- net price	1187	1399
173A	preferred equipment pkg 173A - (includes items in preferred equipment package 172A plus 6-way power passenger seat, conventional spare tire, automatic air conditioner, leather seat trim and full carriage roof)		
	- total package price	3838	4516
	- discount	978	1150
	- net price	2860	3366
	Colony Park		
192A	preferred equipment pkg 192A - (includes illuminated entry system, front carpet floor mats, rear carpet floor mats, 6-way power driver seat, dual inboard facing rear seats, front cornering lamps, fingertip speed control, electric rear window defroster, turbine spoke aluminum wheels, bodyside protection molding, power lock group, light group)		
	- **Colony Park GS Wagon,** total package price	1624	1911
	- discount	510	600
	- net price	1114	1311
	- **Colony Park LS Wagon,** total package price	1585	1865
	- discount	510	600
	- net price	1075	1265
193A	preferred equipment pkg 193A - (includes items in preferred equipment package 192A plus leather-wrapped steering wheel, electronic AM/FM stereo cassette radio, dual illuminated visor mirrors, power radio antenna and premium sound system)		
	- **Colony Park GS Wagon,** total package price	2114	2488
	- discount	765	900
	- net price	1349	1588
	- **Colony Park LS Wagon,** total package price	2075	2442
	- discount	765	900
	- net price	1310	1542

SABLE

SABLE (6 Cylinder)

Code	Model	Base Cost	Sgstd. List
M50	GS Sedan	13224	15311
M53	LS Sedan	13941	16154
M55	GS Wagon	14028	16256
M58	LS Wagon	14766	17124

Destination Charge: 480 480

STANDARD EQUIPMENT:

SABLE: Black bumper rub strips (GS), halogen headlamps, front cornering lamps, roof-mounted luggage rack (Wagons), dual power body-color mirrors, rocker panel moldings (GS), bodyside cladding (LS), dual decklid paint stripes (Sedans), lower door and rocker urethane coating (GS), deluxe wheel covers, front seat center fold-down armrest, rear seat center fold-down armrest (Sedans), driver's left footrest, locking glove box, roof-mounted assist handles, 2-way adjustable front headrests (GS), 4-way adjustable front headrests (LS), 2-way adjustable rear headrests

(Sedans), tachometer, alert lights (LS), front seat map pockets (LS), inside day/night rearview mirrors, dual flip-up illuminated visor mirrors with dual secondary visors (LS), cargo net tie-down hooks, AM/FM stereo radio with four speakers, cloth twin-comfort lounge and dual manual recliners, front seat power lumbar supports (LS), 60/40 split-second seat (Wagons), four-spoke steering wheel with driver side supplemental air bag restraint system, air conditioning, maintenance-free battery, power front disc/rear drum brakes, electronic chimes, electronic digital clock, coolant recovery system, remote decklid release (LS Sedan), 3.0 liter SEFI V6 engine, stainless steel exhaust, front wheel drive, remote-release fuel filler door (LS), tinted glass, inside hood release, dual note horn, light group (LS), automatic parking brake release (LS), front and rear stabilizer bars, rack-and-pinion power steering (GS), tilt steering column, mini-spare tire, P205/70R14 BSW all-season radial tires, electronic automatic 4-speed overdrive transaxle, power side windows (LS), interval windshield wipers.

ACCESSORIES

Code	Description	Base Cost	Sgstd. List
—	**Engines**		
99U	3.0L SEFI V6	STD	STD
	- w/461A, 462A	(472)	(555)
994	3.8L SEFI V6	472	555
44T	**Transaxle** — 4-speed automatic transmission	STD	STD
422	**California Emissions System**	85	100
428	**High Altitude Emissions System**	NC	NC
—	**Tires**		
T78	P205/70R14 BSW	STD	STD
T7G	P205/70R14 WSW	69	82
T32	P205/65R15 BSW	55	65
T3B	P205/65R15 WSW	124	146
T3B	P205/65R15 WSW (with 451A, 461A, or 462A) includes deluxe wheel covers	69	82
508	tire, conventional spare (n/a with 214 third seat on Wagons)	62	73
573	**Air Conditioner, Automatic**	155	183
552	**Anti-Lock Braking System (ABS)**	838	985
473	**Autolamp On/Off Delay Switch**	62	73
631	**Battery, Heavy-Duty** — 3.0L engine only (n/a with 924 insta-clear windshield)	23	27
475	**Cargo Area Cover**	56	66
57Q	**Defroster, Rear Window Electric** — required in NY State. Required with 924 insta-clear windshield, 173 rear window washer/wiper	136	160
	Floor Mats, Front/Rear Carpet	36	43
65Z	**Fuel Tank, Extended Range** — included with 155 electronic instrument cluster	39	46
155	**Instrument Cluster, Electronic** — includes 65Z extended range fuel tank	299	351
144	**Keyless Entry System** — includes illuminated entry system, requires 902 power lock group	186	218
943	**Light Group** — GS	50	59
902	**Lock Group, Power** — GS Sedans	270	317
902	**Lock Group, Power** — GS Wagons	227	267
902	**Lock Group, Power** — LS Sedans and Wagons (required with 144 keyless entry)	192	226
412	**Luxury Trim Option** — (available LS Sedans only; NA w/leather seat trim or individual seats) - w/954 tutone paint	510	600
	- w/monochrome paint	458	539
677	**Mirrors, Dual Illuminated Visor**	85	100
13B	**Moonroof, Power**	659	776
CLG	**Paint, Clearcoat**	160	188
954	**Paint, Tutone** — included and only available w/412 luxury trim		
596	**Picnic Tray (Load Floor Extension)**	77	90

MERCURY

Mfgs. Code	Description	Base Cost	Sgstd. List
—	**Radio Systems**		
58H	AM/FM stereo cassette radio (n/a w/916 JBL sound or 917 compact disc	132	155
586	high-level audio system	417	490
586	high-level audio system (w/451A)	285	335
586	high-level audio system (w/461A)	142	167
917	compact disc, digital, (requires 586 high level audio system)	418	491
916	JBL sound system (requires 586 high-level audio or 916 compact disc) available Sedans only	447	526
913	premium sound system	143	168
91H	antenna, power	69	82
58Y	AM/FM radio delete	(175)	(206)
214	**Seat, Rear Facing Third** — n/a with 508 conventional spare tire	132	155
21A	**Seat, 6-Way Power Driver**	247	290
21J	**Seats, 6-Way Dual Power**	494	580
53J	**Seats, 6-Way Dual Power** — w/451A, 461A, 462A	247	290
88P	**Seats, Bucket with Console**	NC	NC
88N	**Seat Trim, Leather Twin Comfort** — LS	416	489
88R	**Seat Trim, Leather Individual** — LS	416	489
88W	**Seat Trim, Vinyl** — GS Wagon	31	37
525	**Speed Control, Fingertip** — required with 524 leather-wrapped steering wheel	178	210
52A	**Steering, Variable Assist Power**	88	104
524	**Steering Wheel, Leather-Wrapped** — requires 525 speed control	54	63
972	**Stripes, Bodyside Accent**	52	61
662	**Suspension, Heavy-Duty**	22	26
173	**Washer/Wiper, Rear Window** — requires 57Q rear window defroster	107	126
64K	**Wheels, Aluminum** — requires T32 tires	191	224
64J	**Wheels, Polycast** — requires T78 tires	117	138
43R	**Windows, Power Side**	267	315
924	**Windshield, Insta-Clear** — requires 57Q rear window defroster	259	305
57D	**Air Conditioner, Manual-Delete** — GS	(695)	(817)
153	**Bracket, Front License Plate**	NC	NC
41H	**Engine Block Immersion Heater**	17	20
—	**Mandatory New York Warranty Enhancement** — required on all models registered and sold in New York State	95	110
53A	**Luxury Touring Package** — available on LS Sedans only (includes anti-lock, power moonroof and leather individual seats) - total package price	1913	2250
	- discount	170	200
	- net price	1743	2050
—	**Preferred Equipment Packages**		
450A	GS preferred equipment pkg 450A - (includes power side windows, fingertip speed control, electric rear window defroster and power lock group) - **GS Sedan,** total package price	851	1002
	- discount	170	200
	- net price	681	802
	- **GS Wagon,** total package price	808	952
	- discount	170	200
	- net price	638	752
451A	GS preferred equipment pkg 451A - (includes items in GS preferred equipment package 450A plus front and rear carpet floor mats, 6-way power driver's seat, electronic AM/FM stereo cassette radio, P205/65R15 BSW tires, aluminum wheels and light group)		
	- **GS Sedan,** total package price	1562	1838
	- discount	595	700
	- net price	967	1138
	- **GS Wagon,** total package price	1519	1788

Mfgs. Code	Description	Base Cost	Sgstd. List
	- discount	595	700
	- net price	924	1088
461A	LS preferred equipment pkg 461A - (includes front and rear carpet floor mats, 6-way power driver seat, leather-wrapped steering wheel, fingertip speed control, electric rear window defroster, electronic AM/FM stereo cassette radio, P205/65R15 BSW tires, aluminum wheels, power lock group, premium sound system, power radio antenna, bodyside accent stripes and 3.8 liter EFI engine) - total package price	1957	2302
	- discount	680	800
	- net price	1277	1502
462A	LS preferred equipment pkg 462A - (includes front and rear carpet floor mats, 6-way power driver seat, leather-wrapped steering wheel, fingertip speed control, electric rear window defroster, P205/65R15 BSW tires, aluminum wheels, power lock group, power radio antenna, bodyside accent stripes, 3.8 liter EFI engine, keyless entry system, electronic instrument cluster, autolamp on/off delay system, automatic air conditioner and high level electronic AM/FM stereo cassette audio system) - total package price	2801	3294
	- discount	850	1000
	- net price	1951	2294

TOPAZ

Mfgs. Code	Description	Base Cost	Sgstd. List
TOPAZ (4 Cylinder)			
M31	2 Dr GS	9108	10065
M33	2 Dr XR5	9997	11064
M36	4 Dr GS	9248	10222
M37	4 Dr LS	10475	11601
M38	4 Dr LTS	11387	12626
Destination Charge: All Models		455	455

STANDARD EQUIPMENT:

TOPAZ: Black bumper rub strip (GS, LS), body-color front and rear bumpers (GS, LS), dark titanium bumper (XR5), two-tone color bumper (LTS), rectangular halogen headlamps, decklid luggage rack, dual power remote-control mirrors, bodyside moldings, single-color dual bodyside paint stripes (GS, LS), quad-band lower bodyside paint stripe (XR5), tri-band lower bodyside (LTS), lower bodyside urethane coating, decklid spoiler (XR5), turbine style wheel covers (GS, LS), cast aluminum wheels (XR5, LTS), fold-down front seat armrest (LS, XR5, LTS), reminder chimes, coat hooks, full console, cassette tape storage (LS, LTS), diagnostic alert module, front and rear floor mats, lockable glove box, passenger assist grab handles, full instrumentation including tachometer, fuel gauge and trip odometer; map light, illuminated footwell, day/night rearview mirror, dual illuminated visor mirrors (LS, LTS), cargo net tie-down hooks (LS, XR5, LTS), premium sound system (LTS), electronic AM/FM stereo with integral clock (GS), electronic AM/FM stereo with cassette tape player and integral clock (LS, XR5, LTS), front motorized shoulder belt restraint system, low-back individual reclining seats with adjustable headrests (GS, LS), sport bucket seats with power lumbar supports and 2-way adjustable headrests (XR5, LTS), contoured rear seat back (XR5, LTS), 6-way power driver's seat (LTS), all cloth seat trim, 4-spoke color-keyed steering wheel (GS, LS), black leather-wrapped 4-spoke steering wheel, air conditioning (LTS), maintenance-free battery, power front disc/rear drum brakes, power decklid release (LS, XR5, LTS), rear window defroster (LS, XR5, LTS), 2.3 liter EFI HSC engine (GS, LS), 2.3 liter EFI HSO engine (XR5, LTS), front wheel drive, remote-release fuel filler door (LS, XR5, LTS), tinted glass, inside hood release, dual note horn, illuminated entry system (LS, LTS), light group (LS,XR5, LTS), power door locks (LS, LTS), speed control (LS, LTS), power rack-and-pinion steering, tilt steering wheel (LS, XR5,

LTS), sport suspension (LS, XR5, LTS), temporary spare tire, P185/70R14 BSW tires (GS), P185/70R14 BSW performance tires (LS, XR5, LTS), 5-speed manual transaxle, power flow-through ventilation (GS, LS, XR5), power side windows (LS, LTS), interval windshield wipers.

ACCESSORIES

Mfgs. Code	Description	Base Cost	Sgstd. List
—	**Engines**		
99X	2.3L HSC EFI 14 engine	STD	STD
99S	2.3L HSO EFI 14 engine	STD	STD
—	**Transaxles**		
445	5-speed manual transaxle	STD	STD
440	automatic transaxle	479	563
422	**California Emissions System**	85	100
428	**High Alitude Emissions**	NC	NC
—	**Tires**		
T72	P185/70R14 BSW (std. on GS)	STD	STD
T7K	P185/70R14 WSW	69	82
T73	P185/70R14 performance BSW (std. on LS, XR5 and LTS)	STD	STD
T7J	P185/70R14 performance WSW	69	82
572	**Air Conditioner, Manual**	695	817
414	**Comfort/Convenience Group**	147	173
57Q	**Defroster, Electric Rear Window**	136	160
—	**Four-Wheel Drive (4 Door Only)**		
967	GS w/360A or 361A	1267	1490
967	GS w/363A, 364A, or 368A	788	927
967	LS	1256	1478
967	LS w/365A	777	915
967	LTS	1173	1380
—	**Lock Group, Power**		
903	2-door GS	234	276
903	2-door XR5	166	195
903	4-door GS	271	318
903	2-door GS w/comf./conv. group	166	195
903	4-door GS w/comf./conv. group	202	238
548	**Luggage Rack, Decklid**	97	115
CLG	**Paint, Clearcoat**	78	91
954	**Paint, Tu-tone**	135	159
—	**Radio Systems**		
589	AM/FM stereo w/cassette (std. on LS, XR5, LTS)	132	155
913	premium sound system (std. on LTS)	117	138
58Y	AM/FM stereo delete (GS only)	(208)	(245)
58Y	AM/FM stereo w/cassette delete (LS, XR5, LTS)	(340)	(400)
21A	**Seat, 6-Way Power Driver's**	247	290
525	**Speed Control, Fingertip**	178	210
52Q	**Steering Wheel, Tilt**	115	135
—	**Supplemental Restraint System, Driver Air Bag**		
59H	GS	692	815
59H	LS, or LTS	529	622
64J	**Wheels, Polycast**	164	193
43R	**Windows, Power Side** — 4 door only	267	315
153	**Front License Plate Bracket**	NC	NC
41H	**Engine Block Immersion Heater**	17	20
—	**Mandatory New York Warranty Enhancement** — required on vehicles sold and registered in New York State	95	110
—	**Preferred Equipment Packages**		
	GS		
360A	preferred equipment pkg 360A - (includes 5-speed manual transaxle,		

Mfgs. Code	Description	Base Cost	Sgstd. List
	conventional axle and P185/70R14 BSW tires)	STD	STD
361A	preferred equipment pkg 361A - (includes comfort/convenience group, tilt steering wheel, electric rear window defroster, manual air conditioner) - total package price	1093	1285
	- discount	680	680
	- net price	413	485
363A	preferred equipment pkg 363A - (includes automatic transaxle, comfort/convenience group, tilt steering wheel, electric rear window defroster, manual air conditioner) - total package price	1572	1848
	- discount	850	1000
	- net price	722	848
364A	preferred equipment pkg 364A - (includes automatic transaxle, comfort/convenience group, tilt steering wheel, electric rear window defroster, manual air conditioner, power side windows, fingertip speed control, polycast wheels) - GS 4 door only - total package price	2181	2566
	- discount	1148	1350
	- net price	1033	1216
368A	preferred equipment pkg 368A - (includes automatic transaxle, comfort/convenience group, tilt steering wheel, decklid luggage rack, rear window defroster, manual air conditioner, tu-tone paint) - GS 4 door only - total package price	1707	2007
	- discount	893	1050
	- net price	814	957
365A	preferred equipment pkg 365A - (includes 5-speed manual transaxle, conventional axle, P185/70R14 performance BSW tires) - total package price	479	563
	- discount	479	563
	- net price	NC	NC
—	**XR5**		
371A	preferred equipment pkg 371A - (includes 6-way power driver seat, fingertip speed control, power lock group, premium sound system) - total package price	708	833
	- discount	255	300
	- net price	453	533

TRACER

TRACER (4 Cylinder)

Mfgs. Code	Description	Base Cost	Sgstd. List
M10	4 Dr Base Notchback	8503	9386
M15	4 Dr Wagon	9411	10407
M14	4 Dr LTS Notchback	10505	11636

STANDARD EQUIPMENT:

TRACER: Front air dam (LTS), body-color bumpers, halogen headlamps, remote-control manual driver's side mirror (dual electric remote-control mirrors on Wagon and LTS), wide body-color moldings, wide black belt line molding, rear decklid spoiler (LTS), lower bodyside urethane coating, 13" x 5" semi-styled steel wheels with plastic center cap (Base Notchback), 14" x 5" semi-styled steel wheels with full wheel cover (Wagon), 14" x 5.0" 8-spoke aluminum wheels with locking lug nuts (LTS), cargo cover (Wagon), console, grab handles, analog instrumentation including tachometer, light group (LTS), dual non-illuminated visor mirrors (dual illuminated on LTS), front motorized shoulder belt restraint system, low-back cloth reclining seats, map pocket, 60/40 split fold down rear seat, integral rear seat headrests (Base Notchback, LTS), 4-spoke steering wheel (leather-wrapped on LTS), maintenance-free battery, power front disc/rear drum brakes (power 4-wheel disc brakes on LTS), remote decklid release (LTS), rear window defroster (Wagon, LTS), 1.9

liter SEFI 4 cylinder engine (Base Notchback, Wagon), 1.8 liter DOHC 16-valve EFI 4 cylinder engine (LTS), engine low coolant warning light, engine malfunction indicator light, remote fuel door release (LTS), tinted glass, electronic AM/FM stereo radio with integral clock (LTS also includes cassette), speed control (LTS), front and rear stabilizer bars, manual rack-and-pinion steering (power rack-and-pinion steering on Wagon and LTS), tilt steering wheel (LTS), 4-wheel independent suspension, sport handling suspension (LTS), P175/70R13 BSW tires (Base Notchback), P175/65R14 BSW tires (Wagon), P185/60R14 BSW tires (LTS), 5-speed manual overdrive transaxle, rear window wiper/washer (Wagon), interval windshield wipers (Wagon, LTS).

ACCESSORIES

Code	Description	Base Cost	Sgstd. List
—	**Engines**		
99J	1.9L EFI (Base 4-Door/Wagon)	STD	STD
998	1.8L DOHC (LTS)	STD	STD
—	**Transaxles**		
445	5-speed manual	STD	STD
44T	4-speed overdrive automatic	622	732
422	**California Emissions System**	59	70
428	**High Altitude Emissions System**	NC	NC
—	**Tires**		
T15	P175/70R13 BSW (Base 4-Door)	STD	STD
T75	P175/65R14 BSW & full wheel covers (std on Wagon)	112	132
T83	P185/60HRX14 BSW (LTS)	STD	STD
572	**Air Conditioning, Manual**	632	744
613	**Decklid Release, Remote** — Base 4-Door	42	50
57Q	**Defroster, Rear Window** — Base 4-Door	136	160
902	**Door Locks, Power**	174	205
18K	**Fuel Door Release, Remote** — Base 4-Door	21	24
943	**Light Group** — Base 4-Door/Wagon	98	116
548	**Luggage Rack, Deluxe** — Wagon	97	115
54J	**Mirrors, Dual Electric** — Base 4-Door	83	98
13B	**Moonroof, Power** — Base 4-Door/LTS	466	549
CLR	**Paint, Clearcoat**	NC	NC
—	**Radio Systems**		
589	AM/FM stereo/cassette (Base 4-Door/Wagon)	132	155
913	sound system, premium	117	138
58Y	AM/FM stereo delete credit (Base 4-Door/Wagon)	(208)	(245)
58Y	AM/FM stereo/cassette delete credit (LTS)	(340)	(400)
215	**Seat Tilt Adjuster, Driver-Side** — std on LTS	31	37
525	**Speed Control** — Base 4-Door/Wagon	171	201
52H	**Steering Power** — Base 4-Door	200	235
52H	**Steering Column, Tilt**-Base 4-Door/Wagon	115	135
43R	**Windows, Power**	260	306
172	**Wipers, Variable Intermittent**-Base 4-Door	47	55
153	**Front License Plate Bracket**	NC	NC
—	**Mandatory New York Warranty Enhancement** — required on vehicles sold and registered in New York State	95	110
—	**Preferred Equipment Packages**		
	4 Door Base Notchback		
572B	preferred equipment pkg 572B - (includes P175/65R14 BSW tires with full wheel covers, variable speed interval wipers, remote fuel filler door, power steering, dual power mirrors, rear window defroster, decklid release, light group) - total package price	739	870
	- discount	340	400
	- net price	399	470
573B	preferred equipment pkg 573B - (includes P175/65R14 BSW tires with full wheel covers, variable speed interval wipers, remote fuel filler door,		

Mfgs. Code	Description	Base Cost	Sgstd. List
	driver's side seat with tilt adjustment, power steering, tilt steering wheel, dual power mirrors, rear window defroster, manual air conditioner, decklid release, light group) - total package price	1517	1786
	- discount	553	650
	- net price	964	1136
515A	preferred equipment pkg 515A — total package price	1566	1845
	- discount	255	300
	- net price	1311	1543
	4 Door Wagon		
572B	preferred equipment pkg 572B - (includes P175/65R14 BSW tires with full wheel covers, variable speed interval wipers, remote fuel filler door, power steering, dual power mirrors, rear window defroster, decklid release, light group) - total package price	98	116
	- discount	0	0
	- net price	98	116
573B	preferred equipment pkg 573B - (includes P175/65R14 BSW tires with full wheel covers, variable speed interval wipers, remote fuel filler door, driver's side seat tilt adjustment, power steering, tilt steering wheel, dual power mirrors, rear window defroster, manual air conditioner, decklid release, light group) - total package price	876	1032
	- discount	340	400
	- net price	536	632

1991 oldsmobile

BRAVADA

BRAVADA (6 Cylinder)

Code	Description	Base Cost	Sgstd. List
V06	4 Dr	21249	23795
Destination Charge:		455	455

STANDARD EQUIPMENT:

BRAVADA: Gold metallic body side accent stripe, air conditioning, all-wheel drive, front armrests, passenger assist handles, heavy duty maintenance free battery, anti-lock power front disc and rear drum brakes, carpeting, front console with cup holders and dual auxiliary electrical outlets, cruise control, electric rear window defogger, side window defoggers, door locks with remote lock control package (includes two key-chain transmitters), 4.3 liter V6 engine with electronic fuel injection, foglamps, front and rear floor mats, protective rear cargo mat, halogen headlamps, inside hood release, analog instrument panel gauge cluster, power rear tailgate lock release, rooftop luggage carrier, inside day-night rearview mirror, electric driver and passenger side outside mirrors, illuminated driver and passenger side mirrors, color-coordinated moldings (body-side, rocker panel, wheel opening), radio (Delco ETR AM/FM stereo with seek-scan, auto-reverse cassette with music search, digital display clock and mast antenna), front reclining bucket seats, folding rear bench seat with center armrest, power steering, leather-wrapped steering wheel with tilt-away feature, P235/75R15 radial ply blackwall tires including full-size spare, 4-speed automatic transmission, 15" cast aluminum wheels including spare, power side windows, tinted windows plus deep-tint glass in rear doors, rear quarters and tailgate; pulse wiper system includes tailgate wiper and washer.

ACCESSORIES

Code	Description	Base Cost	Sgstd. List
1SA	**Bravada Package 1SA**	STD	STD
QEB	**Tires** — P235/75R15 SBR RWL mud and snow	155	182
U52	**Instrument Panel Cluster, Electronic**	252	296
V10	**Cold Climate Package**	77	90
WJ7	**Custom Leather Trim**	553	650
YF5	**California Emission Equipment and Test**	85	100
Z82	**Towing Package, Heavy-Duty**	348	409

CUSTOM CRUISER

CUSTOM CRUISER (8 Cylinder)

Code	Description	Base Cost	Sgstd. List
P35	3 Seat Wagon	17687	20495
	Destination Charge:	535	535

STANDARD EQUIPMENT:
CUSTOM CRUISER: Air conditioning, assist handles, maintenance-free battery, anti-lock power front disc and rear drum brakes, cargo net, 5.0 liter EFI engine, firm ride and handling package, halogen headlamps, headlamp-on reminder, inside hood release, rallye instrument panel (includes analog speedometer, tachometer, fuel gauge, oil pressure, coolant temperature, voltmeter plus temperature indicators for oil pressure, high engine and trip odometer), rooftop luggage rack, map pockets, remote control driver side mirror and manual passenger side mirror, driver and passenger side visor vanity mirrors, body side moldings, lower body side and wheel opening moldings, radio (Delco ETR AM/FM stereo with seek-scan, digital display clock, dual rear speakers and door speakers), front seat inflatable driver side restraint system, 55/45 divided bench seat with center armrest, rear-facing third seat, power steering, deluxe steering wheel with tilt-away feature, heavy duty suspension, P225/75R15 steel-belted radial ply white stripe all-season tires, automatic overdrive transmission, turn-signal-on reminder chime, vista roof with solarcool glass, 15" x 7" wheels, deluxe wheel discs, rear power window release, tinted glass, pulse wiper system, rear window wiper/washer.

ACCESSORIES

Code	Description	Base Cost	Sgstd. List
1SA	**Custom Cruiser 3-Seat Wagon Package 1SA**	STD	STD
1SB	**Custom Cruiser 3-Seat Wagon Package 1SB** — includes electronic cruise control, power door locks with tailgate lock; power side windows with auto down feature; color-coordinated door edge moldings; front and rear floor mats, AM/FM stereo radio/cassette/clock	888	1045
1SC	**Custom Cruiser 3-Seat Wagon Package 1SC** — includes Package 1SB contents plus 6-way power driver seat adjuster, automatic electric leveling system; power antenna; dual illuminated visor vanity mirrors; door courtesy lamps; reminder package; rearview mirror with read lamps, compass	1569	1846
1SD	**Custom Cruiser 3-Seat Wagon Package 1SD** — includes Package 1SC contents plus automatic electric comfort control air conditioning; front fender cornering lamps; 6-way power passenger seat adjuster; driver and passenger exterior power mirrors; twilight sentinel; remote lock control package	2242	2638
C49	**Defogger, Electric Rear Window** — w/Package 1SA, 1SB, 1SC	136	160
	- w/Package 1SD	166	195
D42	**Security Cover, Rear Storage**	59	69
K05	**Heater, Engine Block**	15	18

Mfgs. Code	Description	Base Cost	Sgstd. List
PD4	**Wheels, Aluminum 15" with Locks**	272	320
UX1	**Radio** — AM stereo/FM stereo/cassette/graphic equalizer/clock	268	315
U1C	**Radio** — AM/FM stereo/compact disc/clock	358	421
V92	**Towing Package**	213	250
WJ7	**Custom Leather Trim**	417	490
YF5	**California Emission Equipment and Test**	85	100

CUTLASS CALAIS

CUTLASS CALAIS (4 Cylinder)

Mfgs. Code	Description	Base Cost	Sgstd. List
L27	Coupe	9502	10295
L69	Sedan	9502	10295
F27	S Coupe	10265	11495
F69	S Sedan	10354	11595
T27	SL Coupe	13480	15095
T69	SL Sedan	13569	15195
K27	International Series Coupe	14551	16295
K69	International Series Sedan	14641	16395
	Destination Charge: All models	455	455

STANDARD EQUIPMENT:
CUTLASS CALAIS: Air conditioning (SL, International), maintenance-free battery, power front disc and rear drum brakes (International Series also has ABS anti-lock brake system), bumper wide rub strips (except International), trunk cargo net (SL, International), full-length console, side window defogger, 2.5 liter 4 cylinder EFI engine (Base Calais, S), 2.3 liter quad 4 cylinder DOHC MFI engine (SL), 2.3 liter quad 4 DOHC high output MFI engine (International), door-pull handles (International), door map storage (SL, International), halogen headlamps, front and rear floor mats (International), foglamps (International), headlamp-on reminder, driver information center (International), inside hood lock release (International), header panel courtesy and map lamps (S, SL, International), under-hood convenience lamp (SL, International), roof rail lamps (S, SL, International), black outside mirrors (driver side remote control on S, SL and International), visor vanity mirror for passenger and driver (SL; illuminated on International), black rocker panel molding (Base Calais, S, SL), wheel opening moldings (Base Calais, SL), deluxe body side molding (S, SL), contour reclining front bucket seats (non-reclining on Sedan), split-folding rear seats with pass-through (SL, International), easy entry seat adjuster for passenger side (Coupes), power rack and pinion steering, deluxe steering wheel (Base Calais, S), deluxe delta sport steering wheel (SL), leather-wrapped sport steering wheel with tilt-away feature (International), MacPherson strut front suspension, P185/75R14 steel-belted radial ply BW all-season tires (Base Calais, S), P195/70R14 touring steel-belted radial ply BW all-season tires, P205/55R16 performance steel-belted radial-ply BW all-season tires (International), 5-speed manual transmission (Base Calais, S), 5-speed manual transmission with overdrive (International), automatic transmission (SL), turn-signal-on reminder chime, 14" x 6" deluxe wheels (Base Calais), 14" x 6" sport wheels with stainless steel trim rings (S), 14" x 6" aluminum styled wheels with locks (SL), 16" x 6" aluminum styled wheels with locks (International), tinted glass, two-tone paint with lower body accent color (SL), pulse wiper system (International).

ACCESSORIES

Mfgs. Code	Description	Base Cost	Sgstd. List
—	**Option Packages**		
1SA	**Cutlass Calais Coupe Package 1SA**	STD	STD
1SB	**Cutlass Calais Coupe Package 1SB** — includes tilt away steering wheel; front and rear floor mats; bodyside moldings; 4-way manual driver seat		

Mfgs. Code	Description	Base Cost	Sgstd. List
	adjuster	226	265
1SC	**Cutlass Calais Coupe Package 1SC** — includes Package 1SB contents plus electronic cruise control; power door locks; 4-season air conditioning; pulse wiper system; driver remote, passenger manual exterior mirrors	1244	1463
1SA	**Cutlass Calais Sedan Package 1SA**	STD	STD
1SB	**Cutlass Calais Sedan Package 1SB** — includes tilt-away steering wheel; front and rear floor mats, bodyside moldings; 4-way manual driver seat adjuster	225	265
1SC	**Cutlass Calais Sedan Package 1SC** — includes Package 1SB contents plus electronic cruise control; power door locks; 4-season air conditioning; pulse wiper system; driver remote, passenger manual exterior mirrors	1278	1503
1SA	**Cutlass Calais S Coupe Package 1SA**	STD	STD
1SB	**Cutlass Calais S Coupe Package 1SB** — includes tilt-away steering wheel; front and rear floor mats; 4-season air conditioner; remote driver and passenger exterior mirrors; 4-way manual driver seat adjuster; pulse wiper system; underhood lamp; dual covered visor vanity mirrors; electronic cruise control	813	957
1SC	**Cutlass Calais S Coupe package 1SC** — includes Package 1SB contents plus power side windows with auto down feature; power front fender antenna; remote lock control package; driver information system	1362	1602
1SA	**Cutlass Calais S Sedan Package 1SA**	STD	STD
1SB	**Cutlass Calais S Sedan Package 1SB** — includes tilt-away steering wheel; front and rear floor mats; 4-season air conditioner; remote driver and passenger exterior mirrors; 4-way manual driver seat adjuster; pulse wiper system; underhood lamp; dual covered visor vanity mirrors; electronic cruise control	813	957
1SC	**Cutlass Calais S Sedan Package 1SC** — includes Package 1SB contents plus power side windows with auto down feature; power front fender antenna; remote lock control package; driver information system	1451	1707
1SA	**Cutlass Calais SL Coupe Package 1SA**	STD	STD
1SB	**Cutlass Calais SL Coupe Package 1SB** — includes power door locks; tilt-away steering wheel; front and rear floor mats; pulse wiper system; electronic cruise control; power front fender antenna; electric rear window defogger, remote driver and passenger exterior mirrors; power side windows with auto down feature; dual illuminated visor vanity mirrors	786	925
1SC	**Cutlass Calais SL Coupe Package 1SC** — includes Package 1SB contents plus 6-way power driver seat adjuster; driver information system; remote lock control package (AU3 required)	1109	1305
1SA	**Cutlass Calais SL Sedan Package 1SA**	STD	STD
1SB	**Cutlass Calais SL Sedan Package 1SB** — includes power door locks, tilt-away steering wheel; front and rear floor mats; pulse wiper system; electronic cruise control; power front fender antenna; electric rear window defogger; remote driver and passenger exterior mirrors; power side windows with auto down feature; dual illuminated visor vanity mirrors	876	1030
1SC	**Cutlass Calais SL Sedan Package 1SC** — includes Package 1SB contents plus 6-way power driver seat adjuster; driver information system; remote lock control package (AU3 required)	1199	1410
1SA	**Cutlass Calais International Series Coupe Package 1SA**	STD	STD
1SB	**Cutlass Calais International Series Coupe Package 1SB** — includes 6-way power driver seat adjuster; power side windows with auto down feature; remote driver and passenger exterior mirrors; electronic cruise control, power front fender antenna; electric rear window defogger; remote lock control package	1105	1300
1SA	**Cutlass Calais International Series Sedan Package 1SA**	STD	STD
1SB	**Cutlass Calais International Series Sedan Package 1SB** — includes 6-way power driver seat adjuster; power side windows with auto down feature; remote driver and passenger exterior mirrors; electronic cruise		

Mfgs. Code	Description	Base Cost	Sgstd. List
	control; power front fender antenna; electric rear window defogger; remote lock control package	1194	1405
AU3	**Door Locks, Power** — F27	162	190
	- F69	196	230
BF9	**Floor Mats, Delete** — L27, L69, F27, F69	(38)	(45)
C49	**Defogger, Electric Rear Window**	136	160
FE3	**Touring Car Ride & Handling Package** — F27, F69	500	588
	- T27, T69	207	244
K05	**Heater, Engine Block**	15	18
LD2	**Engine** — 2.3 liter DOHC L4 quad (MXI required) - L27, L69, F27, F69	561	660
LD2	**Engine** — 2.3 liter quad 4 w/MXI auto transmission - K27, K69	340	400
LG7	**Engine** — 3300 V6 MFI - T27, T69	43	50
MXI	**Transmission** — 3-speed automatic transmission w/console shift - L27, L69, F27, F69	459	540
PD8	**Wheels** — aluminum 14" w/locks - F27, F69	301	354
QFF	**Tires** — P185/75R14 SBR WW - L27, L69, F27, F69	58	68
UB3	**Cluster, Instrument Panel Rallye** — F27, F69, T27, T69	107	126
UM6	**Radio** — AM/FM stereo/cassette/clock - L27, L69, F27, F69	140	165
U1C	**Radio** — AM/FM stereo/CD/clock - F27, F69	358	421
	- T27, T69	233	274
	- K27, K69	233	274
UX1	**Radio** — AM stereo/FM stereo/cassette/graphic equalizer/clock - T27, T69, K27, K69	128	150
V3N	**Column Shift** — (MXI required) - L27, L69	(94)	(110)
V56	**Luggage Carrier, Deck Lid** — F27, F69, T27, T69, K27, K69	98	115
WJ7	**Custom Leather Trim** — K27, K69	340	400
W40	**Quad 442 Sport Performance Package** — F27	1446	1701
YF5	**California Emission Equipment**	85	100

CUTLASS CIERA

Code	Model	Base Cost	Sgstd. List
CUTLASS CIERA (4 Cylinder)			
L69	Sedan	11033	12495
J37	S Coupe	11828	13395
J69	S Sedan	11215	12995
J35	Cruiser 2 Seat Wagon	11991	13895
CUTLASS CIERA (6 Cylinder)			
M69	SL Sedan	13717	15895
M35	Cruiser SL 3 Seat Wagon	14321	16595
Destination Charge: All models		480	480

STANDARD EQUIPMENT:
CUTLASS CIERA: Air conditioning (SL), maintenance-free battery, power front disc and rear drum brakes, front and rear bumper moldings, side window defoggers, convenience group - includes under-hood and trunk lamps, inside day-night mirror with dual reading lamps, visor vanity mirrors, chime tones (SL), front and rear door pull handles, 2.5 liter 4 cylinder EFI engine (Base Ciera, S), V6 MFI engine (SL), front wheel drive, halogen headlamps, headlamp-on reminder, inside hood release, map pockets, black outside mirrors (driver side remote, passenger side manual), body side molding, bright rocker panel and wheel opening moldings, radio-includes Delco ETR AM/FM stereo with seek-scan, digital display clock, dual rear speakers, fixed mast fender antenna (SL also has auto-reverse cassette and extended range speakers), front bench seat with fold-down armrest (Base Ciera, S), 55/45 divided bench front seat plus armrest and driver side power reclining seat back

(SL), power rack-and-pinion steering, deluxe steering wheel, MacPherson strut front suspension, P185/75R14 steel-belted radial-ply all-season white stripe tires, automatic transmission, power trunk-lid lock release (SL), turn-signal-on reminder chime, 14" x 5.5" wheels, deluxe wheel discs, tinted glass.

CUTLASS CRUISER WAGON: Maintenance-free battery, power front disc and rear drum brakes, front and rear bumper moldings, side window defogger, front and rear door-pull handles, 2.5 liter 4 cylinder EFI engine, front wheel drive, halogen headlamps, headlamp-on reminder, inside hood release, map pockets, black outside mirrors (driver side - remote control, passenger side-manual), body side moldings, bright roof drip and belt reveal moldings, radio (Delco ETR AM/FM stereo with seek-scan and digital display clock, dual rear speakers, fixed mast fender antenna), custom bench front seat with fold-down armrest, split-folding rear seat backs, power rack-and-pinion steering, deluxe steering wheel, MacPherson front strut suspension, P185/75R14 steel-belted radial-ply white stripe all-season tires, 3-speed automatic transmission, turn-signal-on reminder chime, 14" x 5.5" wheels, deluxe wheel discs, tinted glass.

ACCESSORIES

Code	Description	Base Cost	Sgstd. List
1SA	**Cutlass Ciera Sedan Package 1SA**	STD	STD
1SB	**Cutlass Ciera Sedan Package 1SB** — includes 4-season air conditioner	684	805
1SC	**Cutlass Ciera Sedan Package 1SC** — includes Package 1SB contents plus tilt-away steering wheel, pulse wiper system	846	995
1SD	**Cutlass Ciera Sedan Package 1SD** — includes Package 1SC contents plus power door locks	1041	1225
1SE	**Cutlass Ciera Sedan Package 1SE** — includes Package 1SD contents plus power side windows with auto down feature	1313	1545
1SA	**Cutlass Ciera S Coupe Package 1SA**	STD	STD
1SB	**Cutlass Ciera S Coupe Package 1SB** — includes 4-season air conditioner; tilt-away steering wheel; pulse wiper system; front and rear floor mats	629	740
1SC	**Cutlass Ciera S Coupe Package 1SC** — includes Package 1SB contents plus electronic cruise control; power driver reclining divided bench seat with storage armrest; body accent stripe; door-edge guard moldings; convenience group; rocker panel and wheel opening moldings; power recliner passenger seat back; remote driver and passenger exterior mirrors; power trunk-lid lock release	1212	1426
1SD	**Cutlass Ciera S Coupe Package 1SD** — includes Package 1SC contents plus lower bodyside moldings; power side windows with auto down feature; power door locks; power front fender antenna	1629	1916
1SA	**Cutlass Ciera S Sedan Package 1SA**	STD	STD
1SB	**Cutlass Ciera S Sedan Package 1SB** — includes 4-season air conditioner, tilt-away steering wheel; pulse wiper system; front and rear floor mats	629	740
1SC	**Cutlass Ciera S Sedan Package 1SC** — includes Package 1SB contents plus electronic cruise control; power driver reclining divided bench seat with storage armrest; body accent stripe; door-edge guard moldings; convenience group; rocker panel and wheel opening moldings; power recline passenger seat back; remote driver and passenger exterior mirrors; power trunk-lid lock release	1221	1436
1SD	**Cutlass Ciera S Sedan Package 1SD** — includes Package 1SC contents plus lower bodyside moldings; power side windows with auto down feature; power door locks; power front fender antenna	1726	2031
1SA	**Cutlass Ciera SL Sedan Package 1SA**	STD	STD
1SB	**Cutlass Ciera SL Sedan Package 1SB** — includes tilt-away steering wheel; pulse wiper system; front and rear floor mats; door-edge guard moldings; electronic cruise control; body accent stripe; power reclining passenger seat back; dual illuminated visor vanity mirrors, power door locks; power side windows with auto down feature; remote driver and passenger		

Mfgs. Code	Description	Base Cost	Sgstd. List
	exterior mirrors	893	1051
1SC	**Cutlass Ciera SL Sedan Package 1SC** — includes Package 1SB contents plus remote lock control package (AU3 required); 6-way power driver seat adjuster; power front fender antenna	1140	1341
1SA	**Cutlass Cruiser S 2-Seat Wagon Package 1SA**	STD	STD
1SB	**Cutlass Cruiser S 2-Seat Wagon Package 1SA** — includes 4-season air conditioner; tilt-away steering wheel; pulse wiper system; rear window air deflector; front and rear floor mats	663	780
1SC	**Cutlass Cruiser S 2-Seat Wagon Package 1SC** — includes Package 1SB contents plus power reclining driver seat divider bench with storage armrest; power reclining passenger seat back; convenience group; electronic cruise control; rooftop luggage carrier; body accent stripe; door -edge guard moldings; remote driver and passenger exterior mirrors	1262	1485
1SD	**Cutlass Cruiser S 2-Seat Wagon Package 1SD** — includes Package 1SC contents plus power door locks with tailgate lock; power side windows with auto down feature; power front fender antenna; rear-facing third seat	1971	2319
1SA	**Cutlass Cruiser SL 3-Seat Wagon Package 1SA**	STD	STD
1SB	**Cutlass Cruiser SL 3-Seat Wagon Package 1SB** — includes tilt-away steering wheel; pulse wiper system; electronic cruise control; front and rear floor mats; body accent stripe; power side windows with auto down feature; power door locks with tailgate lock; dual illuminated visor vanity mirrors; remote driver and passenger exterior mirrors; power reclining passenger seat back	915	1076
1SC	**Cutlass Cruiser SL 3-Seat Wagon Package 1SC** — includes Package 1SB contents plus remote lock control package (AU3 required); power front fender antenna; 6-way power driver seat adjuster	1161	1366
AC3	**Seat Adjuster** — (6-way power bucket, driver) - J37, J35	246	290
AG1	**Seat Adjuster** — (6-way power bench, driver) - J37, J69, J35	246	290
AM6	**Seat** — (divided bench, driver power reclining, storage armrest) - L69	264	311
AR9	**Seat** — (contour reclining bucket/package) - J37	383	451
AS7	**Seat** — (45/55 divided front/package) - M69	234	275
B34/ B35	**Floor Mats** — (front and rear) - L69	38	45
BF9	**Floor Mats, Delete** — J37, J69, J35	(38)	(45)
BX3	**Paneling, Wood Grain Vinyl** — M35	225	265
C49	**Defogger, Electric Rear Window**	136	160
G66	**Lead-Carrying Package** — L69, J69, M69, J35, M35	90	106
K05	**Heater, Engine Block** — J37, J69, M69, J35, M35	15	18
K34	**Cruise Control, Electric** — L69	179	210
LG7	**Engine** — (3300 V6 MFI) - L69, J37, J69, J35	604	710
MX0	**Transmission** — (automatic w/overdrive) - J37, J69, M69, J35	170	200
N91	**Wheel Discs** — (simulated wire w/locks) - L69, J37, J69, M69	183	215
PH5	**Wheels** — (aluminum 14" w/locks) - J37, J69, M69, J35, M35	234	275
QFE	**Tires** — (P185/75R14 SBR BW) - L69, J37, J69, J35	(41)	(48)
QMW	**Tires** — (P195/75R14 SBR BW)	(15)	(18)
UB3	**Cluster, Instrument Panel Rallye** — J37, J69, M69, J35, M35	88	104
TR9	**Convenience Group** — L69	48	57
UM6	**Radio** — (AM/FM stereo/clock/cassette) - L69, J37, J69, J35	140	165
UX1	**Radio** — (AM stereo/FM stereo/cassette/graphic equalizer/clock/6-speakers) - M69, M35	200	235
UW4	**Audio System** — (6-speaker enhanced) - M69, M35	72	85
V08	**Cooling System** — (high capacity)	34	40
V52	**Luggage Rack, Deck Lid** — J37, J69, M69	98	115
WJ7	**Custom Leather Trim** — M69	417	490
YF5	**California Emission Equipment and Testing**	85	100
YP9	**Sport Appearance Package** — J35	706	831

CUTLASS SUPREME

	CUTLASS SUPREME (4 Cylinder)		
H47	Coupe	12941	14995
H69	Sedan	13027	15095
R47	International Series Coupe	16997	19695
R69	International Series Sedan	17083	19795
	CUTLASS SUPREME (6 Cylinder)		
S47	SL Coupe	14580	16895
S69	SL Sedan	14667	16995
T67	Convertible	18119	20995
	Destination Charge: All models	485	485

STANDARD EQUIPMENT:
CUTLASS SUPREME: Air conditioning (automatic comfort control on International), maintenance-free battery, power 4-wheel disc brakes, front and rear body color bumper facias (except International), black bumper moldings (Base Coupe & Sedan, SL), full-length console with armrest (Convertible), full-length sport console with armrest (International), convenience group (except Base Coupe & Sedan), cruise control (International), side window defoggers, door map-storage pockets (except Base Coupe & Sedan), 2.3 liter DOHC MFI 4 cylinder engine (Base Coupe & Sedan), 3.1 liter V6 MFI engine (Convertible, SL), 3.4 liter DOHC MFI V6 engine (International), front wheel drive, dual engine cooling fans, power door locks (International), driver information system (International), dual exhaust outlets (International), halogen headlamps, headlamp-on reminder, inside hood release, electronic instrument panel cluster including tachometer (International), remote lock control package - includes power door locks and power trunk lid lock release (International), black outside mirrors with driver side remote (Base Coupe & Sedan, SL), black remote control outside mirrors (Convertible, International), driver and passenger side visor vanity mirrors (Convertible, SL, International), wheel opening moldings, body side molding (SL, International), automatic front seat belts, pulse wiper system (International), tinted glass, power rack and pinion steering (special ratio on International), 14" x 5.5" deluxe wheel discs (Base Coupe & Sedan), 15" x 6" cast aluminum wheels with locks (Convertible, SL), 16" aluminum-styled wheels with locks (International), deluxe steering wheel (leather-wrapped with tilt-away feature on International), turn-signal-on reminder chime, power trunk-lid lock release (Convertible, SL), P195/75R14 steel-belted radial ply BW all-season tires (Base Coupe & Sedan), P205/70R15 steel-belted radial ply BW touring tires (Convertible, SL), P225/60R16 steel-belted radial ply BW performance tires (International), 4-wheel independent suspension (touring car ride suspension on Convertible and International), automatic transmission (5-speed manual overdrive transmission on International Coupe), power side windows (Convertible), lower body accent stripe (Convertible, International Coupe), front bucket seats with reclining seat backs, contour front bucket seats with lumbar thigh bolster and headrest power articulation (International), 55/45 divided front bench seat with armrest (SL), individual rear bucket seats (International Coupe), split folding rear seat (SL), radio - Delco ETR AM/FM stereo with seek-scan and digital clock, dual rear speakers (Base Coupe & Sedan), radio - Delco ETR AM/FM stereo with seek-scan, digital clock, auto-reverse cassette and 6-speaker enhanced audio system (Convertible), radio -Delco ETR AM/FM stereo with seek-scan, auto-reverse cassette, digital clock, dual rear speakers with extended range (SL), radio -Delco ETR AM/FM stereo with seek-scan, auto-reverse cassette with music search, digital clock, dual rear speakers with extended range (International), front and rear floor mats (International).

ACCESSORIES

1SA	**Cutlass Supreme Coupe Package 1SA**	STD	STD
1SB	**Cutlass Supreme Coupe Package 1SB** — includes tilt-away steering wheel; pulse wiper system; electronic cruise control; electric driver and		

Mfgs. Code	Description	Base Cost	Sgstd. List
	passenger exterior mirrors; front and rear floor mats; convenience group	291	342
1SC	**Cutlass Supreme Coupe Package 1SC** — includes Package 1SB contents plus appearance and molding package; remote lock control package; power side windows with auto down feature	626	737
1SD	**Cutlass Supreme Coupe Package 1SD** — includes Package 1SC contents plus power rear quarter antenna; 6-way power driver seat adjuster	852	1002
1SA	**Cutlass Supreme Sedan Package 1SA**	STD	STD
1SB	**Cutlass Supreme Sedan Package 1SB** — includes tilt-away steering wheel; pulse wiper system; electronic cruise control; electric driver and passenger exterior mirrors; front and rear floor mats; convenience group	291	342
1SC	**Cutlass Supreme Sedan Package 1SC** — includes Package 1SB contents plus appearance and molding package; remote lock control package; power side windows with auto down feature	724	852
1SD	**Cutlass Supreme Sedan Package 1SD** — includes Package 1SC contents plus power rear quarter antenna; 6-way power driver seat adjuster	864	1017
1SA	**Cutlass Supreme SL Coupe Package 1SA**	STD	STD
1SB	**Cutlass Supreme SL Coupe Package 1SB** — includes electronic cruise control; tilt-away steering wheel; pulse wiper system; front and rear floor mats; appearance and molding package; power driver and passenger exterior mirrors	507	597
1SC	**Cutlass Supreme SL Coupe Package 1SC** — includes Package 1SB contents plus power rear quarter antenna; remote lock control package; power side windows with auto down feature; 6-way power driver seat adjuster	877	1032
1SD	**Cutlass Supreme SL Coupe Package 1SD** — includes Package 1SC contents plus auto electric comfort control air conditioner; steering wheel touch controls	1128	1327
1SA	**Cutlass Supreme SL Sedan Package 1SA**	STD	STD
1SB	**Cutlass Supreme SL Sedan Package 1SB** — includes electronic cruise control; tilt-away steering wheel; pulse wiper system; front and rear floor mats; appearance and molding package; power driver and passenger exterior mirrors	516	607
1SC	**Cutlass Supreme SL Sedan Package 1SC** — includes Package 1SB contents plus power rear quarter antenna; remote lock control package; power side windows with auto down feature; 6-way power driver seat adjuster	975	1147
1SD	**Cutlass Supreme SL Sedan Package 1SD** — includes Package 1SC contents plus auto electric comfort control air conditioner; steering wheel touch controls	1141	1342
1SA	**Cutlass Supreme International Series Coupe Package 1SA**	STD	STD
1SB	**Cutlass Supreme International Series Coupe Package 1SB** — includes power side windows with auto down feature; appearance and molding package	281	330
1SC	**Cutlass Supreme International Series Coupe Package 1SC** — includes Package 1SB contents plus 6-way power driver seat adjuster; power rear quarter antenna	561	660
1SA	**Cutlass Supreme International Series Sedan Package 1SA**	STD	STD
1SB	**Cutlass Supreme International Series Sedan Package 1SB** — includes power side windows with auto down feature; appearance and molding package	344	405
1SC	**Cutlass Supreme International Series Sedan Package 1SC** — includes Package 1SB contents plus 6-way power driver seat adjuster; power rear quarter antenna	625	735
1SA	**Cutlass Supreme Convertible Package 1SA**	STD	STD
1SB	**Cutlass Supreme Convertible Package 1SB** — includes electronic cruise		

Mfgs. Code	Description	Base Cost	Sgstd. List
	control; tilt-away steering wheel; pulse wiper system; power driver and passenger exterior mirrors; appearance and molding package; front and rear floor mats	482	567
1SC	**Cutlass Supreme Convertible Package 1SC** — includes Package 1SB contents plus power rear quarter antenna; remote lock control package; 6-way power driver seat adjuster	1060	1247
1SD	**Cutlass Supreme Convertible Package 1SD** — includes Package 1SC contents plus auto electric comfort control air conditioner; steering wheel touch controls	1396	1642
AN3	**Seat** — (front reclining bucket/package) - S47, S69	288	339
AM6	**Seat** — (55/45 divided bench w/dual reclining seat backs) - H47, H69	NC	NC
AU3	**Door Locks, Power** — H47	162	190
	- H69	196	230
BF9	**Floor Mats, Delete** — T67	(38)	(45)
BYP	**Sport Appearance Package** — H47	362	426
	- H69	119	140
	- T67	1275	1500
CF5	**Astroroof** — (electric sliding glass) - S47, S69, R47, R69	553	650
C49	**Defogger, Electric Rear Window**	136	160
C68	**Air Conditioner** — (auto electric comfort control) - H47, H69	128	150
D84	**Paint Scheme, Two-Tone** — S69	86	101
FE3	**Touring Car Ride and Handling Package** — H47, H69	467	549
	- S47	184	216
JL9	**Braking System, Anti-Lock**	786	925
K05	**Heater, Engine Block** — H47, H69, S47, S69, R47, R69	15	18
LH0	**Engine** — (3.1 liter V6 w/MX0 4-speed automatic transmission) - H47, H69	149	175
PH3	**Wheels** — (cast aluminum 15" w/locks) - H47, H69	292	343
QMX	**Tires** — (P195/75R14 SBR WW) - H47, H69	61	72
UB3	**Cluster, Instrument Panel Rallye/Package** — H47, H69, S47, S69, T67	302	355
UK3	**Steering Wheel Touch Controls** — H47, H69	349	410
UM6	**Radio** — (AM/FM stereo/cassette/clock) - H47, H69	140	165
UT6	**Radio** — (AM/FM stereo/cassette/clock/8 speakers) - H47, H69	357	420
	- S47, S69	217	255
	- T67	111	130
	- R47, R69	191	225
UV6	**Head-Up Instrument Display** — R47, R69	251	295
U1C	**Radio** — (AM/FM stereo/CD/clock/8 speakers) - H47, H69	464	546
	- S47, S69	339	399
	- T67	233	274
	- R47, R69	314	369
V08	**Cooling System, High Capacity** — H47, H69, S47, S69	106	125
V56	**Luggage Carrier, Deck Lid** — H47, H69, S47, S69, R47, R69	98	115
WJ7	**Custom Leather Trim** — S47, S69, T67	417	490
	- R47, R69	340	400
NN5/ YF5	**California Emission Equipment and Testing**	85	100

EIGHTY-EIGHT ROYALE

	EIGHTY-EIGHT ROYALE (6 Cylinder		
N37	Coupe	14753	17095
N69	Sedan	14839	17195
Y37	Brougham Coupe	16134	18695

Mfgs. Code	Description	OLDSMOBILE	Base Cost	Sgstd. List
Y69	Brougham Sedan		16220	18795

Destination Charge: All models 535 535

STANDARD EQUIPMENT:

EIGHTY-EIGHT ROYALE: Air conditioning, maintenance-free battery, power front disc and rear drum brakes, front and rear bumper impact strips, cigar lighter, side window defoggers, front and rear door-pull handles, V6 SFI engine, front wheel drive, halogen headlamps, headlamp-on reminder, inside hood release, remote control driver side and manual passenger side mirrors, rocker panel and wheel opening moldings, body side moldings, radio (Delco ETR AM/FM stereo with seek-scan, digital display clock, dual rear speakers with extended range, fixed mast rear quarter antenna), custom front bench seat, power rack-and-pinion steering, deluxe steering wheel with tilt-away features, 4-wheel fully independent suspension, P205/75R14 steel-belted radial-ply BW all-season tires, automatic overdrive transmission, trip odometer, turn-signal-on reminder chime, 14" x 6" wheels, deluxe wheel discs, tinted glass, pulse wiper system. **Eighty-Eight Royale Brougham also has in addition to above standard equipment:** Convenience group (includes underhood and trunk lamps, visor vanity mirror and chime tones), color-coordinated remote control outside mirrors, 55/45 divided front bench seat with reclining seat backs, power trunk-lid lock release, deluxe wheel discs.

ACCESSORIES

Code	Description	Base Cost	Sgstd. List
1SA	**Eighty-Eight Royale Coupe Package 1SA**	STD	STD
1SB	**Eighty-Eight Royale Coupe Package 1SB** — includes divider seat bench with dual recliners with storage armrest; electronic cruise control; convenience group front and rear floor mats	467	549
1SC	**Eighty-Eight Royale Coupe Package 1SC** — includes 1SB contents plus power door locks; power side windows with auto down feature; door-edge guard moldings; power rear quarter antenna; 6-way power driver seat adjuster	1168	1374
1SD	**Eighty-Eight Royale Coupe Package 1SD** — includes Package 1SC contents plus remote control lock package; reminder package	1377	1620
1SA	**Eighty-Eight Royale Sedan Package 1SA**	STD	STD
1SB	**Eighty-Eight Royale Sedan Package 1SB** — includes divider seat bench with dual recliner and storage armrest; electronic cruise control; convenience group; front and rear floor mats	467	549
1SC	**Eighty-Eight Royale Sedan Package 1SC** — includes Package 1SB contents plus power door locks; power side window auto down feature; door-edge guard moldings; power rear quarter antenna; 6 way power driver seat adjuster	1266	1489
1SD	**Eighty-Eight Royale Sedan Package 1SD** — includes Package 1SC contents plus remote control lock package; reminder package	1475	1735
1SA	**Eighty-Eight Royale Brougham Coupe Package 1SA**	STD	STD
1SB	**Eighty-Eight Royale Brougham Coupe Package 1SB** — includes electronic cruise control; power door locks; front and rear floor mats; door-edge guard moldings; power side windows with auto down feature; 6-way power driver seat adjuster	854	1005
1SC	**Eighty-Eight Royale Brougham Coupe Package 1SC** — includes Package 1SB contents plus power rear quarter antenna; reminder package	978	1151
1SD	**Eighty-Eight Royale Brougham Coupe Package 1SD** — includes Package 1SC contents plus auto electric comfort control air conditioner; driver information system; remote control lock package	1365	1606
1SA	**Eighty-Eight Royale Brougham Sedan Package 1SA**	STD	STD
1SB	**Eighty-Eight Royale Brougham Sedan Package 1SAB** — includes electronic cruise control; power door locks; front and rear floor mats, door-		

Mfgs. Code	Description	Base Cost	Sgstd. List
	edge guard moldings; power side windows with auto down feature; 6-way power driver seat adjuster	952	1120
1SC	**Eighty-Eight Royale Brougham Sedan Package 1SC** — includes Package 1SB contents plus power rear quarter antenna; reminder package	1076	1266
1SD	**Eighty-Eight Royale Brougham Sedan Package 1SD** — includes Package 1SC contents plus auto electric comfort control air conditioner; driver information system; remote control lock package	1463	1721
AJ3	**Restraint System, Inflatable** — (driver) - N69, Y69	723	850
AU3	**Door Locks, Power** — N37	162	190
	- N69	196	230
A31	**Windows, Power Side** — N37	217	255
	- N69	272	320
AG2	**Seat Adjuster** — (6-way power, passenger) - Y37, Y69	247	290
BF9	**Floor Mats, Delete** — N37, N69	(38)	(45)
C09	**Rooftop Covering** — (full vinyl) - Y69	170	200
C49	**Defogger, Electric Rear Window**	136	160
D90	**Accent Stripe, Body**	38	45
FE3	**Touring Car Ride and Handling Package** — N37, N69	662	779
	- Y37, Y69	606	713
JM4	**Braking System, Anti-Lock**	786	925
K05	**Heater, Engine Block**	15	18
N91	**Wheel Discs** — (simulated wire w/locks, WW tires) - N37, N69	247	291
N91	**Wheel Discs** — (simulated wire w/locks) - Y37, Y69	183	215
PA3	**Wheels** — (aluminum 15" w/locks) - N37, N69	313	368
	- Y37, Y69	272	320
QJR	**Tires** — (P205/75R14 SBR WW) - N37, N69	65	76
R6T	**Antenna, Delete** — N37, N69	(64)	(75)
R8A	**Convenience Value Group** — N37, N69	269	317
	- Y37, Y69	244	287
UM6	**Radio** — (AM/FM stereo/cassette/clock) - N37, N69	119	140
UX1	**Radio** — (AM stereo/FM stereo/cassette/graphic equalizer/clock) - Y37, Y69	200	235
U1C	**Radio** — (AM/FM stereo/CD/clock/6 speakers) - Y37, Y69	305	359
U39	**Cluster, Instrument Panel**	56	66
U51	**Information, System Driver** — Y37, Y69	128	150
U52	**Cluster, Instrument Panel** — (electronic) - Y37, Y69	254	299
V08	**Cooling System, High Capacity**	56	66
V58	**Luggage Carrier, Deck Lid**	98	115
V81	**Towing Package**	230	271
WJ7	**Custom Leather Trim** — Y37, Y69	417	490
YF5	**California Emission Equipment and Testing**	85	100

NINETY-EIGHT REGENCY

NINETY-EIGHT REGENCY (6 Cylinder)

		Base Cost	Sgstd. List
W69	Regency Elite Sedan	20449	23695
Destination Charge:		580	580

STANDARD EQUIPMENT:

NINETY-EIGHT REGENCY ELITE: Automatic electronic comfort control air conditioning with rear seat ducts, rear seat center armrest, maintenance-free battery, anti-lock power front disc and rear drum brakes, cigar lighters, convenience group, cruise control, side window and electric rear window defoggers, power door locks, front and rear door-pull handles, V6 tuned port fuel injection, front wheel drive, front and rear floor mats, headlamp-on reminder, halogen headlamps, inside hood release, trip odometer, front and rear reading lamps, electric driver and passenger outside mirrors,

release, trip odometer, front and rear reading lamps, electric driver and passenger outside mirrors, color-coordinated body side moldings, radio (Delco ETR AM/FM stereo with seek-scan music search, cassette, digital display clock and 6 speakers), power antenna, power remote fuel filler door,driver side inflatable restraint system, 55/45 divided front bench seat with dual controls (driver side - 6-way power, passenger side - manual), power rack-and-pinion steering, deluxe steering wheel with tilt-away feature, four-wheel fully independent suspension plus automatic load leveling, P205/70R15 steel-belted radial-ply white-stripe all-season tires, electronic shift automatic overdrive transmission with column shift, power trunk-lid lock release, turn-signal-on reminder chime, 15" simulated wire wheels with locks, power side windows, tinted glass, pulse wiper system.

ACCESSORIES

Code	Description	Base Cost	Sgstd. List
1SA	**Ninety-Eight Regency Elite Sedan Package 1SA**	STD	STD
1SB	**Ninety-Eight Regency Elite Sedan Package 1SB** — includes reminder package; rearview automatic day/night mirror; dual illuminated visor vanity mirrors; 6-way power driver seat adjuster; steering wheel touch controls; aluminum 15" wheels w/locks; front fender cornering lamps	726	854
1SC	**Ninety-Eight Regency Elite Sedan Package 1SC** — includes Package 1SB contents plus power pull-down trunk; remote accessory control package; twilight sentinel; cargo net	1040	1224
CF5	**Astroroof, Electric Sliding Glass**	1046	1230
C50	**Heated Windshield, Self-Defrosting**	213	250
D90	**Accent Stripe, Body**	38	45
FE3	**Touring Car Ride and Handling Package**	200	235
FW1	**Computer Command Ride System**	368	434
K05	**Heater, Engine Block**	15	18
N91	**Wheel Discs — Simulated Wire** — w/Package 1SB, 1SC	(103)	(121)
PH6	**Wheels** — (aluminum 15" w/locks - w/Package 1SA	103	121
QGY	**Tires** — (P205/70R15 SBR BW touring	NC	NC
UX1	**Radio** — (AM stereo/FM stereo/cassette/graphic equalizer/clock)	102	120
U1H	**Radio** — (AM/FM stereo/CD/graphic equalizer/clock)	439	516
U1J	**Radio** — (AM/FM stereo/CD/clock)	337	396
U2A	**Instrument Cluster, Electronic w/Driver Information Center**	382	449
V1F	**Paint, Glamour Metallic**	179	210
V92	**Towing Package**	128	150
WJ7	**Custom Leather Trim** — (Package 1SB or 1SC required)	417	490
YF5	**California Emission Equipment and Testing**	85	100

NINETY-EIGHT TOURING SEDAN

NINETY-EIGHT TOURING SEDAN (6 Cylinder)

Code	Description	Base Cost	Sgstd. List
V69	Touring Sedan	24677	28595
	Destination Charge:	580	580

STANDARD EQUIPMENT:

NINETY-EIGHT TOURING SEDAN: Automatic electronic comfort control air conditioning, rear seat center armrest, maintenance-free battery, anti-lock power front disc and rear drum brakes, luggage compartment cargo net, cigar lighters, convenience group, full console with floor shifter, cruise control, side window defoggers, electric rear window defoggers, V6 TPI engine, front wheel drive, front and rear floor mats, foglamps, halogen headlamps, tachometer, driver information center, front-fender cornering lamps, courtesy lamps, front and rear reading lamps, inside day-night automatic electrochromic mirror, driver and passenger side illuminated visor vanity mirror, electrically operated driver and passenger outside mirrors (driver side has electric defog feature), color-coordinated body side moldings, bright belt reveal moldings, radio (Delco ETR AM/FM stereo with seek-scan, auto-reverse cassette, graphic equalizer and digital display clock, power antenna, dimensional sound six-speaker system), remote accessory control package (includes illuminated package, retained accessory power, remote lock control for doors and trunk plus two key-chain transmitters), power remote fuel filler door, driver side inflatable restraint system, front bucket seats with 6-way power adjuster and articulated headrests, rear fixed seat headrests, power rack-and-pinion steering, leather-wrapped sport steering wheel with tilt-away feature, 4-wheel independent suspension with automatic electronic load leveling and special touring car ride and handling system, P215/60R16 steel-belted radial-ply touring BW tires, automatic overdrive transmission, turn-signal-on reminder chime, automatic headlight control twilight sentinel, "pass-key" vehicle anti-theft system, cast aluminum 16-inch wheels with locks, power side windows, tinted glass with EZ KOOL solar control, pulse wiper system.

ACCESSORIES

Code	Description	Base Cost	Sgstd. List
CF5	**Astroroof, Electric Sliding Glass**	1046	1230
C50	**Heated Windshield, Self-Defrosting**	213	250
D90	**Accent Stripe, Body**	38	45
KA1	**Heated Bucket Seats**	200	235
K05	**Heater, Engine Block**	15	18
U1H	**Radio** — (AM/FM stereo/CD/graphic equalizer/clock	337	396
V92	**Towing Package**	128	150
YF5	**California Emission Equipment and Testing**	85	100

SILHOUETTE

SILHOUETTE (6 Cylinder)

Code	Description	Base Cost	Sgstd. List
M06	Silhouette	16248	18195
	Destination Charge:	510	510

STANDARD EQUIPMENT:

SILHOUETTE: Air conditioning, Freedom battery, power front disc and rear drum brakes, body color front and rear bumper fascias, cigar lighter, overhead console, front and rear side window defoggers, 3.1 liter V6 TBI engine, front wheel drive, carpeting, front and rear floor mats, halogen headlamps, headlamp-on reminder, inside hood release, rallye cluster instrument panel includes speedometer, tachometer, trip and total odometer, voltmeter, temperature and oil pressure gauges; electrically operated driver and passenger mirrors, body color body side moldings, concealed auxiliary power outlet, radio (Delco ETR AM/FM stereo with seek-scan, digital display clock, dual front and rear speakers, fixed mast antenna), front bucket seats with folding armrests, 3 center and 2 rear modular seats, power rack-and-pinion steering, deluxe steering wheel with tilt-away feature, P205/70R14 steel-belted radial ply BW all-season tires, automatic transmission, 14" x 6" aluminum styled wheels with locks, deep tint windows, solar treated windshield, pulse wiper system, rear window wiper.

ACCESSORIES

Code	Description	Base Cost	Sgstd. List
1SA	**Silhouette Package 1SA**	STD	STD
1SB	**Silhouette Package 1SB** — includes power door locks; electronic cruise control; power side windows with auto down feature	625	735
1SC	**Silhouette Package 1SC** — includes Package 1SB contents plus 6-way power driver seat adjuster	616	725
AB3	**6-Passenger Modular Seating**	(94)	(110)

Mfgs. Code	Description	Base Cost	Sgstd. List

OLDSMOBILE

B4A	**Black Roof Delete**	NC	NC
C49	**Defogger, Electric Rear Window**	136	160
FE3	**Touring Car Ride and Handling Package**	207	243
K05	**Heater, Engine Block**	15	18
UM6	**Radio** — (AM/FM stereo/cassette/clock)	119	140
U1C	**Radio** — (AM/FM stereo/CD/clock)	337	396
V54	**Luggage Carrier, Rooftop**	123	145
WJ7	**Custom Leather Trim w/6-Passenger Seating**	553	650
WJ7	**Custom Leather Trim w/7-Passenger Seating**	740	870
YF5	**California Emission Equipment and Testing**	85	100

TORONADO

TORONADO (6 Cylinder)

Z57	Coupe	20535	23795

Destination Charge: 580 580

STANDARD EQUIPMENT:

TORONADO: Electronic automatic air conditioning with manual override, front and rear center armrests, passenger side assist handle, maintenance-free battery, anti-lock power 4-wheel disc brakes, console with rear courtesy lamps, convenience group (includes under-hood and trunk lamps, visor vanity mirror and chime tones), cruise control, side window defoggers, electric rear window defogger, power door locks with central (trunk) unlocking feature, V6 TPI engine, front wheel drive, front and rear floor mats, fuel filler door with remote lock release, power retractable halogen headlamps, headlamp-on reminder, instrument panel analog gauge cluster with tachometer and electronic reminder package, front-fender cornering lamps, courtesy lamps, inside day-night rearview mirror, black remote control driver and passenger outside mirrors (driver side has defog feature), color-coordinated body side moldings, belt reveal wheel opening moldings, oil change and level reminder, radio (Delco ETR AM/FM stereo with seek-scan, auto-reverse cassette with music search, digital display clock, dimensional 6-speaker system, power antenna), driver side inflatable restraint system, contour reclining bucket seats with console and floor shifter, 6-way power driver side seat adjuster, driver and passenger seat back recliners, power rack-and-pinion steering, leather-wrapped steering wheel with tilt-away feature MacPherson front strut suspension with independent rear suspension plus automatic leveling system, P215/65R15 steel-belted radial-ply blackwall touring tires, automatic overdrive transmission, trunk cargo net, power trunk-lid lock release, turn-signal-on reminder chime, twilight sentinel automatic headlight control, "pass key" vehicle anti-theft security system, 15" x 6" aluminum styled wheels with locks, power side windows, tinted glass, pulse wiper system.

ACCESSORIES

1SA	**Toronado Coupe Package 1SA**	STD	STD
1SB	**Toronado Coupe Package 1SB** — includes 6-way power passenger seat adjuster; illumination package; dual illuminated visor vanity mirrors; rearview, automatic day/night rearview mirror; remote lock control package; steering wheel touch controls	683	804
AM6	**Seat, Divider Bench w/Electronic Instrument Cluster**	NC	NC
CF5	**Astroroof, Electric Sliding Glass**	1046	1230
C50	**Heated Windshield, Self-Defrosting**	213	250
D84	**Paint Scheme, Two-Tone**	86	101
FE3	**Touring Car Ride and Handling Package**	51	60
K05	**Heater, Engine Block**	15	18

QPJ	**Tires** — (P215/65R15 SBR WW touring)	68	80
UX1	**Radio** — (AM stereo/FM stereo/cassette/graphic equalizer/clock)	102	120
UZ3	**Telephone** — (mobile keypad control)	846	995
U1A	**Radio** — (AM stereo/FM stereo/CD/graphic equalizer/clock)	335	394
U1H	**Radio** — (AM stereo/FM stereo/cassette/CD/graphic equalizer/clock)	439	516
U68	**Visual Information Center** — (UX1 or U1A required)	1101	1295
V1F	**Paint, Glamour Metallic**	179	210
WJ7	**Custom Leather Trim**	340	400
YF5	**California Emission Equipment and Testing**	85	100

TORONADO TROFEO

TORONADO TROFEO (6 Cylinder)

V57	Trofeo Coupe	22865	26495
	Destination Charge:	580	580

STANDARD EQUIPMENT:

TORONADO TROFEO: Electronic comfort control air conditioning with manual override, front and rear center armrests, passenger assist handle, maintenance-free battery, anti-lock power 4-wheel disc brakes, electronic digital compass, convenience group, cruise control, side window defoggers, electric rear window defogger, V6 TPI engine, front-wheel drive, front and rear floor mats, body color grille with headlamp covers, halogen power retractable headlamps, headlamp-on reminder, illumination package (front door locks and interior), instrument panel gage cluster with tachometer and electronic reminder package, front fender cornering lamps, remote lock control package, remote control fuel filler door lock, electrochromic automatic inside day-night rearview mirror, black electric remote control driver and passenger side outside mirrors (driver side has defog feature), driver and passenger side illuminated visor vanity mirrors, black moldings (wheel-opening, beltline and quarter windows), color-coordinated body side moldings, radio (Delco ETR AM/FM stereo with seek-scan auto-reverse cassette with music search, digital display clock, dimensional sound 6-speaker system, power antenna), driver side inflatable restraint system, front bucket seats with 6-way power adjusters, rear seat headrests, power rack-and-pinion steering, leather-wrapped steering wheel with tilt-away feature, touring car ride and handling suspension plus automatic leveling system, P215/60R16 performance steel-belted radial-ply BW all-season tires, automatic overdrive transmission, trunk cargo net, power trunk-lid lock release, turn-signal-on reminder chime, twilight sentinel automatic headlight control, "pass key" vehicle anti-theft security system, 16" x 7" aluminum styled wheels with locks, power side windows, tinted glass, pulse wiper system.

ACCESSORIES

1SA	**Toronado Trofeo Coupe Package 1SA**	STD	STD
CF5	**Astroroof, Electric Sliding Glass**	1045	1230
C50	**Heated Windshield, Self-Defrosting**	213	250
K05	**Heater, Engine Block**	15	18
UX1	**Radio** — (AM stereo/FM stereo/cassette/graphic equalizer/clock)	102	120
UZ3	**Telephone** — mobile keypad control	846	995
U1A	**Radio** — (AM stereo/FM stereo/CD/graphic equalizer/clock)	335	394
U1H	**Radio** — (Am stereo/FM stereo cassette/CD/graphic equalizer/clock)	439	516
U68	**Visual Information Center** — (UX1 or U1A required)	1101	1295
V1F	**Special Paint**	179	210
YF5	**California Emission Equipment and Testing**	85	100

1991 plymouth

ACCLAIM

ACCLAIM (4 Cylinder)

		Base Cost	Sgstd. List
PH41	4 Dr Base Sedan	9696	10825
PH41	4 Dr LE Sedan	11504	12880

ACCLAIM (6 Cylinder)

		Base Cost	Sgstd. List
PX41	4 Dr LX Sedan	12824	14380

	Base Cost	Sgstd. List
Destination Charge:	465	465

STANDARD EQUIPMENT:

ACCLAIM: Maintenance-free battery, power disc front drum rear brakes, soft fascia with integral nerf and 5 mph protection bumpers, full passenger compartment carpeting (Base Acclaim), warning chime for headlights on, seatbelt and key in ignition, lower body protective urethane coating, electric rear window defroster (LE, LX), side window demisters, 2.5 liter 4 cylinder electronic fuel injection engine (Base Acclaim, LE), 3.0 liter V6 multi-port injection engine including front air dam (LX), fascia integral fog lamps (LX), tinted glass rear window (Base Acclaim), all tinted glass windows (LE, LX), locking glove box, single halogen aerostyle headlights, cloth covered headliner, inside hood release, dual electric horn, instrument panel (mechanical cluster includes 120 mph speedometer, odometer, trip odometer, gauges for fuel, temperature, voltmeter, warning light for high beam, seatbelt, brakes, check engine, low fuel, oil pressure, turn signal, air bag), tachometer, oil pressure gauge, check gauges warning light (LE, LX), standard sound insulation (Base Acclaim), premium sound insulation (LE, LX), deck lid mounted luggage rack (LE, LX), message center (LE, LX), mirrors (outside dual remote control black - vanity visor left), bright wheel lip moldings (LE, LX), wide bodyside moldings (Base Acclaim), narrow bodyside moldings (LE, LX), AM mono/FM stereo radio with digital clock and two speakers (Base Acclaim), AM mono/FM stereo ETR with digital clock and four speakers (LE), AM mono/FM stereo ETR cassette radio (non seek and scan), with digital clock and four speakers (LX), electronic speed control (LE, LX), tilt steering column (LE, LX), power rack and pinion type steering, luxury steering wheel (Base Acclaim, LE), luxury leather-wrapped steering wheel (LX), bodyside stripe (Base Acclaim), bodyside and deck stripe (LE, LX), P185/70R14 SBR BSW all-season touring tires (Base Acclaim), P195/70R14 SBR BSW all-season touring tires (LE), P205/60R15 SBR BSW all-season touring tires (LX), compact T125/70D14 spare tire, 5 speed manual transmission with center console (N/A with bench seat) (Base Acclaim), automatic 3 speed transmission (LE), automatic 4 speed transmission (LX), trip computer (LX), dress up trunk, remote release trunk, Delta 14" wheel cover (Base Acclaim), Impeller 14" wheel cover (LE), cast aluminum 15" wheel cover (LX), deluxe windshield wiper/washer with intermittent wipe.

ACCESSORIES

		Base Cost	Sgstd. List
AWN	**Super Discount Package A** — (includes Popular Equipment - AAM, and Deluxe Convenience - AJK; N/A with Super Discount package B - AWP); includes: manual air conditioning, electric rear window defroster, front and rear floor mats, tinted glass, 4 speakers, electronic speed control and tilt steering column - Base, total retail price - 1565, discount - 650, net price	778	915
AWP	**Super Discount Package B** — includes all equipment in Super Discount Package A plus dual power remote heated black mirrors, power windows, power door locks - Base, total retail price - 2241, discount - 750, net price	1267	1492
AWR	**Super Discount Package C** — includes manual air conditioning, dual		

	power remote heated black mirrors, power windows, power door locks - LE, LX, total retail price - 1497, discount - 525, net price	826	972
AAC	**Premium Equipment Discount Package** — includes split folding 55/45 rear seat, premium body sound insulation, lights (map, underhood, cigarette lighter), message center - Base, total retail price - 319, discount - 78, net price	204	241
AJK	**Deluxe Convenience Discount** — (included in Super Discount Package A - AWN and Super Discount Package B - AWP); includes front and rear floor mats, electronic speed control, tilt steering column - Base, total retail price - 409, discount - 50, net price	305	359
AFH	**Overhead Convenience Discount** — includes console which includes reading lamps, compass and outside temp readouts, sunglass and storage - LE, LX, total retail price - 383, discount - 50, net price	283	333
EDM	**Engine** — 2.5 liter electronic fuel injection - Base, LE	STD	STD
EFA	**Engine** — 3.0 liter multi-point fuel injection V6 - Base, LE	590	694
DDM	**Transmission** — 5 speed manual - Base	STD	STD
DGA	**Transmission** — 3 speed automatic - Base	465	547
DGB	**Transmission** — 4 speed electronic automatic - Base	544	640
DGB	**Transmission** — 4 speed electronic automatic - LE	79	93
HAA	**Air Conditioning** — (only available in AEN or AWP on LE)	698	821
MDA	**Bracket** — front license plate	NC	NC
BRF	**Brakes** — four wheel disc with anti-lock	776	899
CUF	**Console/Armrest** — center mounted required for floor shift auto trans - Base	132	155
GFA	**Defroster** — electric rear window (in AWN, AWP); required in New York State - Base	139	163
JPB	**Door Locks** — power (in AWP, AWR, AJP)	208	245
NAE	**Emissions** — California control and testing	87	102
P	**Paint** — extra cost	65	77
RAS	**Radio** — AM mono/FM stereo w/cassette, digital clock, 4 speakers - Base	174	205
	- (w/package AWN or AWP on Base) - Base, LE	132	155
RAN	**Radio** — AM stereo/FM stereo w/cassette, digital clock, seek/scan, 4 infinity speakers (requires Package AWN or AWP on Base) - Base, LE	366	430
RAY	**Radio** — AM stereo/FM stereo w/cassette, digital clock, seek scan, 4 infinity speakers, graphic equalizer - LE	548	645
	- LX	417	490
JPS	**Seat** — power drive side (requires AWN or AWP on Base)	252	296
BF	**Seat** — front bench, rear full fixed bench; N/A w/floor shift trans - Base	87	102
N7	**Seat** — front buckets, rear 55/45 split fold cown; requires AAC - Base		
NF	**Seat** — front bench, rear 55/45 split fold down; requires AAC; N/A w/floor shift trans - Base	52	61
VF	**Seat** — premium front bench, 55/45 split fold down; N/A w/floor shift trans		
GWB	**Sunroof** — glass, pop-up; includes deflector, removable shade, stowage bag, tie down straps - LE, LX	344	405
JFH	**Tachometer** — Base	91	107
TKS	**Tires** — P195/70R14 SBR BSW all season touring (requires WHH on Base) - Base	26	31
TKT	**Tires** — P195/70R14 SBR WSW all season touring (N/A w/WHH) - Base	88	104
TBB	**Tires** — conventional spare 14" (available w/14" tires only) - Base	72	85
	- w/TKS or TKT tires on Base, LE	81	95
WHH	**Wheels** — cast aluminum 14" (requires TKS tires) - Base, LE	279	328
—	**Windows** — power (only available in package AWP, AWR or AJP)		

LASER

LASER (4 Cylinder)

Code	Description	Base Cost	Sgstd. List
PM24	2 Dr Laser	10012	10864
PH24	2 Dr RS Laser	11673	12770
PH24	2 Dr RS Turbo Laser	12739	13954
	Destination Charge: All models	328	328

STANDARD EQUIPMENT:

LASER: Power front and rear disc brakes, floor console, lower body protective coating, electric rear window defroster (RS, RS Turbo), 1.8 liter multi-point fuel injection engine (Base Laser), 2.0 liter DOHC turbo-charged MP engine with intercooler (RS Turbo), gauges (fuel, odometer, oil pressure, speedometer, temperature, tachometer, trip odometer, turbo boost (with turbo engine only), tinted glass with windshield sun shade, remote release fuel filler door, automatic extinguish retractable headlights, single note horn (Base Laser), dual note horn (RS, RS Turbo), remote liftgate release, interior day/night mirror, outside dual remote control mirror (Base Laser), power outside dual remote control mirror (RS, RS Turbo), non-illuminating right and left side vanity mirrors, AM/FM stereo ETR radio with digital clock and four speakers (Base Laser), AM/FM stereo ETR radio cassette with digital clock and four speakers (RS, RS Turbo), black roof with body color target band (RS, RS Turbo), highback bucket seats with folding rear seat - cloth and vinyl (Base Laser), highback with driver's adjustable lumbar with folding rear seat - cloth (RS, RS Turbo), tilt steering column, power assisted rack and pinion type steering (RS, RS Turbo), MacPherson type struts, front/rear suspension, sport suspension (Base Laser, RS), performance suspension (RS Turbo), P185/70R14 all-season radial tires with compact spare (Base Laser, RS), P205/55VR16 all-season performance radial tires with compact spare (RS Turbo), rear tonneau cover (RS, RS Turbo), 5 speed manual transmission, 14" styled steel wheels with center cap and exposed lugs (Base Laser), 14" full wheel cover (RS), 16" steel wheel with full turbine wheel cover (RS Turbo), variable intermittent windshield wipers.

ACCESSORIES

Code	Description	Base Cost	Sgstd. List
—	**Customer Preferred Equipment Packages**		
A	**Laser A Package** — (includes models and specific equipment mentioned) - 2 Dr with 5 speed manual transmission	10012	10864
B	**Laser B Package** — (includes power steering, rear defroster, wheel covers, tonneau cover, floor mats, console cupholder) - 2 Dr with 5 speed manual transmission	10501	11439
	- 2 Dr with automatic transmission	10085	12127
C	**Laser C Package** — (includes Laser B Pkg plus air conditioning) - 2 Dr with 5 speed manual transmission	11190	12250
	- 2 Dr with automatic transmission	11775	12930
D	**Laser D Package** — (includes Laser C Pkg plus AM/FM cassette and speed control) - 2 Dr with 5 speed manual transmission	11513	12630
E	**Laser RS E Package** — (includes specific equipment mentioned) - 2 Dr with 5 speed manual transmission	11673	12770
F	**Laser RS F Package** — (includes air conditioning) - 2 Dr with 5 speed manual transmission	12362	13581
	- 2 Dr with automatic transmission	12947	14269
G	**Laser RS G Package** — (includes air conditioning, AM/FM cassette with equalizer, floor mats, console cupholder, speed control, rear liftgate wiper/washer) - 2 Dr with 5 speed manual transmission	12889	14200
	- 2 Dr with automatic transmission	13473	14888
H	**Laser RS H Package** — (includes Laser RS G Pkg plus power windows and door locks) - 2 Dr with 5 speed manual transmission	13261	14638

Mfgs. Code	Description	Base Cost	Sgstd. List
	- 2 Dr with automatic transmission	13846	15326
J	**Laser RS J Package —** (includes Laser RS H Pkg plus compact disc player) - 2 Dr with 5 speed manual transmission	13795	15266
	- 2 Dr with automatic transmission	14379	15954
E	**Laser RS Turbo E Package —** (includes models and specific equipment mentioned) - 2 Dr with 5 speed manual transmission	12739	13954
F	**Laser RS Turbo F Package —** (includes air conditioning) - 2 Dr with 5 speed manual transmission	13428	14765
	- 2 Dr with automatic transmission	14128	15588
G	**Laser RS Turbo G Package —** (includes air conditioning, AM/FM cassette with equalizer, floor mats, console cupholder, speed control, rear liftgate wiper/washer) - 2 Dr with 5 speed manual transmission	13954	15384
	- 2 Dr with automatic transmission	14654	16207
K	**Laser RS Turbo K Package —** (includes Laser RS Turbo G Pkg plus power windows and power door locks) - 2 Dr with 5 speed manual transmission	14326	15822
	- 2 Dr with automatic transmission	15026	16645
L	**Laser RS Turbo L Package —** (includes Laser RS Turbo K Pkg plus compact disc player) - 2 Dr with 5 speed manual transmission	14860	16450
	- 2 Dr with automatic transmission	15560	17273

SUNDANCE

SUNDANCE (4 Cylinder)

Mfgs. Code	Description	Base Cost	Sgstd. List
PL24	2 Dr America	7172	7699
PL44	4 Dr America	7447	7999
PH24	2 Dr Highline	8149	8899
PH44	4 Dr Highline	8419	9199
PS24	2 Dr RS	9219	10099
PS44	4 Dr RS	9523	10425
	Destination Charge: All models	465	465

STANDARD EQUIPMENT:

SUNDANCE: Power front vented disc and rear drum brakes, black bumpers with 5 mph protection, warning chimes for headlights on, seatbelts, and key-in-ignition (Highline, RS), cigarette lighter, mini console (America, Highline), full center console with armrest (RS), side window demisters, childproof door locks (4 door only), 2.2 liter 4 cylinder electronic fuel injection engine (America, Highline), 2.5 liter 4 cylinder electronic fuel injection engine (RS), quiet tuned exhaust system, clear glass with tinted backlight, bright grille, single rectangular halogen aerostyle headlights, inside release hood, instrument panel (mechanical includes 85 mph speedometer, on RS odometer, trip odometer with reset, gauges for fuel, voltage and temperature, warning lights for oil pressure, turn signal, high beam, seatbelts, brakes, engine, air bag), premium sound insulation (Highline, RS), hood pad insulation, remote release liftgate (RS), light (ash receiver, cargo compartment, glove box, underhood dome)(RS), outside left remote control black mirror (America, Highline), dual outside remote control black mirror (RS), inside day/night rearview mirror, covered vanity driver and passenger side mirror, narrow bodyside black molding (Highline), wide bodyside bright insert molding (RS), monotone paint (America, Highline), two tone paint (RS), AM/FM stereo radio and two speakers (Highline), AM/FM stereo cassette radio with four speakers (RS), liftgate mounted luggage rack (RS), passive driver air bag and active 3-point front and rear restraint system, removable shelf panel, power rack and pinion steering, (firm feel 16:1), luxury steering wheel tachometer (RS), P185/70R14 SBR blackwall tires (America, Highline), PS185/70R14 SBR blackwall all-season touring tires (RS), T115/70D14 compact spare tire, 5 speed manual transmission, vinyl color-keyed trim (America), premium cloth color-keyed trim (Highline), performance cloth color-keyed trim (RS), 4 Argent wheels with black hub center and nut covers (America), Impeller design wheel cover (Highline, RS), windshield wiper/washer with 2 speed intermittent wipe (RS).

ACCESSORIES

Mfgs. Code	Description	Base Cost	Sgstd. List
HAA	**Air Conditioning** — (includes tinted glass) - America w/W pkg	672	791
	- Highline w/A pkg	672	791
	- RS w/E pkg	672	791
—	**Tinted Glass** — (required with air conditioning) - America w/W pkg	90	107
	- Highline w/E pkg	90	107
	- RS w/G pkg	90	107
MDA	**Front License Plate Bracket**	NC	NC
CUN	**Overhead Console** — (includes thermometer, compass, reading lights and storage bins) - Highline w/C, D, E pkgs	225	265
	- RS w/G, H pkgs	225	265
GFA	**Electric Rear Window Defroster** — (required in New York State) - America w/W pkg	138	163
	- Highline w/A pkg	138	163
	- RS w/G pkg	139	163
JPB	**Power Door Locks**		
	- (2 Dr) Highline w/A, B, C, D pkgs	165	194
	- (2 Dr) RS w/G pkg	165	194
	- (4 Dr) Highline w/A, B, C, D pkgs	200	235
	- (4 Dr) RS w/G pkg	200	235
NAE	**California Emissions**	87	100
CLE	**Floor Mats** – (front and rear) - America w/X, Y pkgs	39	46
	- Highline w/A, B, C, D pkgs	39	46
	- RS w/G pkg	39	46
JHA	**Intermittent Wipers** — Highline w/A, B pkgs	48	56
GTE	**Mirrors** — (dual outside remote) - Highline w/A, B pkgs	59	69
GTK	**Mirrors** — (dual outside remote) (requires power door locks) - Highline w/C, D, pkgs	48	57
	- RS w/G pkg	48	57
	- Highline w/A, B pkgs	107	126
P	**Paint** — extra cost	65	77
JPS	**Power Seat** — driver's side (requires power mirrors, power locks and power windows) - Highline w/C, D, E pkgs	252	296
	- RS w/G, H pkgs	252	296
JPA	**Power Windows** — (requires power mirrors and power locks) - (2 Dr) Highline w/C, D, E pkgs	213	250
	- (2 Dr) RS w/G, H pkgs	213	250
	- (4 Dr) Highline w/C, D, E pkgs	269	316
	- (4 Dr) RS w/G, H pkgs	269	316
RAL	**Radio** — (AM/FM stereo with digital clock and 2 speaker sound system) - America w/W pkg	241	284
RAS	**Radio** — (deluxe AM/FM stereo w/cassette and 4 speaker sound system)		
	- America w/W pkg	416	489
	- America w/X, Y pkgs	174	205
	- Highline w/A, B pkgs	174	205
	- Highline w/C, D pkgs	132	155
RAN	**Radio** — (Infinity I sound system) - Highline w/E pkg	234	275
	- RS w/G pkg	234	275
NHM	**Speed Control** — electronic (requires tilt steering wheel) - Highline w/A, B, C, D pkgs	182	214
	- RS w/G pkg	182	214
GWB	**Sunroof** — (flip-up, manual) - Highline, RS	322	379

Mfgs. Code	Description PLYMOUTH	Base Cost	Sgstd. List
SUA	**Tilt Steering Column** — Highline w/A pkg	117	138
	- RS w/G pkg	117	138
TBB	**Tire** — (conventional spare) - America, Highline	72	85
	- RS	88	103
WHH	**Wheels** — cast aluminum (4) - Highline, RS	279	328
—	**Customer Preferred Equipment Packages**		
W	**America W Package** — (includes models and specific equipment mentioned)		
	- 2 Dr and 5 speed manual transmission	7207	7599
	- 4 Dr and 5 speed manual transmission	7393	7799
	- 2 Dr and automatic transmission	7672	8146
	- 4 Dr and automatic transmission	7858	8346
X	**America X Package** — (includes rear defroster, light package, dual outside remote mirrors, floor mats, AM/FM stereo radio, narrow bodyside and moldings) - 2 Dr and 5 speed manual transmission	7795	8291
	- 4 Dr and 5 speed manual transmission	7991	8503
	- 2 Dr and automatic transmission	8260	8838
	- 4 Dr and automatic transmission	8456	9050
Y	**America Y Package** — (includes America X Pkg plus air conditioning and tinted glass) - 2 Dr and 5 speed manual transmission	8559	9189
	- 4 Dr and 5 speed manual transmission	8755	9401
	- 2 Dr and automatic transmission	9024	9736
	- 4 Dr and automatic transmission	9220	9948
C	**Highline "Special" C Package** — (includes rear defroster, intermittent wipers, tilt steering, light package, wide bodyside moldings, floor console, 4 radio speakers, liftgate release, dual note horn, tachometer with mph speedometer, manual outside remote mirrors) - 2 Dr and 5 speed manual transmission	9036	9932
	- 4 Dr and 5 speed manual transmission	9226	10144
	- 2 Dr and automatic transmission	9501	10479
	- 4 Dr and automatic transmission	9691	10691
D	**Highline "Special" D Package** — (includes Highline "Special" C Pkg plusair conditioning and tinted glass) - 2 Dr and 5 speed manual transmission	9544	10530
	- 4 Dr and 5 speed manual transmission	9734	10742
	- 2 Dr and automatic transmission	10009	11077
	- 4 Dr and automatic transmission	10199	11289
E	**Highline "Special" E Package** — (includes air conditioning, tinted glass, rear defroster, intermittent wipers, tilt steering, light package, wide bodyside molding, floor console, 4 speakers, liftgate release, dual note horn, tachometer with 125 mph speedometer, power outside remote mirrors, speed control, power door locks, AM/FM stereo cassette radio, floor mats) - 2 Dr and 5 speed manual transmission	10110	11196
	- 4 Dr and 5 speed manual transmission	10335	11449
	- 2 Dr and automatic transmission	10575	11743
	- 4 Dr and automatic transmission	10800	11996
A	**Highline A Package** — (includes models and specific equipment mentioned)		
	- 2 Dr w/2.2 liter engine and 5 speed manual transmission	8303	9070
	- 4 Dr w/2.2 liter engine and 5 speed manual transmission	8483	9270
	- 2 Dr w/2.2 liter and automatic transmission	8768	9617
	- 4 Dr w/2.2 liter and automatic transmission	8948	9817
	- 2 Dr w/2.5 liter engine and 5 speed manual transmission	8546	9356
	- 4 Dr w/2.5 liter engine and 5 speed manual transmission	8726	9556
	- 2 Dr w/2.5 liter engine and automatic transmission	9011	9903
	- 4 Dr w/2.5 liter engine and automatic transmission	9191	10103
B	**Highline B Package** — (includes air conditioning, tinted glass, rear defroster, tilt steering)		

Mfgs. Code	Description	Base Cost	Sgstd. List
	- 2 Dr w/2.2 liter engine and 5 speed manual transmission	9131	10044
	- 4 Dr w/2.2 liter engine and 5 speed manual transmission	9311	10244
	- 2 Dr w/2.2 liter engine and automatic transmission	9596	10591
	- 4 Dr w/2.2 liter engine and automatic transmission	9776	10791
	- 2 Dr w/2.5 liter engine and 5 speed manual transmission	9374	10330
	- 4 Dr w/2.5 liter engine and 5 speed manual transmission	9554	10530
	- 2 Dr w/2.5 liter engine and automatic transmission	9839	10877
	- 4 Dr w/2.5 liter engine and automatic transmission	10019	11077
C	**Highline C Package —** (includes rear defroster, tilt steering, light package, floor console, 4 radio speakers, liftgate release, dual note horn, wide bodyside molding, bodyside accent stripe, intermittent wipers, tachometer with 125 mph speedometer, manual outside mirrors)		
	- 2 Dr w/2.5 liter engine and 5 speed manual transmission	9097	10004
	- 4 Dr w/2.5 liter engine and 5 speed manual transmission	9287	10216
	- 2 Dr w/2.5 liter engine and automatic transmission	9562	10551
	- 4 Dr w/2.5 liter engine and automatic transmission	9752	10763
D	Highline D Package — (includes Highline C Pkg plus air conditioning and tinted glass)		
	- 2 Dr w/2.5 liter engine and 5 speed manual transmission	9605	10602
	- 4 Dr w/2.5 liter engine and 5 speed manual transmission	9795	10814
	- 2 Dr w/2.5 liter engine and automatic transmission	10070	11149
	- 4 Dr w/2.5 liter engine and automatic transmission	10260	11361
E	**Highline E Package —** (includes Highline D Pkg except manual mirrors are replaced by power mirrors plus also includes speed control, power door locks, AM/FM stereo cassette radio, floor mats)		
	- 2 Dr w/2.5 liter engine and 5 speed manual transmission	10171	11268
	- 4 Dr w/2.5 liter engine and 5 speed manual transmission	10396	11521
	- 2 Dr w/2.5 liter engine and automatic transmission	10636	11815
	- 4 Dr w/2.5 liter engine and automatic transmission	10861	12068
G	**RS G Package —** (includes models and specific equipment mentioned)		
	- 2 Dr w/2.5 liter engine and 5 speed manual transmission	9383	10270
	- 4 Dr w/2.5 liter engine and 5 speed manual transmission	9586	10495
	- 2 Dr w/2.5 liter engine and automatic transmission	9848	10817
	- 4 Dr w/2.5 liter engine and automatic transmission	10050	11042
	- 2 Dr w/2.5 liter turbo engine and 5 speed manual transmission	10003	10999
	- 4 Dr w/2.5 liter turbo engine and 5 speed manual transmission	10205	11224
	- 2 Dr w/2.5 liter turbo engine and automatic transmission	10468	11546
	- 4 Dr w/2.5 liter turbo engine and automatic transmission	10670	11771
H	**RS H Package —** (includes air conditioning, tinted glass, tilt steering wheel, speed control, power door locks, power outside remote mirrors, AM/FM stereo cassette radio w/seek, floor mats)		
	- 2 Dr w/2.5 liter engine and 5 speed manual transmission	10475	11555
	- 4 Dr w/2.5 liter engine and 5 speed manual transmission	10713	11821
	- 2 Dr w/2.5 liter engine and automatic transmission	10940	12102
	- 4 Dr w/2.5 liter engine and automatic transmission	11178	12368
	- 2 Dr w/2.5 liter turbo engine and 5 speed manual transmission	11094	12284
	- 4 Dr w/2.5 liter turbo engine and 5 speed manual transmission	11332	12550
	- 2 Dr w/2.5 liter turbo engine and automatic transmission	11560	12831
	- 4 Dr w/2.5 liter turbo engine and automatic transmission	11797	13097

VOYAGER FRONT WHEEL DRIVE

VOYAGER (4 Cylinder)

Mfgs. Code	Description	Base Cost	Sgstd. List
L52	Base Voyager	11859	13215
H52	Special Edition	12854	14345

Code	Description	Base Cost	Sgstd. List
P52	Limited Edition	15758	17645
P52 w/ASP	LX	17073	19140

GRAND VOYAGER (6 Cylinder)

Code	Description	Base Cost	Sgstd. List
H53	Special Edition	14394	16095
P53	Limited Edition	17174	19255

Destination Charge: All models 520 520

STANDARD EQUIPMENT:

VOYAGER: Front air conditioning (Voyager LE/ES, Grand Voyager LE), power assisted front disc/rear drum brakes, chimes (headlights on, seatbelt and key in ignition), console (front storage, overhead with compass, trip computer) (Voyager LE/ES, Grand Voyager LE), lower body protect urethane coating, stainless steel exhaust, electric rear window defroster (Voyager LE/ES, Grand Voyager LE), power front and rear door locks (Voyager LE/ES, Grand Voyager LE), 2.5 liter 4 cylinder electronic fuel injected engine (Base Voyager, Voyager SE, Voyager LE/ES), 3.3 liter 6 cylinder multi-point injection engine (Grand Voyager SE, Grand Voyager LE), floor mats (Voyager LE/ES, Grand Voyager LE), remote fuel filler door (Base Voyager, Voyager LE/ES, Grand Voyager LE), tinted glass, aerostyle halogen headlamps, inside hood release, single note horn (Base Voyager), dual note horn (Voyager SE, Voyager LE/ES, Grand Voyager SE, Grand Voyager LE), instrument panel (electro/mechanical 100 mph speedometer, odometer, trip odometer with reset, gauges for fuel, temperature, warning light for low fuel, oil pressure, voltage, liftgate open, check engine), tachometer, voltmeter gauges, check gauges (Voyager LE/ES, Grand Voyager LE), special body sound insulation (Base Voyager, Voyager SE, Grand Voyager SE), deluxe body sound insulation (Voyager LE/ES, Grand Voyager LE), power liftgate release (Voyager SE, Voyager LE/ES, Grand Voyager SE, Grand Voyager LE), exterior aeroblack power fold-away mirror (Base Voyager, Voyager SE, Grand Voyager SE), heated exterior power fold-away aeroblack mirror (Voyager LE/ES, Grand Voyager LE), non-illuminated visor vanity mirror (Base Voyager, Voyager SE, Grand Voyager SE), illuminated visor vanity mirror (Voyager LE/ES, Grand Voyager LE), AM mono/FM stereo ETR radio with digital clock, active 3-point unibelt restraint system, 5 passenger driver and passenger bucket seats with 3 passenger quick release rear bench seats (Base Voyager), 7 passenger driver and passenger quick release rear bench seats (Voyager SE, Voyager LE/ES, Grand Voyager SE, Grand Voyager LE), electronic speed control (Voyager LE/ES, Grand Voyager LE), power rack and pinion steering, tilt steering column (Voyager LE/ES, Grand Voyager LE), deluxe steering wheel (Base Voyager, Voyager SE, Grand Voyager SE), sport steering wheel (Voyager LE/ES, Grand Voyager LE), bodyside tape stripe (Voyager SE, Grand Voyager SE), upper and lower tape stripe (Voyager LE/ES, Grand Voyager LE), P195/75R14 SBR BSW tires (Base Voyager, Voyager SE, Voyager LE/ES), P205/70R15 SBR BSW tires (Grand Voyager SE, Grand Voyager LE), compact spare tire (Base Voyager, Voyager SE, Grand Voyager SE), under body spare tire carrier with cable winch, 3 speed automatic transmission (Base Voyager, Voyager SE, Voyager LE/ES, 4 speed electronic automatic transmission (Grand Voyager SE, Grand Voyager LE), two tone paint (Voyager LE/ES, Grand Voyager LE), 4 deluxe wheel covers (Base Voyager), sport wheel covers (Voyager SE, Voyager LE/ES, Grand Voyager SE, Grand Voyager LE), four styled road wheels (Voyager SE, Voyager LE/ES, Grand Voyager LE), liftgate window wiper/washer with intermittent wipe, deluxe windshield wipers with intermittent wipe

ACCESSORIES

Code	Description	Base Cost	Sgstd. List
—	**Seating**		
CYD	5-passenger (2 buckets, 3-passenger bench) - L52	STD	STD
CYE	7-passenger (2 buckets, 2 passenger and 3-passenger bench) - L52	337	397
CYS	7-passenger, quad command seating (2 buckets, 2 inter buckets and 3 -passenger bench) - all except L52	507	597
—	converta bed seating (7-passenger, 2 buckets, 2-passenger bench and 3		

Mfgs. Code	Description	Base Cost	Sgstd. List
	-passenger bench, converta bed) - H52, H53	470	553
AAB	**Popular Value Discount Package** — (includes light package, deluxe convenience package, floor mats, gauges, dual horns, deluxe sound insulation, power liftgate release, dual illuminated visor vanity mirrors [except L52], power door locks, 7-passenger seating)		
	- L52	1216	1431
	- L52 w/AFW pkg	896	1054
	- H52	900	1059
	- H52 w/AFW pkg	632	743
	- H53	900	1059
	- H53 w/AFW pkg	632	743
AFF	**Luxury Value Discount Package** — (includes popular value discount pkg, storage convenience pkg, overhead console, electric rear window defroster, time delay headlamps, power heated foldaway mirrors, radio [AM stereo and FM stereo cassette, "Infiniti I"], power driver seat [P52, P53 only], power front windows, rear quarter vent windows)		
	- H52	1973	2321
	- H52 w/AFW pkg	1561	1837
	- H53	1973	2321
	- H53 w/AFW pkg	1561	1837
	- P52	197	232
	- P53	197	232
AFW	**Family Value Discount Package** — (includes front air conditioning, electric rear window defroster, dual horns, deluxe sound insulation, power liftgate release, light package)		
	- L52	937	1102
	- L52 w/6 cylinder engine	1192	1402
	- H52	885	1041
	- H53	885	1041
ASP	**LX Decor Package** — (not available w/AHT trailer tow) (includes heavy duty brakes, 3.0L MPI engine, 4-speed automatic ultradrive transmission, bodyside and sill molding, fog lamps, P205/70R15 BSW tires, 15" cast aluminum wheels) - P52	STD	STD
AHT	**Heavy Duty Trailer Tow Package** — (not available with AGA or ASP) (includes 120 amp alternator, 625 amp battery, heavy duty [brakes, flasher, radiator, suspension, transmission, oil cooler], 15" conventional spare tire, P205/70R15 BSW SBR tires, 15" wheel covers, trailer tow wiring harness)		
	- H52	473	557
	- H53	377	443
	- P52	473	557
	- P53	377	443
AFM	**Storage Convenience Package** — (includes forward storage console and storage drawer) - H52, H53	127	149
AJK	**Deluxe Convenience Package** — (included in AAB popular value pkg) (includes electronic speed control, tilt steering column, luxury steering wheel)		
	- L52	343	404
	- H52	343	404
	- H53	343	404
AJP	**Power Convenience Package** — (included in luxury value pkg) (includes power door locks and power windows)		
	- H52	417	490
	- H52 w/AAB	213	250
	- H53	417	490
	- H53 w/AAB	213	250
AGA	**Sport Handling Package** — (not available w/ASO LX Decor or SDB heavy		

Mfgs. Code	Description	Base Cost	Sgstd. List
	duty suspension) (includes heavy duty brakes, rear sway bar, P205/70R15 BSW SBR tires, 15" luxury wheel covers)		
	- H52	117	138
	- P52	117	138
	- H53	20	24
	- P53	20	24
—	**Light Package** — (not included in AAB popular value pkg and AFW family value pkg; not available otherwise) (includes ash receiver, storage drawer [if so equipped], map/reading, glove box, underhood, ignition, illuminated entry, liftgate dual floor, door ajar, low washer fluid warning)		
EDM	**Engine** — 2.5 liter electronic fuel injection - L52, H52, P52	STD	STD
EFA	**Engine** — 3.0 liter MPI - L52, H52, P52	590	694
EGA	**Engine** — 3.3 liter MPI - H52, P52	677	796
DGA	**Transmission** — 3 speed automatic (not available w/3.0L engine on P52) - L52, H52, P52	STD	STD
DGB	**Transmission** — 4 speed automatic - H52, P52	147	173
EL	**Leather Trim** — low back bucket seats (requires AFF) - P52, P53	735	865
HAA	**Air Conditioning** — front; included in AFW - L52, H52, H53	728	857
HBB	**Air Conditioning** — rear; includes deluxe insulation and 120 mph alternator - P53	396	466
HBB	**Air Conditioning** — rear; includes deluxe insulation and 120 amp alternator (requires AFM, GFA, HAA) - H53	485	571
	- with AFW, AAB or AFF on H53 - H53	396	466
	- with AHT on H53 - H53	433	509
	- with AFW, AAB or AFF and AHT on H53 - H53	343	404
BRK	**Brakes** — anti-lock - H53, P53	679	799
	- with AGA, AHT or ASP (requires EHA) - H52, P52	679	799
	- includes 15" tires and wheels (requires EGA) - H52, P52	754	887
MPA	**Applique** — Woodgrain; n/a with ASP - P52, P53	NC	NC
MDA	**Bracket** — front license plate	NC	NC
GFA	**Defroster** — electric rear window (includes power liftgate release); included in AFW - L52	184	217
GFA	**Defroster** — electric rear window; included in AFW and AFF - H52, H53	143	168
JPH	**Door Locks** — Power - speed sensitive actuation; included in AJP, AAB and AFF - L52, H52, H53	204	240
NAE	**Emissions** — California control and testing	87	102
GAE	**Glass** — sunscreen	352	414
MWA	**Luggage Rack**	122	143
P	**Paint** — extra cost	65	77
APB	**Paint** — two tone - H52, H53	252	296
APB	**Paint** — two tone - P52, P53	NC	NC
RAS	**Radio** — AM mono/FM stereo w/cassette non seek and scan w/4 speakers; n/a w/AFF	132	155
RAN	**Radio Infinity I** — AM stereo/FM stereo w/cassette and seek and scan; n/a w/AFF		
	- with 6 infinity speakers - H52, P52, H53, P53	392	461
RAY	**Radio Infinity II** — AM stereo/FM stereo w/cassette, seek/scan and graphic equalizer (requires AAB or AFF)		
	- with 6 infinity speakers (w/AAB) - H52, P52, H53, P53	574	675
	- with 6 infinity speakers (w/AFF) - H52, P52, H53, P53	182	214
SDB	**Suspension** — heavy duty; in AHT; n/a w/AGA	59	69
—	**Seat** — power left (included in AFF) - P52, P53TLB		
—	**Tires** — 205/70R14 SBR WSW (requires AAB on L52/H52) - L52, H52, P52	122	143
TPC	**Tires** — 205/70R15 SBR WSW; (requires AHT or AGA on H52/P52 and AAB on H52/H53) - H52, P52, H53, P53	59	69
TBB	**Tire** — conventional spare 14"; (requires 14" tires and wheel) - L52, H52,		

Mfgs. Code	Description	Base Cost	Sgstd. List
	P52	93	109
	- conventional spare 15" (requires 15" tires and wheels on L52, H52,P52)	93	109
—	**Windows** — power - front doors; included in AJP and AFF - H52, P52, H53, P53		
WJL	**Wheels** — cast aluminum 15"; included in ASP or requires AGA on 52's - H52, P52, H53, P53	309	363
W49	**Wheel Covers (4)** — wire 14; n/a w/AGA, AHT or ASP) - L52, H52, P52	208	245
MP8	**Woodgrain Delete** — includes bodyside stripe with monotone paint - P52, P53	NC	NC

VOYAGER ALL WHEEL DRIVE

VOAYGER ALL WHEEL DRIVE (6 Cylinder)

Code	Description	Base Cost	Sgstd. List
H52	Special Edition	15401	17240
P52	Limited Edition	18301	20535
P52 w/ASP	LE	18753	21049
H53	Grand Voyager Special Edition	16022	17945
P53	Grand Voyager Limited Edition	18802	21105
	Destination Charge: All models	520	520

STANDARD EQUIPMENT:

VOYAGER ALL WHEEL DRIVE: Front air conditioning (LE, Grand Voyager LE), power front disc/rear drum brakes, warning chimes, front storage console (LE, Grand Voyager LE), mini trip computer (LE, Grand Voyager LE), lower body protective urethane coating, rear window defroster (LE, Grand Voyager LE), power door locks (LE, Grand Voyager LE), 3.3 liter 6 cylinder MFI engine, floor mats (LE, Grand Voyager LE), fuel filler door remote release (LE, Grand Voyager LE), tinted glass, aero-style halogen headlamps, inside hood release, dual note horn, tachometer and gauges (LE, Grand Voyager LE), deluxe body sound insulation (LE, Grand Voyager LE), power liftgate release, power foldaway mirrors (heated on LE and Grand Voyager LE), visor vanity mirror (illuminated on LE and Grand Voyager LE), AM mono and FM stereo ETR w/digital clock, electronic speed control (LE, Grand Voyager LE), power steering, tilt steering column (LE, Grand Voyager LE), luxury steering wheel (LE, Grand Voyager LE), bodyside stripe (SE, Grand Voyager SE), P205/70R15 SBR BSW tires, compact spare, automatic 4-speed ultradrive transmission, woodgrain bodyside (LE, Grand Voyager LE), luxury wheel covers, liftgate window wiper/washer.

ACCESSORIES

Code	Description	Base Cost	Sgstd. List
—	**Seating**		
CYE	7-passenger (2 bucket, 2-passenger bench and 3-passenger bench)	STD	STD
CYS	7-passenger, quad command seating (2 buckets, 2 inter buckets and 3 passenger bench)	507	597
—	converta bed seating (7-passenger, 2 buckets, 2-passenger bench and 3 -passenger bench, converta bed) - H52, H53	470	553
AAB	**Popular Value Discount Package** — (not available w/AFF luxury value package) (includes light package, deluxe convenience package, floor mats, gauges, deluxe sound insulation, dual illuminated visor vanity mirrors, power door locks)		
	- H52	900	1059
	- H52 w/AFW	632	743
	- H53	900	1059
	- H53 w/AFW	632	743
AFF	**Luxury Value Discount Package** — (includes popular value package,		

Mfgs. Code	Description	Base Cost	Sgstd. List
	storage convenience package, overhead console, electric rear window defroster, headlamps time delay, power dual heated mirrors, AM stereo and FM stereo cassett "Infinity I", power driver seat [P52 and P53 only], power windows, rear quarter vent windows)		
	- H52	1973	2321
	- H52 w/AFW pkg	1561	1837
	- H53	1973	2321
	- H53 w/AFW pkg	1561	1837
	- P52	197	232
	- P53	197	232
AFW	**Family Value Discount Package** — (includes front air conditioning, electric rear window defroster, deluxe sound insulation, light package)		
	- H52	885	1041
	- H53	885	1041
ASP	**ES Decor Package** — (not available w/AHT trailer tow package) (includes bodyside and sill molding, fog lamps, cast aluminum 15" wheels) - P52	STD	STD
AHT	**Heavy Duty Trailer Tow Package** — (includes 120 amp alternator, 625 amp battery, heavy duty [flasher, radiator, transmission oil cooler], trailer tow wiring harness) - H52, H53, P52, P53	225	265
AFM	**Storage Convenience Package** — (includes console and storage drawer) - H52, H53	127	149
AJK	**Deluxe Convenience Package** — (included in AAB popular value package) (includes electronic speed control, tilt steering column, luxury steering wheel) - H52, H53	343	404
AJP	**Power Convenience Package** — (included in AFF luxury value package) (includes power door locks, power windows)		
	- H52	417	490
	- H52 w/AAB	213	250
	- H53	417	490
	- H53 w/AAB	213	150
—	**Light Package** — (included in AAB popular value package and AFW family value package; not available otherwise) (includes lights for ash receiver, storage drawer [if so equipped], map/reading, glove box, underhood, ignition, illuminated entry, liftgate dual flood, door ajar, low washer warning fluid warning)		
EL	**Leather Trim** — low back bucket seats (requires AFF) - P52, P53	735	865
HAA	**Air Conditioning** — front; included in AFW - H52, H53	728	857
MPA	**Applique** — woodgrain; n/a w/ASP - P52, P53	NC	NC
MDA	**Bracket** — front license plate	NC	NC
GFA	**Defroster** — electric rear window; included in AFW and AFF - H52, H53	143	168
JPH	**Door Locks** — power; included in AJP, AAB and AFF - H52, H53	204	240
NAE	**Emissions** — California control and testing	87	102
GAE	**Glass** — sunscreen	352	414
P	**Paint** — extra cost	65	77
APB	**Paint** — two tone - H52, H53	252	296
APB	**Paint** — two tone - P52, P53	NC	NC
RAS	**Radio** — AM mono/FM stereo w/cassette, non seek and scan w/4 speakers	132	155
RAN	**Radio Infinity I** — AM stereo/FM stereo w/cassette and seek and scan; included in (AFF) - w/6 Infinity speakers	392	461
RAY	**Radio Infinity II** — AM stereo/FM stereo w/cassette and seek/scan and graphic equalizer (requires AAB or AFF) - w/6 Infinity speakers (w/AAB) - w/6 Infinity speakers (w/AFF)	574	675
—	**Seat** — power left; included in AFF - P52, P53		
TPC	**Tires** — 205/70R15 SBR WSW; (requires AAB or AFF on H52/H53)	59	69
—	**Windows** — power - front doors; included in AJP and AFF		
WJL	**Wheels** — cast aluminum 15"; included in ASP	309	363

Code	Description	Base Cost	Sgstd. List
MP8	**Woodgrain Delete** — includes bodyside stripe with monotone paint - P52, P53	NC	NC
—	**Warranty Enhancement for New York** — mandatory	106	125

1991 pontiac

BONNEVILLE LE & SE

BONNEVILLE LE (6 Cylinder)

Code	Description	Base Cost	Sgstd. List
X69	LE Sedan	14528	16834

BONNEVILLE SE (6 Cylinder)

Code	Description	Base Cost	Sgstd. List
Z69	SE Sedan	17660	20464

Destination Charge: All models 535 535

STANDARD EQUIPMENT:

BONNEVILLE: Fixed-mast black antenna, front/rear bumper rub strip, deck lid spoiler (SE), fog lamps (SE), sport left remote/RH manual mirrors, belt reveal wide moldings (bright on LE, gray on SE), wide bodyside moldings with bright insert, soft-ray tinted glass, P215/65R15 steel-belted blackwall tires (LE), P215/60R16 Goodyear Eagle GT +4 (SE), compact spare with cover, trunk security net (SE), 15" wheel covers (LE), 16" x 7" six-spoke sport cast aluminum wheels (SE), acoustical insulation, manual air conditioning, front center seat armrest (LE), front seat storage armrest (SE), rear seat pull-down armrest (SE), cigarette lighter, cluster warning lights include check engine, brake system, remote control deck lid release (SE), front/rear floor mats, headlamp-on warning (SE), hood release, dual horns, simulated woodgrain instrument panel trim, front header dual reading lamp (SE), rear-quarter upper courtesy lamp (SE), lower door RH/LH map pocket, inside, day/night mirror, covered RH/LH visor vanity mirrors, power windows with door pod switches and express-down feature (SE), Delco ETR AM/FM stereo radio w/seek-scan and clock, Delco ETR AM/FM stereo radio with seek-scan and clock and auto-reverse cassette (SE), rear window defogger (SE), automatic passive safety belts, 45/55 split seats with armrest and manual recliners (LE), 45/55 split seats with storage armrest (SE), manual seat recliner - right and left, monitor system includes voltage lights, oil pressure light and seatbelt light, 4-spoke urethane steering wheel (LE), 4-spoke leather-wrapped steering wheel (SE), 3.8 liter 3800 SFI V6 engine, Delco Freedom II battery power, front disc/rear drum brakes (LE, SE), engine coolant recovery system, extensive anti-corrosion protection, front-wheel drive, independent front/rear suspension, rack-and-pinion power steering, 4-speed automatic transmission, dual fluidic concealed windshield wipers, controlled cycle windshield wipers (SE).

ACCESSORIES

Code	Description	Base Cost	Sgstd. List
LN3	**Engine** — 3.8L 3800 V6	NC	NC
MXO	**Transmission** — 4-speed automatic	NC	NC
C49	**Defogger, Electric Rear Window** — Bonneville LE	136	160
	- Bonneville SE	NC	NC
NB2	**Emission Requirements for California**	85	100
D84	**Paint, Custom Two-Tone** — Bonneville LE (n/a w/option package 1SA)	89	105
	Bonneville SE		
	- w/o value option package R6A	89	105
	- t/w value option package R6A	NC	NC
JM4	**Power Brakes, Front Disc, Rear Drum** — anti-lock braking system		

Mfgs. Code	Description	Base Cost	Sgstd. List
	(requires option package 1SD or 1SE on Bonneville LE)	786	925
AU3	**Power Door Locks —** Bonneville LE	196	230
	- Bonneville SE	NC	NC
A31	**Power Windows —** express down, driver; includes front and rear courtesy lamps (included w/B20 custom trim) - Bonneville LE	332	390
	- with Bonneville SE	NC	NC
AU0	**Remote Keyless Entry**	106	125
Z05	**Convenience Package —** (includes illuminated entry, dual illuminated visor vanity mirrors, twilight sentinel, power mirrors) - Bonneville LE	268	315
—	**Radio Equipment**		
US7	power antenna		
	Bonneville LE (NA w/option package 1SA or 1SB)		
	- w/o UX1 or U1A radio	64	75
	- t/w UX1 or U1A radio	NC	NC
UM6	AM/FM ETR stereo w/cassette and clock - consists of Delco AM/FM ETR stereo radio and cassette w/automatic reverse, electronic seek-up/down tuning, integral digital clock, and dual front and rear acoustically matched response speakers - w/o value option package R6A	119	140
	- t/w value option package R6A	NC	NC
UX1	AM stereo/FM stereo ETR w/cassette, graphic equalizer and clock - consists of Delco AM stereo/FM stereo ETR radio and cassette w/automatic reverse and search and replay, electronic seek-up/down tuning, integral 5-band graphic equalizer, integral digital clock, 6-speaker performance sound system, electronic air conditioning, leather-wrapped steering wheel w/radio controls, US7 power antenna and anti-theft feature		
	Bonneville LE		
	- w/o value option package R6A	684	805
	- t/w value option package R6A	565	665
	Bonneville SE		
	- w/o value option package R6A	523	615
	- t/w value option package R6A	NC	NC
U1A	AM/FM stereo ETR w/compact disc player, graphic equalizer and clock - (requires K34 cruise control, N33 tilt steering, CD4 controlled cycle wipers, C49 rear window defogger and A31 power windows) consists of Delco AM/FM stereo ETR radio and compact disc player w/electronic seek-up/down tuning, integral 5-band graphic equalizer, integral digital clock, 6-speaker performance sound system, leather-wrapped steering wheel w/radio controls, electronic air conditioning, US7 power antenna and anti-theft feature		
	Bonneville LE		
	- w/o value option package R6A	876	1031
	- t/w value option package R6A	757	891
	Bonneville SE		
	- w/o value option package R6A	715	841
	- t/w value option package R6A	192	226
—	**Seats**		
AM6	45/55 split - 'pallex' cloth trim - Bonneville LE	NC	NC
	- 'London/Empress' cloth trim - Bonneville SE	NC	NC
AS7	45/45 split - includes console and flash-to-pass - 'London/Empress' cloth trim - Bonneville LE & SE	200	235
B20	**Custom Interior Trim —** (Bonneville LE only; requires option package 1SC, 1SD or 1SE) consists of 45/55 split seat in 'London/Empress' cloth, gauges, power windows and trunk security net) - w/o option package 1SD or 1SE	527	620
	- t/w option package 1SD or 1SE	111	130
AG1	**Power Seat, Driver 6-Way —** Bonneville LE	247	290
	- Bonneville SE	NC	NC

Mfgs. Code	Description	Base Cost	Sgstd. List
CF5	**Sunroof, Power Glass** — includes dual reading lamps and rear quarter courtesy lamps (NA Bonneville LE)	1046	1230
—	**Tires**		
QPH	P215/65R15 BW steel belted radial (NA Bonneville SE) - Bonneville LE	NC	NC
QPJ	P215/65R15 WW steel belted radial (NA Bonneville SE) - Bonneville LE	60	70
QGW	P215/60R16 BW steel belted radial Bonneville LE		
	- w/o value option package R6A	75	88
	- t/w value option package R6A	NC	NC
	- Bonneville SE	NC	NC
WDV	**Warranty Enhancements for New York** — required on all models sold and registered in New York state	55	65
—	**Wheels**		
PF7	15" diamond spoke aluminum with locking package (NA Bonneville SE) - Bonneville LE	252	296
PX0	16" six spoke aluminum with locking package - Bonneville LE - w/o value option package R6A	281	330
	- t/w value option package R6A	NC	NC
	- Bonneville SE	NC	NC
N60	16" cross-lace aluminum, bright faced with locking package	NC	NC
1SA	**Bonneville LE** — model w/standard equipment		
1SB	**Bonneville LE Package 1** — includes tilt steering wheel, controlled cycle wipers and lamp group	229	269
1SC	**Bonneville LE Package 2** — includes Bonneville LE Package 1 plus cruise control, remote deck lid release, rally gauges and tachometer	535	629
1SD	**Bonneville LE Package 3** — includes Bonneville LE Package 2 plus power windows, power door locks, power driver seat	898	1039
1SE	**Bonneville LE Package 4** — includes Bonneville LE Package 3 plus illuminated entry system, LH and RH remote power sport mirrors, dual illuminated visor mirrors, twilight sentinel	1166	1354
1SA	**Bonneville SE** — model w/standard equipment		
1SB	**Bonneville SE Package 1** — includes illuminated entry system, LH and RH remote power sport mirrors, dual illuminated visor vanity mirrors, twilight sentinel	217	255
1SC	**Bonneville SE Package 2** — includes Bonneville SE Package 1 plus twilight sentinel	268	315
R6A	**Bonneville LE Package R6A** — includes 16" aluminum wheels, P215/60R16 BSW steel belted radials, AM/FM stereo w/cassette	408	558
R6A	**Bonneville SE Package R6A** — includes custom two-tone paint, AM/FM stereo w/cassette and graphic equalizer	523	610

BONNEVILLE SSE

BONNEVILLE SSE (6 Cylinder)

Y69	SSE Sedan	21803	25264
	Destination Charge: All models	535	535

STANDARD EQUIPMENT:

BONNEVILLE SSE: Front/rear bumper rub strip, deck lid spoiler, fog lamps, power heated blue-tinted mirrors, belt reveal wide moldings, wide bodyside moldings with special cladding and gold insert, soft-ray tinted glass, P215/60R16 Goodyear Eagle GT +4, compact spare with cover, trunk security net, deluxe trunk trim with deck lid liner, 16" x 7" aero-light cast aluminum wheels, acoustical deluxe insulation, automatic air conditioning w/outside air temperature indicator and steering wheel controls, rear seat armrest w/storage, cigarette lighter, cluster warning lights include: check engine, brake system, console with storage, remote control deck lid release, electric key-activated side door fuel filler, flash-to-pass, deluxe front/rear full retention floor mats, specific gauges with driver information center, headlamp-on warning, remote hood release, dual horns, illuminating entry, simulated woodgrain instrument panel trim, front header dual reading lamp, rear-quarter upper courtesy lamp, lower door RH/LH map pocket, power windows with door pod switches and express-down feature, Delco ETR AM/FM stereo radio w/seek-scan, auto-reverse cassette and graphic equalizer, 8-speaker performance sound system, rear window defogger, remote keyless entry system, automatic passive safety belts, 45/45 12-way bucket seats with deluxe console, 4-spoke leather-wrapped steering wheel with redundant radio controls, 3.8 liter 3800 SFI V6 engine, Delco Freedom II battery, power front/disc rear drum brakes, engine coolant recovery system, extensive anti-corrosion protection, front-wheel drive, headlamp washers, independent front/rear suspension, rack-and-pinion power steering, 4-speed automatic transmission, dual fluidic concealed windshield wipers, controlled cycle windshield wipers.

ACCESSORIES

Code	Description	Base Cost	Sgstd. List
LN3	**Engine** — 3.8L SFI 3800 V6	NC	NC
MX0	**Transmission** — 4-speed automatic	NC	NC
C68	**Air Conditioning** — w/electronic controls	NC	NC
K34	**Cruise Control**	NC	NC
A90	**Deck Lid Release, Remote**	NC	NC
C49	**Defogger, Electric Rear Window**	NC	NC
Y98	**Electronic Ride Control**	NC	NC
B41	**Accessory Kit** — consists of light sticks, raincoat, first aid kit, gloves and utility spotlight (12 volt)	NC	NC
NB2	**Emission Requirements for California**	85	100
T96	**Fog Lamps**	NC	NC
U50	**Gauges, Rally Cluster** — includes tachometer, trip odometer, electronic compass, and driver information center	NC	NC
—	**Headlamps**		
T82	twilight sentinel	NC	NC
TU6	flash-to-pass control	NC	NC
CE4	headlamp washer system	NC	NC
C97	illuminated entry system	NC	NC
BS1	insulation, additional acoustical	NC	NC
C75	lamp, courtesy and dual reading	NC	NC
TR9	**Lamp Group** — consists of dual reading lamps, rear quarter lamp, engine compartment lamp and headlamp-on warning system	NC	NC
B48	**Luggage, Compartment Trim**	NC	NC
B53	**Mats, Deluxe Front and Rear Floor**	NC	NC
—	**Mirrors**		
DK2	heated power remote, tinted - LH and RH	NC	NC
D64	illuminated visor vanity - RH	NC	NC
D74	illuminated visor vanity - LH	NC	NC
JM4	**Power Brakes, Front Disc, Rear Drum** — anti-lock braking system	NC	NC
AU1	**Power Door Locks** — key activated (includes remote fuel filler door lock	NC	NC
A31	**Power Windows**	NC	NC
AU0	**Remote Keyless Entry**	NC	NC
—	**Radio Equipment**		
UX1	AM/FM stereo ETR w/cassette, graphic equalizer and clock - consists of Delco AM stereo/FM stereo ETR radio and cassette w/automatic reverse and search and replay, electronic seek-up/down tuning, integral 5-band graphic equalizer, integral digital clock, dual front and rear acoustically matched response speakers, leather-wrapped steering wheel w/radio		

Mfgs. Code	Description **PONTIAC**	Base Cost	Sgstd. List
	controls and anti-theft feature	NC	NC
U1A	AM stereo/FM stereo ETR w/compact disc player, graphic equalizer and clock - consists of Delco AM stereo/FM stereo ETR radio and compact disc player w/electronic seek-up/down tuning, integral 5-band graphic equalizer, integral digital clock, leather-wrapped steering wheel w/radio controls, and anti-theft feature	192	226
U85	performance sound system, eight-speakers (dual front, front doors, four in package shelf)	NC	NC
US7	**Antenna, Power**	NC	NC
—	**Seats**		
AL7	45/45 split, articulating; includes console - 'metrix' cloth trim	NC	NC
	- 'Ventura' leather trim	662	779
AP9	**Security Net, Luggage Compartment**	NC	NC
T43	**Spoiler, Rear Deck**	NC	NC
NP5	**Leather Wrapped Steering Wheel**	NC	NC
N33	**Tilt Steering Wheel**	NC	NC
CD4	**Windshield Wipers, Controlled Cycle**	NC	NC
CF5	**Sunroof, Power Glass** — (dual reading lamps replaced w/single lamp)	1046	1230
UA6	**Theft Deterrent System**	128	150
WDV	**Warranty Enhancements for New York**	55	65
QGW	**Tires** — P215/60R16 BW steel belted radial	NC	NC
—	**Wheels**		
PF4	16" aero-lite aluminum; w/locking package	NC	NC
N73	16" gold cross-lace aluminum; w/locking package	NC	NC
R6A	**Bonneville SSE Value Option Package R6A** — includes power glass sunroof and theft deterrent system	927	1080
1SB	**Bonneville SSE Option Package 1** — includes power glass sunroof and 45/55 split seat with leather trim	1093	1259

FIREBIRD

FIREBIRD (6 Cylinder)			
S87	Firebird	11332	12690
FIREBIRD (8 Cylinder)			
S87	Formula	13868	15530
W87	Trans Am	15654	17530
W87	Trans Am GTA	21905	24530
Destination Charge: All models		480	480

STANDARD EQUIPMENT:

FIREBIRD: Aero package (includes specific front and rear fascias, rocker panel extensions and quarter panel extensions) (Trans Am), black-finish stationary antenna, black-finish door handles and key lock cylinders, body color one-piece resilient Endura front panel and front bumper, concealed rectangular quartz halogen headlamps (electrically operated), Endura rear bumper, front air dam, front fender air extractors (Trans Am), hood air extractors (Trans Am), hood air louvers (Trans Am), sport body-color mirrors - LH remote control, RH manual convex, rear deck spoiler (Firebird), rear hatch "power pull-down" feature, P215/65R15 steel-belted radial blackwall tires (Firebird), P215/60R16 touring radial tires (Trans Am), P245/50ZR16 steel-belted blackwall radial tires (standard on Formula, Trans Am and GTA), compact spare tire (T125/70D15 "deep-dish" hi-tech turbo wheels (charcoal, 15" x 7" (Firebird) "deep-dish" hi-tech turbo wheels (16" x 8" silver metallic) (Formula), Diamond-spoke aluminum wheels (16" x 8") (charcoal - T/A, gold - GTA), aero rear deck spoiler (Trans Am), wraparound soft-ray tinted liftback glass, cargo area carpeting, cigarette lighter, day/night rearview mirror, Delco ETR AM/FM stereo radio with cassette and clock, dual horns, front and rear floor mats, folding rear seat, full-length front console integral with instrument panel, full instrumentation gauges (including tachometer, and trip odometer), graphite-finished instrument panel, inside hood release, rear compartment and console lamp, leather appointment group (Trans Am), lockable storage compartment in left rear quarter panel, power upper vent system, reclining front bucket seats, side window defoggers, four-spoke steering wheel (leather-wrapped on T/A and GTA), tilt steering wheel, tone warning (seatbelts and headlamps-on warning), visor vanity mirror, 3.1 liter multi-port fuel-injected V6 engine (Firebird), 5.0 liter TPI V8 engine (Trans Am), 5-speed manual transmission, Delco Freedom II battery, MacPherson strut front suspension, power front disc/rear drum brake system, power steering, rally tuned suspension (Trans Am), rear-wheel drive, torque arm/track bar rear suspension.

ACCESSORIES

Code	Description	Base Cost	Sgstd. List
1SB	**Firebird (w/V6 Engine) Package 1** — includes custom air conditioning, inside rearview mirror w/flood lamp	755	888
1SB	**Firebird (w/V8 Engine) Package 1** — includes bodyside moldings, power windows, power door locks, inside rear view mirror w/flood lamp	43	33
1SB	**Firebird Formula & Trans Am Package 1** — includes bodyside moldings, power windows, power door locks, inside rear view mirror w/flood lamp	166	183
1SC	**Firebird (w/V6 Engine) Package 2** — includes custom air conditioning, inside rear view mirror w/flood lamp, bodyside moldings, power windows, power door locks, remote control decklid release, sport LH power & RH power convex mirrors	847	979
1SC	**Firebird (w/V8 Engine) Package 2** — includes body side moldings, power windows, power door locks, inside rear view mirror w/flood lamp, manual 4-way driver seat adjuster, cruise control, remote decklid release, sport LH power & RH power convex mirrors	341	384
R6A	**Value Option Package R6A** — (Firebird & Firebird Formula) - includes T-top roof (NA w/B2L engine), AM/FM stereo w/cassette and graphic equalizer - total retail price - 1070, discount - 250, net price	705	820
R6B	**Value Option Package R6B** — (Firebird & Firebird Formula) - includes T-top roof (NA w/B2L engine), power antenna and cargo screen - total retail price - 1064, discount - 250, net price	699	814
R6A	**Value Option Package R6A** — (Trans Am) - includes T-top roof (NA w/B2L engine), AM/FM stereo w/cassette and graphic equalizer, cargo screen - total retail price - 1139, discount - 250, net price	763	889
R6A	**Value Option Package R6A** — (Trans Am GTA) - includes T-top roof (NA w/B2L engine), leather interior - total retail price - 1370, discount - 350, net price	878	1020
—	**Engines**		
LH0	3.1L MPFI V6 (Firebird only)	NC	NC
L03	5.0L TBFI V8 (NA Trans Am or Trans Am GTA) - Firebird (requires C60 air conditioning	298	350
	- Firebird Formula	NC	NC
LB9	5.0L MPFI V8 (NA Firebird; requires G80 limited slip axle; requires performance enhancement group w/MM5 manual transmission on Trans Am GTA and Firebird Formula) - Firebird Formula	633	745
	- Trans Am	NC	NC
	- Trans Am GTA	(255)	(300)
B2L	5.7L MPFI V8 (NA Firebird or w/CC1 hatch roof; requires MX0 automatic transmission, performance enhancement group, G80 limited slip axle, and QLC tires) - Firebird Formula	888	1045
	- Trans Am	255	300
	- Trans Am GTA	NC	NC

Mfgs. Code	Description **PONTIAC**	Base Cost	Sgstd. List
—	**Transmissions**		
MM5	5-speed manual (NA Firebird w/LH0 3.1L V6 engine; NA w/B2L 5.7L V8 engine) - Firebird Formula & Trans Am	NC	NC
	- Firebird w/L03 5.0L V8 engine and Trans Am GTA	(438)	(515)
MX0	4-speed automatic - Firebird Formula & Trans Am	438	515
	- Firebird & Trans Am GTA	NC	NC
C60	**Air Conditioning, Custom** — (required on Firebird w/L03 engine - Firebird	684	805
	- Firebird Formula, Trans Am, & Trans Am GTA	NC	NC
G80	**Axle, Limited Slip Differential** — (available only and required w/LB9 engine or B2L engine) - Firebird & Firebird Formula	85	100
	- Trans Am & Trans Am GTA	NC	NC
K34	**Cruise Control** — (requires 1SB Option Package; included in 1SC Option Package) - Firebird, Firebird Formula & Trans Am	179	210
	- Trans Am GTA	NC	NC
C49	**Defogger, Electric Rear Window** — Firebird, Firebird Formula & Trans Am	136	160
	- Trans Am GTA	NC	NC
NB2	**Emission Requirements for California**	85	100
CC1	**Hatch Roof, Locking** — removable glass panels, includes sunshades (NA w/B2L engine) - w/o value option package R6A	782	920
	- t/w value option package R6A	NC	NC
AU3	**Power Door Locks** — (available only w/A31 power windows - Firebird, Firebird Formula & Trans Am	162	190
	- Trans Am GTA	NC	NC
A31	**Power Windows** — (available only w/AU3 power door locks) includes door map pockets - Firebird, Firebird Formula & Trans Am	221	260
	- Trans Am GTA	NC	NC
—	**Radio Equipment**		
U75	antenna power		
	Firebird & Firebird Formula		
	- w/o value option pkg R6B	64	75
	- w/value option pkg R6B	NC	NC
	- Trans Am	64	75
	- Trans Am GTA	NC	NC
UM6	AM/FM ETR stereo w/cassette and clock - consists of Delco AM/FM ETR stereo radio and cassette w/automatic reverse, electronic seek-up/down tuning, integral digital clock, and dual front and rear coaxial speakers (NA Trans Am GTA) - Firebird, Firebird Formula & Trans Am	NC	NC
UX1	AM/FM stereo w/cassette, graphic equalizer and clock - consists of Delco Am stereo/FM ETR stereo radio and cassette w/automatic reverse and search and replay, electronic seek-up/down tuning, integral 5-band graphic equalizer, integral digital clock, and dual front and rear coaxial speakers		
	Firebird, Firebird Formula & Trans Am		
	- w/o value option package R6A	128	150
	- t/w value option package R6A	NC	NC
	Trans Am GTA	NC	NC
U1A	AM/FM stereo w/compact disc player, clock and graphic equalizer - consists of Delco AM stereo/FM ETR stereo radio and compact disc player, electronic seek-up/down tuning, integral 5-band graphic equalizer, integral digital clock, and dual front and rear coaxial speakers		
	Firebird, Firebird Formula & Trans Am		
	- w/o value option package R6A	320	376
	- t/w value option package R6A	192	226
	Trans Am GTA	192	226
A90	**Deck Lid Release, Remote Control** — (requires 1SB Option Pkg on Firebird w/L03 5.0L V8 engine, Firebird Formula & Trans Am; Incl in 1SC Option Pkg on Firebird w/L03 5.0L V8 engine, Firebird Formula & Trans		

Mfgs. Code	Description	Base Cost	Sgstd. List
	Am; available only & included in 1SC Option Package on Firebird w/LH0 3.1L V6 engine)		
	- Firebird, Firebird Formula, & Trans Am	43	50
	- Trans Am GTA	NC	NC
DG7	**Mirrors, Sport LH Power & RH Power Convex —** (requires 1SB Option Package on Firebird w/L03 5.0L V8 engine, Firebird Formula & Trans Am; included in 1SC Option Package on Firebird w/L03 5.0L V8 engine, Firebird Formula & Trans Am; available only & included in 1SC Option Package on Firebird w/LH0 3.1L V6 engine)		
	- Firebird, Firebird Formula & Trans Am	77	91
	- Trans Am GTA	NC	NC
R6P	**Performance Enhancement Group —** (NA Firebird; NA w/LB9 5.0L engine w/MX0 automatic Transmission; required w/B2L 5.7L engine w/MX0 automatic transmission; required w/LB9 5.0L engine w/MM5 manual transmission on Firebird Formula & Trans Am GTA); includes N10 dual converter exhaust, J41/J42 front disc and rear drum power brakes, KC4 engine oil cooler, and GU6 (w/LB9 5.0L engine)/GU5 (w/B2L 5.7L engine) Performance Axle Ratios		
	- Firebird Formula & Trans Am	225	265
	Trans Am GTA - w/LB9 5.0L V8 engine w/MM5 manual transmission or w/B2L 5.7L V8 engine	NC	NC
	- w/LB9 5.0L V8 engine w/MX0 automatic transmission (delete for credit)	(225)	(265)
D42	**Screen, Cargo Security**		
	Firebird & Firebird Formula		
	- w/o value option package R6B	59	69
	- t/w value option package R6B	NC	NC
	Trans Am		
	- w/o value option package R6A	59	69
	- t/w value option package R6A	NC	NC
	Trans Am GTA	NC	NC
AH3	**Seat Adjuster, Manual 4-Way Driver —** (not available on Firebird w/LH0 3.1L V6 engine; available only and included in 1SC Option Package on Firebird w/L03 5.0L V8 engine; available with 1SB Option Package on Formula; included in 1SC Option Package on Formula)		
	- Firebird & Firebird Formula	30	35
	- Trans Am & Trans Am GTA	NC	NC
—	**Seats**		
AR9	custom reclining bucket - 'pallex' cloth trim (NA Trans Am GTA)	NC	NC
AQ9	articulating luxury bucket seats		
	Trans Am GTA		
	- w/'Pallex' cloth trim	NC	NC
	w/'Ventura' leather trim		
	- w/o value option package R6A	383	450
	- t/w value option package R6A	NC	NC
W68	**Sport Appearance Package —** (Firebird only; requires 1SB Option Package w/LH0 3.1L engine) includes Trans Am aero front and rear fascias, fog lamps and Trans Am aero side moldings	383	450
—	**Tires**		
QPH	touring P215/65R15 BW steel belted radial; includes N24 wheels		
	- Firebird	NC	NC
QPE	touring P215/60R16 BW steel belted radial (NA w/B2L engine) includes PW7 wheels - Trans Am	NC	NC
QLC	high performance P245/50ZR16 BW steel belted radial (NA Firebird) includes WS6 performance suspension and PW7 wheels (Trans Am and Trans Am GTA)/PE0 Wheels (Firebird Formula) - Trans Am	266	313
	- Firebird Formula & Trans Am GTA	NC	NC

Mfgs. Code	Description	Base Cost	Sgstd. List
WDV	**Warranty Enhancements for New York**	55	65
—	**Wheels**		
N24	15" charcoal deep dish hi-tech turbo aluminum w/locking package (Firebird only)	NC	NC
PE0	16" deep dish hi-tech turbo aluminum w/locking package (Firebird Formula only)	NC	NC
PW7	16" diamond-spoke aluminum; black on Trans Am or Gold on Trans Am GTA	NC	NC

GRAND AM

Code	Description	Base Cost	Sgstd. List
GRAND AM (4 Cylinder)			
G27	Coupe	9391	10174
G69	Sedan	9575	10374
GRAND AM LE (4 Cylinder)			
E27	Coupe	9934	11124
E69	Sedan	10112	11324
GRAND AM SE (4 Cylinder)			
W27	Coupe	14595	16344
W69	Sedan	14774	16544

Destination Charge: All models 455 455

STANDARD EQUIPMENT:

GRAND AM: Aero-body front side and rear skirts (SE Coupe, SE Sedan), fixed-mast antenna, base coat/clearcoat paint, soft-fascia front/rear bumpers, composite headlamps, dual/dual chrome-tipped exhaust outlets (SE Coupe, SE Sedan), fog lamps (SE Coupe, SE Sedan), soft-ray glass, mirrors (sport LH remote control, RH manual) (black), belt reveal bright/black molding, body side bright/black molding, gloss black rocker panel (LE Coupe, LE Sedan), monotone paint treatment (includes color-keyed emblems and aluminum wheels on SE models), P185/75R14 all-season blackwall steel-belted radial tires (LE Coupe, LE Sedan), P205/55R16 all-season blackwall steel-belted Goodyear Eagle GT +4 tires (SE Coupe, SE Sedan), compact spare tire, tri-lace 14" wheel cover (LE Coupe, LE Sedan), SE specific color-coordinated 16" aluminum wheels (SE Coupe, SE Sedan), acoustic insulation package, air conditioning (SE Coupe, SE Sedan), cigarette lighter and lighted ashtray, full floor mounted console, controlled-cycle wipers (SE Coupe, SE Sedan), electronic cruise control with resume speed and accelerate feature (SE Coupe, SE Sedan), day/night rearview mirror, deck lid release (SE Coupe, SE Sedan), deluxe cloth interior (SE Coupe, SE Sedan), deluxe color-keyed seatbelts, dual front/dual rear radio speakers, easy-entry front bucket seats (passenger side) (LE Coupe, SE Coupe), carpeted front and rear floor mats, remote release fuel filler door, locking glove compartment, headlamp-on warning, inside hood release, instrument panel cluster with telltales and electrically controlled speedometer (LE Coupe, LE Sedan), instrument panel cluster with full gauges and tachometer (SE Coupe, SE Sedan), dome reading lamp, trunk and courtesy lamp, leather appointment group includes rally, four-spoke, leather-wrapped steering wheel and leather-wrapped shift knob and parking brake handle (SE Coupe, SE Sedan), dual covered visor vanity mirror, dual power sport mirrors (SE Coupe, SE Sedan), power door locks (SE Coupe, SE Sedan), power windows with "express-down" feature (SE Coupe, SE Sedan), Delco ETR AM/FM stereo radio with seek-scan and clock (LE Coupe, LE Sedan), Delco ETR AM/FM stereo radio with seek-scan, auto-reverse cassette and clock (SE Coupe, SE Sedan), rear-seat integral headrest, reclining front bucket seats, split folding rear seat (SE Coupe, SE Sedan), side window defogger, sport steering wheel (LE Coupe, LE Sedan), four spoke, leather-wrapped rally steering wheel (SE Coupe, SE Sedan), tilt steering wheel (SE Coupe, SE Sedan), upshift indicator light (on manual cars only) (LE Coupe, LE Sedan), 2.5 liter 4-cylinder engine with electronic fuel injection (LE Coupe, LE Sedan), 2.3 liter HO 4-cylinder DOHC 16V engine with 5-speed manual transmission (SE Coupe, SE Sedan), 5-speed manual transmission, anti-lock ABS braking system (SE Coupe, SE Sedan), Delco Freedom II battery, dual horns, extensive anti-corrosion protection, front-wheel drive, full coil suspension, low-noise electric cooling fan, MacPherson strut front suspension, power front disc/rear drum brake system, power rack-and-pinion steering, front 24mm stabilizer bar (SE Coupe, SE Sedan), front 21mm stabilizer bar (LE Coupe, LE Sedan).

ACCESSORIES

Mfgs. Code	Description	Base Cost	Sgstd. List
—	**Engines**		
L68	2.5 liter FI 4-cylinder - Grand Am & Grand Am LE	NC	NC
LD2	2.3 liter DOHC FI 4-cylinder (quad 4) (only available with automatic transmission; LE requires UB3 gauges) - Grand Am LE	561	660
	- Grand Am LE (w/W32 sport performance package)		
	- Grand Am SE	119	140
LG0	2.3L DOHC FI high output 4-cylinder (quad 4 HO) (only available with 5-speed manual transmission) - Grand Am LE (only available w/W32 sport performance package)	NC	NC
	- Grand Am SE	NC	NC
—	**Transmissions**		
MM5	5-speed manual	NC	NC
MX1	3-speed automatic	459	540
W32	**Sport Performance Package —** (NA Grand Am SE) consists of LG0 2.3 liter DOHC FI 4-cylinder (quad 4 HO) engine, monotone paint treatment, N78 hi-tech turbo wheels w/locking package, QME P195/70R14 BSW tires, T96 fog lamps w/front and rear courtesy lamps, FE2 specific suspension, aero-body front, side and rear skirts, dual/dual chrome tipped exhaust outlets and UB3 rally cluster gauges w/tachometer and trip odometer		
	Grand Am LE		
	- w/o value option package R6A	1394	1640
	- t/w value option package R6A	1072	1261
UB3	**Rally Cluster Gauges —** includes tachometer and trip odometer (required on LE with LD2 engine) - Grand Am LE	108	127
	- Grand Am LE (w/W32 sport performance package)	NC	NC
	- Grand Am SE	NC	NC
C60	**Air Conditioning —** Grand Am & Grand Am LE	612	720
	- Grand Am SE	NC	NC
C41	**Non Air Conditioning —** Grand Am & Grand Am LE	NC	NC
NB2	**Emission Requirements for California**	85	100
K34	**Cruise Control —** Grand Am & Grand Am LE	179	210
	- Grand Am SE	NC	NC
A90	**Remote Deck Lid Release —** Grand Am LE	43	50
	- Grand Am SE	NC	NC
C49	**Defogger, Electric Rear Window**	136	160
VK3	**Front License Plate Bracket**	NC	NC
V56	**Luggage Carrier, Deck Lid —** black (includes integrated high mounted stop lamp) - Grand Am LE & Grand Am SE	98	115
AU3	**Power Door Locks —** Grand Am LE Coupe	162	190
	- Grand Am LE Sedan	196	230
	- Grand Am SE	NC	NC
AC3	**Power Seat, Driver —** Grand Am SE	247	290
A31	**Power Windows —** (driver's express down) - Grand Am LE Coupe	217	255
	- Grand Am LE Sedan	272	320
	- Grand Am SE	NC	NC
AM9	**Split Folding Rear Seat —** Grand Am LE	128	150
	- Grand Am SE	NC	NC
N33	**Tilt Steering Wheel —** Grand Am & Grand Am LE	115	135

Mfgs. Code	Description **PONTIAC**	Base Cost	Sgstd. List
	- Grand Am SE	NC	NC
AD3	**Sunroof, Glass** — (removable, includes air deflector) - Grand Am LE & Grand Am SE	298	350
CD4	**Controlled Cycle Wipers** — Grand Am & Grand Am LE	47	55
	- Grand Am SE	NC	NC
D84	**Paint, Two-Tone Custom** — Grand Am LE	86	101
AR9	**Custom Reclining Bucket Seats** — 'Pallex' cloth trim (Grand Am & Grand Am LE)	NC	NC
	- 'metrix' cloth trim (Grand Am SE)	NC	NC
WDV	**Warranty Enhancements for New York** — required on all vehicles sold or registered in New York state	55	85
—	**Radio Equipment**		
UM7	AM/FM ETR stereo and clock - consists of Delco AM/FM ETR stereo radio, electronic seek-up/down tuning, integral digital clock, and dual front and rear acoustically matched response speakers - Grand Am & Grand Am LE	NC	NC
UM6	AM/FM ETR stereo w/cassette and clock - consists of Delco AM/FM ETR stereo radio and cassette w/automatic reverse, electronic seek-up/down tuning, integral digital clock, and dual front and rear acoustically matched response speakers - Grand Am	119	140
	Grand Am LE		
	- w/o value option package R6A	119	140
	- t/w value option package R6A	NC	NC
	Grand Am SE	NC	NC
U1D	AM stereo/FM ETR stereo w/compact disc player, graphic equalizer and clock - consists of Delco AM stereo/FM stereo ETR radio and compact disc player w/automatic reverse and search and replay, electronic seek-up/down tuning, integral 5-band graphic equalizer, integral digital clock, weather band, and dual front and rear acoustically matched response speakers		
	Grand Am LE		
	- w/o option package R6A	463	545
	- t/w option package R6A	344	405
	Grand Am SE	344	405
—	**Tires**		
QFE	P185/75R14 BW steel belted radial - Grand Am & Grand Am LE	NC	NC
QME	P195/70R14 BW steel belted radial (touring) (requires N78 hi-tech turbo wheels)		
	Grand Am LE		
	- w/o W32 or value option package R6A	97	114
	- t/w W32 or value option package R6A	NC	NC
QLG	P205/55R16 BW steel belted radial (includes FE3 performance suspension) - Grand Am SE	NC	NC
—	**Wheels**		
P08	tri-lace wheel covers - Grand Am & Grand Am LE	NC	NC
N78	14" hi-tech turbo aluminum w/locking package (requires QME tires)		
	Grand Am LE		
	- w/o W32 or value option package R6A	225	265
	- t/w W32 or value option package R6A	NC	NC
PG0	16" color-keyed aluminum - Grand Am SE	NC	NC
V2C	16" bright faced aluminum - Grand Am SE	NC	NC
—	**Preferred Equipment Packages (PEPS)**		
1SB	**Grand Am LE Coupe Package 1** — includes air conditioning, tilt steering wheel, controlled cycle wipers, cruise control, power door locks	704	810
1SC	**Grand Am LE Coupe Package 2** — includes Grand Am LE Package 1 plus remote deck lid release, split folding rear seat, power windows	1090	1265
1SB	**Grand Am LE Sedan Package 1** — includes air conditioning, tilt steering		

Mfgs. Code	Description	Base Cost	Sgstd. List
	wheel, controlled cycle wipers, cruise control, power door locks	738	850
1SC	**Grand Am LE Sedan Package 2** — includes Grand Am LE Sedan Package 1 plus remote deck lid release, split folding rear seat, power windows	1180	1370
R6A	**Grand Am LE Coupe & Sedan Value Option Package R6A** — includes 14" aluminum wheels, P195/70R14 touring tires, AM/FM stereo w/cassette	339	394

GRAND PRIX GT

Mfgs. Code	Description	Base Cost	Sgstd. List
GRAND PRIX GT (6 Cylinder)			
P37	Coupe	16530	19154
Destination Charge:		485	485

STANDARD EQUIPMENT:
GRAND PRIX GT: Power door locks, power deck lid release, power windows, leather-wrapped tilt steering wheel with radio controls, cruise control, power 6-way driver seat, front bucket seats (with metrix cloth, power articulating split thighs, headrest, lateral support, 3-position lumbar), 2-passenger rear bucket seats with headrest, console, luggage compartment pass-through, leather-wrapped shift knob, front/rear carpeted floor mats, Delco ETR AM stereo/FM stereo auto-reverse cassette w/search replay/5-band graphic equalizer/digital clock, high performance 6-speaker sound system with separate power amplifiers/coaxial speakers, black fixed mast antenna, anti-theft steering column lock/key system, right roof rail assist grips, dual stainless steel exhaust system, gas-shock hood assists, cigarette lighter, dual horns, 3.1 liter V6 engine, 4-speed automatic transmission, rallye tuned suspension, Goodyear P215/60R16 Eagle GT +4 tires, 16" cast aluminum wheels, air conditioning.

ACCESSORIES

Mfgs. Code	Description	Base Cost	Sgstd. List
—	**Engines**		
LH0	3.1 liter MFI V6 (available only w/4-speed automatic transmission	NC	NC
—	**Transmissions**		
MX0	4-speed automatic - w/3.1 liter V6 (LH0)	NC	NC
NB2	**Emission Requirements for California**	85	100
WDV	**Warranty Enhancements for New York** — required on vehicles registered and sold in New York state	55	65
JL9	**Power Brakes** — anti-lock - w/o value option package R6B	786	925
	- t/w value option package R6B	NC	NC
CF5	**Power Sunroof** — Glass - w/o value option package R6A	553	650
	- t/w value option package R6A	NC	NC
C49	**Defogger, Electric Rear Window**	136	160
U68	**Electronic Compass w/Trip Computer & Service Reminder**	234	275
UV6	**Head-Up Display** — (requires slate gray or camel interior trim)	213	250
AU0	**Remote Keyless Entry** — (includes two transmitters)	106	125
V56	**Luggage Carrier, Deck Lid** — (black)	98	115
DH6	**Dual Illuminated Visor Vanity Mirrors**	73	86
US7	**Power Antenna**	64	75
B4U	**Aero Performance Package** — includes aero ground effects, wheel flares, wide body applique, specific front/rear fascias, 16" cross-lace aluminum wheel, and P225/60R16 Goodyear Eagle GT +4 tires (requires 3.1 liter V6 engine)	2206	2595
—	**Radio Equipment**		
UX1	AM stereo/FM stereo ETR w/cassette, graphic equalizer and clock - consists		

Mfgs. Code	Description	Base Cost	Sgstd. List
	of Delco AM stereo/FM stereo ETR radio and electronic seek-up/down tuning, integral 5-band graphic equalizer, integral digital clock, leather-wrapped steering wheel w/radio controls, and 6-speaker performance sound system	NC	NC
U1A	AM/FM ETR stereo w/compact disc player, 5-band graphic equalizer and clock - consists of Delco AM stereo/FM stereo and compact disc player w/electronic seek-up/down tuning, integral 5-band graphic equalizer, 6-speaker performance sound system and anti-theft feature - w/o value option package R6B	192	226
	- t/w value option package R6B	NC	NC
—	**Seats**		
AQ9	articulating sport bucket - 'metrix' cloth trim	NC	NC
	'Ventura' leather trim		
	- w/o value option package R6A	383	450
	- t/w value option package R6A	NC	NC
AC3	**Power Sear, Driver 6-Way**	NC	NC
—	**Tires**		
QGW	P215/60R16 BW steel belted radial	NC	NC
1SB	**Grand Prix GT Coupe Package 1 —** includes power antenna, dual illuminated visor vanity mirrors, remote keyless entry, electronic compass w/trip computer and service reminder, head-up instrument display	361	411
R6A	**Grand Prix GT Coupe Package R6A —** includes articulating seats with leather trim, sunroof	710	825
R6B	**Grand Prix GT Coupe Package R6B —** includes anti-lock brakes and AM/FM stereo w/compact disc player	691	801

GRAND PRIX LE & SE

	GRAND PRIX (6 Cylinder)		
H19	LE Sedan	12622	14294
J37	SE Coupe	12854	14894
J19	SE Sedan	13190	15284
	Destination Charge: All models	485	485

STANDARD EQUIPMENT:

GRAND PRIX LE & SE: Fixed-mast antenna, black-finish door window frames, soft-fascia type bumpers w/integral rub strips, tinted glass, mini-quad headlamps, composite halogen headlamps (LE Sedan), flash-to-pass feature, fog lamps, mirrors - sport LH remote, RH manual (LE Coupe, LE Sedan), mirrors - sport, LH and RH power remote (body color on SE) (SE Coupe), belt reveal moldings (SE Coupe), wide body side, body color/red insert molding (LE Coupe, SE Coupe), wide body color, black with bright insert body side molding (LE Sedan), wheel-lip black moldings (LE Sedan), P205/70R15 blackwall steel-belted radial touring tires (LE Coupe, LE Sedan), P215/60R16 blackwall steel-belted radial Eagle GT +4 tires (SE Coupe), compact spare tire, custom 15" wheel covers with "bolt-on" feature (LE Coupe, LE Sedan), cast aluminum 16" x 6.5" wheels w/wheel locks (color-keyed or machine-faced) (SE Coupe), controlled cycle windshield wipers (SE Coupe), extensive acoustical insulation, electronic push-button control air conditioning, roof rail assist grip (SE Coupe), passive driver and front passenger seat and shoulder belts, rear seat shoulder and lap belts, cigarette lighter, front floor console w/storage (SE Coupe), rear floor console w/storage and cupholders (SE Coupe), front-overhead console w/storage and reading lamps (SE Coupe), cruise control (SE Coupe), deck lid release (SE Coupe), side window defoggers, metrix cloth interior (SE Coupe), Pallex cloth interior (LE Coupe, LE Sedan), dual horns, instrumentation (mechanical analog speedometer, coolant temperature, fuel and trip odometer) (LE Coupe, LE Sedan), instrumentation (mechanical analog speedometer, odometer, tachometer, coolant temperature, oil pressure, voltmeter and trip odometer) (SE Coupe), luggage, underhood and IP courtesy lighting, fully carpeted luggage compartment trim, cargo net luggage compartment (SE Coupe), carpeted front and rear door mats, day/night rearview mirrors, RH and LH covered mirrors (LE Coupe, LE Sedan, SE Coupe), power door locks (SE Coupe), power windows w/"express down" feature (SE Coupe), Delco ETR AM/FM stereo radio w/clock (LE Coupe, LE Sedan), Delco ETR AM stereo/FM stereo radio with auto-reverse cassette, graphic equalizer, clock, leather steering wheel with radio controls (SE Coupe), high performance six-speaker sound system with separate power amplifier and coaxial speakers (SE Coupe), 40/60 split front seats w/folding armrest and reclining RH and LH seatbacks (LE Coupe, LE Sedan), bucket seats w/power articulating split thighs, headrest, lateral support and 3-position lumbar (SE Coupe), bucket seats w/power recliners, articulating split thighs, and 3-position lumbar (manually articulating), 6-way power driver's seat (SE Coupe), rear seat (three passenger w/integrated headrests), leather-wrapped shift knob (SE Coupe), four-spoke urethane sport steering wheel (LE Coupe, LE Sedan), leather-wrapped sport steering wheel w/radio controls (SE Coupe), tilt column steering wheel (SE Coupe), seatback pockets (SE Coupe), 2.3 liter 16-valve DOHC L4 engine with multi-port fuel injection (LE Coupe, LE Sedan), 3.1 liter V6 engine with multi-port fuel injection (SE Coupe), four-wheel power disc brakes, engine coolant recovery system, dual exhaust system (SE Coupe), stainless steel exhaust system, extensive anti-corrosion protection, front-wheel drive, GM computer command control, power rack-and-pinion steering, four-wheel independent suspension, MacPherson strut front suspension, rally tuned suspension (SE Coupe), 3-speed automatic transmission (w/2.3 liter DOHC L4 only) (LE Coupe, LE Sedan), 4-speed automatic transmission w/overdrive (w/3.1 liter V6 or 3.4 liter V6) (SE Coupe).

ACCESSORIES

Code	Description	Base Cost	Sgstd. List
—	**Transmissions**		
MX1	3-speed automatic - only available w/LD2 engine	NC	NC
MX0	4-speed automatic (NA w/LD2 engine) - w/3.1 liter V6 (LH0)	170	200
A90	**Deck Lid Release, Remote Control**	43	50
C49	**Defogger, Electric Rear Window**	136	160
NB2	**Emission Requirements for California**	85	100
D84	**Paint, Two-Tone** — (NA w/option package 1SA, SE Sedan, BYP sport appearance package, or B4U aero performance package)	89	105
JL9	**Power Brakes** — anti-lock (NA w/LE Sedan)	786	925
CF5	**Power Sunroof Glass** — (includes mirror w/dual reading lamps, NA Grand Prix LE) Grand Prix SE Coupe (requires option package 1SC/1SD/1SE)		
	- w/o B20 custom trim	574	675
	- t/w B20 custom trim	553	650
	Grand Prix SE Sedan		
	- w/o B20 custom trim	574	675
	- t/w B20 custom trim	553	650
—	**Engines**		
LD2	2.3 liter DOHC MFI 4-cylinder quad 4 (only available w/3-speed automatic transmission)	NC	NC
LH0	3.1 liter MFI V6 (only available w/4-speed automatic transmission	NC	NC
AU0	**Remote Keyless Entry** — (includes two transmitters, NA Grand Prix LE Sedan)	106	125
UB3	**Gauge Cluster** — (includes tachometer, oil pressure, and voltmeter; required w/bucket seats) - Grand Prix LE Sedan (requires option package 1SC)	72	85
	Grand Prix SE Coupe		
	- w/o value option package R6A, R6B, or BYP appearance	72	85
	- t/w value option package R6A, R6B, or BYP appearance	NC	NC
	Grand Prix SE Sedan		
	- w/o value option package R6A or BYP	72	85
	- t/w value option package R6A or BYP	NC	NC
UV6	**Head-Up Display (n/a Grand Prix LE Sedan)** — Grand Prix SE Coupe		

Mfgs. Code	Description	Base Cost	Sgstd. List
	(requires slate gray or camel interior trim)	213	250
	Grand Prix SE Sedan (requires slate gray or camel interior trim)		
	- w/o value option package R6B	213	250
	- t/w value option package R6B	NC	NC
V56	**Luggage Carrier, Deck Lid (black)**	98	115
B37	**Mats, Carpet Front & Rear** — Grand Prix LE Sedan	38	45
	- Grand Prix SE	NC	NC
DG7	**LH & RH Power Sport Mirrors** — (NA Grand Prix LE)	66	78
DH6	**Illuminated Visor Vanity Mirrors** — (NA Grand Prix LE)	73	86
A31	**Power Windows** — Grand Prix SE Coupe	217	255
	- Grand Prix LE/SE Sedan	272	320
AU3	**Power Door Locks** — Grand Prix SE Coupe	162	190
	- Grand Prix LE/SE Sedan	196	230
US7	**Power Antenna** — Grand Prix LE Sedan (requires option package 1SC)	64	75
	- Grand Prix SE	64	75
B20	**Custom Interior Trim** — consists of luggage compartment, cargo net, leather-wrapped steering wheel, 'metrix' cloth seats, overhead mini console with reading lamps, and rear seat pass-through (NA Grand Prix LE)		
	Grand Prix SE Coupe		
	- w/o value option package R6A or R6B	279	328
	- t/w value option package R6A or R6B	NC	NC
	Grand Prix SE Sedan		
	- w/o value option package R6A or R6B	275	324
	- t/w value option package R6A or R6B	NC	NC
B4U	**Aero Performance Package** — includes aero ground effects, wheel flares, wide bodyside applique, specific front and rear fascias, 16" cross-lace aluminum wheels, and P225/60R16 Goodyear Eagle GT +4 tires (requires bucket seats and UB3 Gauge Cluster, and LH0 3.1 liter engine) - Grand Prix SE Coupe	2206	2595
—	**Radio Equipment**		
UM7	AM/FM ETR stereo and clock - consists of Delco AM/FM ETR stereo radio, electronic seek-up/down tuning, integral digital clock, and dual front and rear acoustically matched response speakers	NC	NC
UM6	AM/FM ETR stereo w/cassette and clock - consists of Delco AM/FM ETR stereo radio and cassette w/automatic reverse, electronic seek-up/down tuning, integral digital clock, and dual front and rear acoustically matched response speakers - Grand Prix LE Sedan (NA w/option package 1SA)	119	140
	- Grand Prix SE Coupe/Sedan	119	140
UX1	AM stereo/FM stereo ETR w/cassette, graphic equalizer and clock - consists of Delco AM stereo/FM stereo ETR radio and cassette w/auto reverse and search & replay, electronic seek-up/down tuning, integral 5-band graphic equalizer, integral digital clock, leather-wrapped steering wheel w/radio controls, and 6-speaker performance sound system (NA w/LD2 engine or Grand Prix LE)		
	Grand Prix SE Coupe (NA w/option packages 1SA or 1SB)		
	- w/o value option package R6A/R6B or B20	502	590
	- t/w value option package R6B or B20	459	540
	- t/w value option package R6A	NC	NC
	Grand Prix SE Sedan (NA w/option package 1SA)		
	- w/o value option package R6A/R6B or B20	502	590
	- t/w value option package R6B or B20	459	540
	- t/w value option package R6A	NC	NC
U1A	AM/FM ETR stereo w/compact disc player, 5-band graphic equalizer and clock - consists of Delco AM stereo/FM stereo and compact disc player w/electronic seek-up/down tuning, integral 5-band graphic equalizer, integral digital clock, steering wheel controls, 6-speaker performance		

Mfgs. Code	Description	Base Cost	Sgstd. List
	sound system and anti-theft feature (NA w/LD2 engine or Grand Prix LE)		
	Grand Prix SE Coupe (NA w/option packages 1SA or 1SB)		
	- w/o value option package R6A/R6B or B20	694	816
	- t/w value option package R6B or B20	651	766
	- t/w value option package R6A	192	226
	Grand Prix SE Sedan (NA w/option package 1SA)		
	- w/o value option package R6A/R6B or B20	694	816
	- t/w value option package R6B or B20	651	766
	- t/w value option package R6A	192	226
—	**Seats**		
AM6	45/55 split w/center armrest (3-passenger seating) - 'pallex' cloth trim	NC	NC
	- 'metrix' cloth trim (included in B20)		
AR9	bucket (requires UB3 Gauge Cluster) 'pallex' cloth trim, includes console - Grand Prix LE	94	110
	Grand Prix SE Coupe		
	- w/o value option package R6B or BYP appearance	94	110
	- t/w value option package R6B or BYP appearance	NC	NC
	Grand Prix SE Sedan	94	110
AN3	custom sport bucket (requires UB3 Gauge Cluster, only available w/B20custom interior trim, includes console, 'metrix' cloth trim)		
	- Grand Prix LE	119	140
	Grand Prix SE Coupe		
	- w/o value option package R6B or BYP appearance	119	140
	- t/w value option package R6B or BYP appearance	NC	NC
	Grand Prix SE Sedan	119	140
AC3	**Power Seat, Driver 6-Way** — Grand Prix LE (requires option package 1SC)	247	290
	- Grand Prix SE	247	290
BYP	**Sport Appearance Package** — includes lower aero ground effects, bucket seats w/console, UB3 Gauge Cluster, PH3 15" aluminum sport wheel, high gloss greenhouse moldings, and dual outlet exhaust (requires LH0 3.1 liter engine)		
	Grand Prix SE Coupe		
	- t/w B20 (w/o value option package R6A or R6B)	578	680
	- w/o B20, value option package R6A or R6B	553	650
	- t/w value option package R6A	506	595
	- t/w value option package R6B	NC	NC
—	**Tires**		
QIN	P205/70R15 BW steel belted radial - Grand Prix LE/SE	NC	NC
WDV	**Warranty Enhancements for New York** — required on all vehicles registered and sold in New York state	55	65
—	**Wheels**		
PH3	15" aluminum sport w/locking package (optional w/QIN 15" tires only)		
	- Grand Prix LE Sedan (NA w/option package 1SA)	225	265
	Grand Prix SE Coupe (NA w/option package 1SA)		
	- w/o value option package R6B or BYP	225	265
	- t/w value option package R6B or BYP	NC	NC
	Grand Prix SE Sedan	225	265
1SB	**Grand Prix SE Coupe Package 1** — includes tilt steering wheel and controlled cycle wipers	162	190
1SC	**Grand Prix SE Coupe Package 2** — includes Grand Prix SE Coupe Package 1 plus cruise control and illuminated entry system	353	415
1SD	**Grand Prix SE Coupe Package 3** — includes Grand Prix SE Coupe Package 2 plus power windows, power door locks, 6-way driver power seat, LH & RH power sport mirrors	388	428
1SE	**Grand Prix SE Coupe Package 4** — includes Grand Prix SE Coupe Package 3 plus remote control deck lid release, power antenna, dual		

Mfgs. Code	Description	Base Cost	Sgstd. List
	illuminated visor mirrors, remote keyless entry	673	764
1SB	**Grand Prix LE Sedan Package 1 —** includes controlled cycle wipers and tilt steering wheel	162	190
1SC	**Grand Prix LE Sedan Package 2 —** includes Grand Prix LE Sedan Package 1 plus cruise control	340	400
1SB	**Grand Prix SE Sedan Package 1 —** includes tilt steering wheel, controlled cycle wipers, cruise control and illuminated entry system	326	415
1SC	**Grand Prix SE Sedan Package 2 —** includes Grand Prix SE Sedan Package 1 plus power windows, power door locks, 6-way driver power seat LH & RH power sport mirrors	477	533
1SD	**Grand Prix SE Sedan Package 3 —** includes Grand Prix SE Sedan Package 2 plus remote deck lid release, power antenna, illuminated visor vanity mirror, remote keyless entry	763	869
R6A	**Grand Prix SE Coupe Package R6A —** includes AM/FM stereo w/cassette and graphic equalizer, custom trim, rallye gauges and tachometer	605	703
R6B	**Grand Prix SE Coupe Package R6B —** includes custom trim, sport appearance package	657	763
R6A	**Grand Prix SE Sedan Package R6A —** includes AM/FM stereo w/cassette and graphic equalizer, custom trim, rallye gauges and tachometer	602	699
R6B	**Grand Prix SE Sedan Package R6B —** includes custom trim, head-up instrument display	344	399

GRAND PRIX STE

GRAND PRIX STE (6 Cylinder)			
T19	Sedan	17255	19994
Destination Charge:		485	485

STANDARD EQUIPMENT:

GRAND PRIX STE: Power antenna, black-finish door window frames, soft-fascia type bumpers w/integral rub strips, tinted glass, composite halogen headlamps, flash-to-pass feature, fog lamps, body side molding with bright insert, P215/60R16 blackwall steel-belted radial Eagle GT +4 tires, compact spare tire, cast aluminum 16" x 6.5" STE wheels w/wheel locks, controlled cycle windshield wipers, extensive acoustical insulation, electronic push-button control air conditioning, roof rail assist grip, passive driver and front passenger seat and shoulder belts, rear seat shoulder and lap belts, cigarette lighter, front floor console w/storage, cruise control, deck lid release, side window defoggers, metrix cloth interior, dual horns, instrumentation (mechanical analog speedometer, odometer, tachometer, coolant temperature, oil pressure, voltmeter and trip odometer), illuminated entry system, luggage, underhood and IP courtesy lighting, fully carpeted luggage compartment trim, cargo net luggage compartment, carpeted front and rear floor mats, day/night rearview mirrors, illuminated visor vanity, RH and LH mirrors, power door locks, power windows w/"express down" feature, Delco ETR AM stereo/FM stereo radio with auto-reverse cassette, graphic equalizer, clock, leather steering wheel with radio controls, high-performance eight-speaker sound system with sub-woofer amplifier, bucket seats w/power recliners, articulating split thighs and 3-position lumbar (manually articulating headrest), 6-way power driver's seat, rear seat (three passenger w/integrated headrests, folding armrest and luggage compartment pass-through), leather-wrapped shift knob, leather-wrapped sport steering wheel w/radio controls, tilt column steering wheel, front door map pockets, rear door map pockets, seatback pockets, 3.1 liter V6 engine with multi-port fuel injection, four-wheel power disc brakes, engine coolant recovery system, dual exhaust system, stainless steel exhaust system, extensive anti-corrosion protection, front-wheel drive, GM computer command control, power rack-and-pinion steering, four-wheel independent suspension, MacPherson strut front suspension, rally tuned suspension, 4-speed automatic transmission w/overdrive (w/3.1 liter V6 and

3.4 liter V6).

ACCESSORIES

Code	Description	Base Cost	Sgstd. List
—	**Engines**		
LH0	3.1 liter MFI V6 (available only w/4-speed automatic transmission)	NC	NC
—	**Transmissions**		
MX0	4-speed automatic - w/3.1 liter V6 (LH0)	NC	NC
NB2	**Emission Requirements for California**	85	100
WDV	**Warranty Enhancements for New York** — required on all models registered and sold in New York state	55	65
JL9	**Power Brakes** — anti-lock - w/o value option package R6A	786	925
	- t/w value option package R6A	NC	NC
CF5	**Power Sunroof, Glass**	553	650
UV6	**Head-Up Display** — (requires slate gray interior trim)	213	250
V56	**Luggage Carrier, Deck Lid** — (black)	98	115
—	**Radio Equipment**		
UX1	AM stereo/FM stereo ETR w/cassette, graphic equalizer and clock - consists of Delco AM stereo/FM stereo ETR radio and electronic seek-up/down tuning, integral 5-band graphic equalizer, integral digital clock, leather-wrapped steering wheel w/radio controls, and 6-speaker performance sound system	NC	NC
U1A	AM/FM ETR stereo w/compact disc player, 5-band graphic equalizer and clock - consists of Delco AM stereo/FM stereo and compact disc player w/electronic seek-up/down tuning, integral 5-band graphic equalizer, 6-speaker performance sound system and anti-theft feature - w/o value option package R6A	192	226
	- t/w value option package R6A	NC	NC
—	**Seats**		
AQ9	articulating sport bucket - 'metrix' cloth trim	NC	NC
	'Ventura' leather trim	383	450
—	**Power Seat, Driver 8-Way**	NC	NC
QGW	**Tires** — P215/60R16 BW steel belted radial	NC	NC
1SB	**Grand Prix STE Sedan Package 1** — includes articulating seats with leather trim and sunroof	443	500
R6A	**Grand Prix STE Package R6A** — includes anti-lock power brakes, AM/FM stereo w/compact disc player	691	801

LE MANS

Code	Description	Base Cost	Sgstd. List
	LE MANS (4 Cylinder)		
X08	2 Dr Aerocoupe (Value Leader)	7006	7574
N08	2 Dr Aerocoupe	7640	8304
N19	4 Dr LE Sedan	8054	8754
	Destination Charge: All models	325	325

STANDARD EQUIPMENT:

LE MANS: Body color deck lid molding (LE Sedan), full wheel covers (Value Leader Aerocoupe, LE Aerocoupe, LE Sedan), integral roof luggage rack mounting provision, lower accent gray paint theme (LE Aerocoupe), remote sport mirrors (driver's side only on Value Leader) (body color on LE Sedan and GSE), halogen headlamps, roll-down rear windows (LE Sedan), soft-ray tinted glass (LE Aerocoupe, LE Sedan), P175/70R13 steel-belted blackwall tires (Value Leader Aerocoupe, LE

instruments (trip odometer, tachometer, (not available on Value Leader and LE Sedan), temperature gauge and upshift lamp (manual transmission only and not available on Value Leader), luggage compartment security cover (Value Leader Aerocoupe, LE Aerocoupe), motorized, 2-point passive shoulder belts with manual lap belts for driver and right front passenger, one-key locking system, rear assist handles, rear seat lap and shoulder belts (outboard positions), side window defroster, 1.6L L4 engine with electronic fuel injection, extensive anti-corrosion protection, full-size spare wheel and tire, MacPherson strut front suspension with stabilizer bar, power front disc/rear drum brakes, rack-and-pinion steering, semi-independent trailing arm torsion beam rear suspension with coil springs, sport suspension tuning, 4-speed manual transmission (Value Leader Aerocoupe), 5-speed manual transmission (LE Aerocoupe, LE Sedan).

ACCESSORIES

Code	Description	Base Cost	Sgstd. List
R6A	**Value Option Pkg R6A** — (includes removable sunroof, front and rear floor mats, AM/FM stereo radio w/cassette) - Le Mans Value Leader - suggested list price - 812, discount - 150, net price	567	662
	- Le Mans LE - suggested list price - 505, discount - 150, net price	306	355
L73	**Engine** — 1.6 liter TBI 4 cylinder	NC	NC
—	**Transmissions**		
MM4	4-speed manual (Value Leader only)	NC	NC
MM5	5-speed manual (NA Value Leader)	NC	NC
MX1	3-speed automatic (NA Value Leader)	378	445
C60	**Air Conditioning** — (requires power steering, NA Value Leader)	578	680
NB2	**Emission Requirements for California**	NC	NC
B37	**Floor Mats, Front & Rear**		
	- w/o value option package R6A	28	33
	- t/w value option package R6A	NC	NC
N40	**Power Steering** — (requires air conditioning, and auto transmission, NA Value Leader)	182	214
—	**Radio Equipment**		
UM7	AM/FM ETR stereo and clock - (consists of Delco AM/FM ETR stereo radio, integral digital clock, electronic seek-up/down tuning, dual front and rear acoustically matched response speakers, and fixed mast antenna)		
	- Value Leader	261	307
	- LE Aerocoupe & LE Sedan	NC	NC
UM6	AM/FM ETR stereo w/cassette and clock - (consists of Delco AM/FM ETR stereo radio, cassette with automatic reverse, integral digital clock, electronic seek-up/down tuning, dual front and rear acoustically matched response speakers, and fixed mast antenna)		
	Value Leader		
	- w/o value option package R6A	365	429
	- t/w value option packge R6A	NC	NC
	LE Aerocoupe & LE Sedan		
	- w/o value option package R6A	104	122
	- t/w value option package R6A	NC	NC
AD3	**Sunroof, Removable**		
	- w/o value option package R6A	298	350
	- t/w value option package R6A	NC	NC
WDV	**Warranty Enhancements for New York**	55	65
Q97	**Tires** — P175/70R13 BW steel belted radial	NC	NC

SUNBIRD

		Base Cost	Sgstd. List
SUNBIRD (4 Cylinder)			
C37	Coupe	8015	8684
C69	Sedan	8108	8784
B37	LE Coupe	8433	9444
B69	LE Sedan	8523	9544
B67	LE Convertible	12872	14414
D37	SE Coupe	9550	10694
SUNBIRD (6 Cylinder)			
U37	GT Coupe	11112	12444
Destination Charge: All models		455	455

STANDARD EQUIPMENT:

SUNBIRD: Acoustical insulation, aero extensions (GT Coupe), front air dam, black-finish door window frames, black-finish windshield wipers, convertible top with electrohydraulic operation (LE Convertible), composite headlamps (LE Coupe, LE Sedan, LE Convertible), fog lamps (GT Coupe), full-dropping rear quarter window (LE Convertible), GT specific front and rear fascia with partially hidden headlamps (GT Coupe), mirrors (LH remote control, RH manual convex) (LE Convertible, GT Coupe), wide body-side moldings (LE Coupe, LE Sedan), narrow, black body-side moldings (SE Coupe, GT Coupe), soft-fascia, front and rear bumpers with rub strip moldings, rear deck spoiler (SE Coupe, GT Coupe), P185/75R14 blackwall all-season steel-belted radial tires (LE Coupe, LE Sedan, LE Convertible, SE Coupe), P215/60R14 blackwall, steel-belted Goodyear Eagle GT +4 tires including WS6 suspension (GT Coupe), compact spare tire, custom wheel covers (LE Coupe, LE Sedan, LE Convertible), hi-tech aluminum 14" wheels (requires P195/70R14 touring tires) (SE Coupe), GT specific 15" aluminum wheels (GT Coupe), cigarette lighter, color-keyed seat belts, driver and passenger covered visor vanity mirror, day/night rearview mirror, Delco ETR AM/FM stereo radio with seek and scan and clock (LE Coupe, LE Sedan, LE Convertible, SE Coupe), Delco ETR AM/FM stereo radio with seek and scan and auto-reverse cassette (GT Coupe), front floor console, inside hood release, Pontiac warm red instrument panel lighting, power top convertible switch (LE Convertible), reclining front bucket seats, side window defoggers, deluxe vinyl four-spoke steering wheel (LE Coupe, LE Sedan, LE Convertible, SE Coupe), tinted glass (LE Convertible, GT Coupe), upshift indicator light (manual transmission-equipped cars only), 2.0 liter OHC 4-cycle engine with electronic fuel injection (LE Coupe, LE Sedan, LE Convertible, SE Coupe), 3.1 liter V6 engine with MPFI (GT Coupe), 5-speed manual transmission with overdrive, Delco Freedom II battery, dual/dual exhaust system (GT Coupe), extensive anti-corrosion protection, front-wheel drive, dull-coil suspension, MacPherson strut front suspension, power front disc/rear drum brake system, power rack-and-pinion steering, 24mm front stabilizer bar (LE Coupe, LE Sedan, SE Coupe), 21mm rear stabilizer bar (LE Convertible, GT Coupe), stainless steel exhaust system.

ACCESSORIES

		Base Cost	Sgstd. List
—	**Engines**		
LT2	2.0 liter OHC FI 4-cylinder - Sunbird, Sunbird LE & Sunbird SE	NC	NC
LH0	3.1 liter FI 6-cylinder (requires UB3 rally gauges w/tachometer, N78 hi-tech turbo wheels and QME tires)		
	Sunbird LE		
	- w/o value option package R6B	561	660
	- t/w value option package R6B	NC	NC
	Sunbird SE	561	660
	Sunbird GT	NC	NC
—	**Transmissions**		
MM5	5-speed manual	NC	NC

PONTIAC

Mfgs. Code	Description	Base Cost	Sgstd. List
MX1	3-speed automatic	395	465
C60	**Air Conditioning —** (requires A01 tinted glass)	612	720
C41	**Non Air Conditioning**	NC	NC
D06	**Front Seat Armrest** - Sunbird LE	49	58
	- Sunbird GT	NC	NC
NB2	**Emission Requirements for California**	85	100
K34	**Cruise Control —** Sunbird LE, Sunbird SE & Sunbird GT	179	210
A90	**Remote Decklid Release —** Sunbird LE	43	50
C49	**Defogger, Electric Rear Window —** Sunbird, Sunbird LE Coupe & Sedan, Sunbird SE & Sunbird GT	136	160
A01	**Tinted Glass —** Sunbird & Sunbird LE Coupe/Sedan	89	105
	- Sunbird LE Convertible	NC	NC
	- Sunbird SE & Sunbird GT	NC	NC
TR9	**Lamp Group —** (includes glove box lamp, IP courtesy lamp, and headlamp -on warning system) - Sunbird LE	25	29
	- Sunbird GT	NC	NC
VK3	**Front License Plate Bracket**	NC	NC
AU3	**Power Door Locks —** Sunbird LE Coupe, SE Coupe, & GT Coupe	162	190
	- Sunbird LE Sedan	196	230
	- Sunbird LE Convertible	NC	NC
A31	**Power Windows —** (requires AU3 power door locks) - Sunbird LE Coupe, SE Coupe, & GT Coupe	208	245
	- Sunbird LE Sedan	264	310
	- Sunbird LE Convertible	NC	NC
—	**Radio Equipment**		
UM7	AM/FM ETR stereo and clock - consists of Delco AM/FM ETR stereo radio, integral radio, integral digital clock, electronic seek-up/down tuning, dual front and rear acoustically matched response speakers and fixed mast antenna - Sunbird, Sunbird LE & Sunbird SE	NC	NC
UN6	AM/FM ETR stereo w/cassette and clock - consists of Delco AM/FM ETR stereo radio and cassette w/automatic reverse, search and repeat, tape equalizer, electronic seek-up/down tuning, integral digital clock, dual front and rear acoustically matched response speakers and fixed mast antenna - Sunbird & Sunbird LE	145	170
	Sunbird LE		
	- w/o value option package R6A/R6B	145	170
	- t/w value option package R6A/R6B	NC	NC
	Sunbird GT	NC	NC
U1C	AM/FM ETR stereo w/compact disc player and clock (NA Sunbird) - consists of Delco AM/FM ETR stereo radio, w/compact disc player, integral digital clock, electronic seek-up/down tuning, dual front and rear acoustically matched response speakers and fixed mast antenna		
	Sunbird LE		
	- w/o value option package R6A/R6B	337	396
	- t/w value option package R6A/R6B	192	226
	Sunbird SE	337	396
	Sunbird GT	192	226
U39	**Rally Gauges —** Sunbird LE	42	49
UB3	**Rally Gauges with Tachometer —** (requires LH0 3.1 liter V6 engine)		
	Sunbird LE Coupe & Sedan		
	- w/o option package 1SC, 1SD, or value option package R6B	108	127
	- t/w option package 1SC, 1SD	66	78
	- t/w value option package R6B	NC	NC
	Sunbird LE Convertible		
	- w/o option package 1SC, or value option package R6B	108	127
	- t/w option package 1SC	66	78
	- t/w option package R6B	NC	NC

Mfgs. Code	Description	Base Cost	Sgstd. List
	Sunbird SE & GT	NC	NC
AM9	**Split Folding Rear Seat** — Sunbird LE Coupe & Sedan	128	150
T43	**Spoiler, Rear Deck Lid** — Sunbird LE Convertible	60	70
	- Sunbird SE & Sunbird GT	NC	NC
N33	**Tilt Steering Wheel**	115	135
AD3	**Sunroof, Glass** — (removable) - Sunbird LE Coupe, Sunbird SE, & Sunbird GT	298	350
CD4	**Controlled Cycle Wipers** — Sunbird LE	47	55
B20	**White Vinyl Interior Trim** — Sunbird LE Convertible	64	75
D84	**Paint, Two-Tone Custom** — Sunbird LE	86	101
AR9	**Seats, Reclining Bucket** — 'Pallex' cloth trim (all models)	NC	NC
WDV	**Warranty Enhancements for New York** — required on vehicles sold or registered in New York state (see dealer for details)	55	65
—	**Tires**		
QFE	P185/75R14 BW steel belted radial (NA w/LH0 3.1 liter V6 engine - Sunbird & Sunbird LE	NC	NC
QME	P195/70R14 BW steel belted radial (touring) requires N78 hi-tech turbo aluminum wheels		
	Sunbird LE		
	- w/o value option package R6A/R6B	97	114
	- t/w value option package R6A/R6B	NC	NC
	Sunbird SE	NC	NC
QHF	P205/60R15 BW steel belted radial - Sunbird GT	NC	NC
—	**Wheels**		
P08	tri-lace wheel cover - Sunbird & Sunbird LE		
N78	14" hi-tech turbo aluminum w/locking package (requires QME tires)		
	Sunbird LE		
	- w/o value option package R6A/R6B	225	265
	- t/w value option package R6A/R6B	NC	NC
	Sunbird SE	NC	NC
N78	14" white hi-tech turbo aluminum w/locking package (requires QME tires)		
	Sunbird LE Convertible		
	- w/o value option package R6A/R6B	225	265
	- t/w value option package R6A/R6B	NC	NC
PF7	15" aluminum wheels - Sunbird GT	NC	NC
1SB	**Sunbird LE Coupe/LE Sedan Package 1** — includes tinted glass and LH remote and RH manual sport mirrors	134	158
1SC	**Sunbird LE Coupe/LE Sedan Package 2** — includes Sunbird LE Coupe/LE Sedan Package 1 plus tilt steering wheel, controlled cycle wipers, air conditioning, lamp group, front seat armrest, rally gauges, cruise control	792	914
1SD	**Sunbird LE Coupe/LE Sedan Package 3** — includes Sunbird LE Coupe/LE Sedan Package 2 plus split folding rear seat, remote deck lid release	962	1114
1SB	**Sunbird LE Convertible Package 1** — includes tilt steering wheel, controlled cycle wipers, air conditioning	774	910
1SC	**Sunbird LE Convertible Package 2** — includes Sunbird LE Convertible Package 1 plus lamp group, front seat armrest, rally gauges, cruise control, remote deck lid release	700	806
1SB	**Sunbird SE Coupe Package 1** — includes tilt steering wheel, controlled cycle wipers, air conditioning	774	910
1SC	**Sunbird SE Coupe Package 2** — includes Sunbird SE Coupe Package 1 plus lamp group, front seat armrest, cruise control, split folding rear seat, remote deck lid release	1196	1407
1SB	**Sunbird GT Coupe Package 1** — includes tilt steering wheel, controlled cycle wipers, air conditioning	774	910
1SC	**Sunbird GT Coupe Package 2** — includes Sunbird GT Coupe Package 1 plus cruise control, split folding rear seat, remote deck lid release	1122	1320
R6A	**Sunbird LE Package R6A** — includes 14" turbo aluminum wheels,		

Mfgs. Code	Description	Base Cost	Sgstd. List
	P195/70R14 touring tires, AM/FM stereo w/cassette	323	374
R6B	**Sunbird LE Package R6B —** includes 3.1 liter FI 6-cylinder engine, rally gauges with tachometer, 14" turbo aluminum wheels, P195/70R14 touring tires, AM/FM stereo w/cassette	787	911
	- w/o 1SC or 1SD	787	911
	- w/1SC or 1SD	745	862

TRANS SPORT

TRANS SPORT (6 Cylinder)

Mfgs. Code	Description	Base Cost	Sgstd. List
M06	Base Trans Sport	13948	15619
M06	SE Trans Sport	16868	18889

Destination Charge: All models ... 510 510

STANDARD EQUIPMENT:

TRANS SPORT: Fixed-mast black antenna, soft-fascia type bumpers with integral rub strips, sliding right-hand side door, four rear flip-out side glass windows, rear lift gate, 2-speed rear window washer/wiper, heat-repelling solar-coated glass windshield, tinted glass (Trans Sport), deep-tinted tinted glass (Trans Sport SE), dual remote sport mirrors, composite halogen headlamps, lower aero molding (accent color on Trans Sport, upper color on SE models), black bodyside molding (Trans Sport SE), black roof treatment (may be deleted on base model), two-tone paint theme (Trans Sport), monotone paint theme (Trans Sport SE), 14" styled wheel cover (Trans Sport), 15" sport cast aluminum wheel (Trans Sport SE), P205/70R14 steel-belted blackwall tires (Trans Sport), P205/65R15 steel-belted touring tires (Trans Sport SE), remote fuel filler door release, exterior composite body panels that resist dents, dings, and rust, color-keyed shoulder belts (outboard positions on all seating rows), front and rear position floor mats, Metrix cloth trim (Trans Sport SE), Pallex cloth trim (Trans Sport), front bucket seats with headrest, recline feature, armrest with 5-passenger capacity (2nd row bench) (Trans Sport), front bucket seats with 6-passenger capacity (2nd and 3rd row modulars) (Trans Sport SE), front air conditioning (Trans Sport SE), analog instrumentation with tachometer and gauges, cruise control (Trans Sport SE), day/night rearview mirror, Delco ETR AM/FM stereo radio with clock (Trans Sport), Delco ETR AM/FM stereo with auto-reverse cassette and clock (Trans Sport SE), dual note horns, flash-to-pass feature, hose and attachment inflator pump (Trans Sport SE), intermittent wipers, side front window defoggers, four-spoke sport steering wheel (Trans Sport), leather-wrapped sport steering wheel (Trans Sport SE), tilt steering wheel (Trans Sport SE), covered RH and LH visor vanity mirrors, front and side door map pockets, mesh net front seatback pockets, overhead consolette (Trans Sport SE), seatback cup holders (with modular seating) (Trans Sport SE), under dash cup and mug holder, 3.1 liter V6 engine with electronic fuel injection, power disc/drum brakes, compact spare tire with hoist cable, composite body panels that resist dents, dings and rust, electronic ride control (ERC) (Trans Sport SE), engine coolant recovery system, front-wheel drive, GM computer command control, power rack-and-pinion steering, stainless steel exhaust system, fully independent front MacPherson struts, trailing axle rear suspension, 3-speed automatic transmission.

ACCESSORIES

Mfgs. Code	Description	Base Cost	Sgstd. List
LG6	**Engine —** 3.1 liter FI V6	NC	NC
MX1	**Transmission —** 3-speed automatic	NC	NC
C67	**Air Conditioning —** (electronic controls) - Trans Sport	684	805
	- Trans Sport SE	NC	NC
C41	**Non Air Conditioning —** (available on Trans Sport option package 1SA only)	NC	NC
B2Q	**Black Roof, Delete —** (NA Trans Sport SE)	NC	NC

Mfgs. Code	Description PONTIAC	Base Cost	Sgstd. List
NB2	**California Emission Requirements**	85	100
C49	**Defogger, Electric Rear Window**	136	160
AJ1	**Glass, Deep Tint** — (excludes windshield and front doors) - Trans Sport	208	245
	- Trans Sport SE	NC	NC
V54	**Luggage Carrier, Roof —**		
	Trans Sport		
	- w/o value option package R6A	123	145
	- t/w value option package R6A	NC	NC
	Trans Sport SE	123	145
DG7	**Mirrors, Sport LH Power & RH Power Convex**		
	Trans Sport		
	- w/o value option package R6A	41	48
	- t/w value option package R6A	NC	NC
	Trans Sport SE	NC	NC
AB5	**Power Door Locks** — key activated	230	270
AG9	**Power Seat, Driver 6-Way**		
	Trans Sport		
	- w/o value option package R6A	247	290
	- t/w value option package R6A	NC	NC
	Trans Sport SE	247	290
A31	**Power Windows** — (express down, driver's side; available only with AB5 power door locks)	217	255
—	**Radio Equipment**		
UM7	AM/FM ETR stereo w/clock - consists of Delco AM/FM ETR stereo radio, electronic seek-up/down tuning, integral digital clock, and dual front and rear acoustically matched response speakers (NA Trans Sport SE)	NC	NC
UM6	AM/FM stereo w/cassette and clock - consists of Delco AM/FM ETR stereo radio and cassette w/automatic reverse, electronic seek-up/down tuning, integral digital clock, and dual front and rear coaxial speakers		
	- Trans Sport	119	140
	- Trans Sport SE	NC	NC
U1A	AM stereo/FM stereo w/compact disc player, clock and graphic equalizer - consists of Delco AM/FM ETR stereo radio and compact disc player, electronic seek-up/down tuning, integral 5-band graphic equalizer, integral digital clock and dual front and rear coaxial speakers - Trans Sport	439	516
	- Trans Sport SE	320	376
—	**Seats**		
ZP5	5-passenger seating - NA Trans Sport SE - consists of dual reclining front bucket seats and 3-passenger bench seat in second row	NC	NC
AB3	6-passenger seating - consists of dual reclining front bucket seats, 2 modular seats in 2nd row and 2 modular seats in 3rd row; also includes rear air distribution, 3rd row shoulder belts and 3rd row floor mats		
	- Trans Sport	446	525
	- Trans Sport SE	94	110
ZP7	7-passenger seating - consists of dual reclining front bucket seats, 3 modular seats in 2nd row and 2 modular seats 3rd row; also includes rear air defroster, 3rd row shoulder belts and 3rd row floor mats		
	- Trans Sport	574	675
	- Trans Sport SE (rear air distributor, 3rd row shoulder belts and 3rd row floor mats standard	94	110
—	**Tires**		
XHX	P205/70R14 BW steel belted radial (NA Trans Sport SE)	NC	NC
XMR	P205/65R15 BW steel belted radial touring (requires PH3 aluminum wheel on Trans Sport; requires PH3/13P aluminum wheel on Trans Sport SE)		
	- Trans Sport	53	62
	- Trans Sport SE	NC	NC
WDV	**Warranty Enhancements for New York** — required on all models sold and		

Mfgs. Code	Description	Base Cost	Sgstd. List
	registered in New York state	55	65
—	**Wheels**		
PH3	15" aluminum sport (requires XMR touring tires) - (w/locking package)		
	- Trans Sport	225	265
	- Trans Sport SE	NC	NC
13P	15" bright faced aluminum (NA Trans Sport; requires XMR touring tires) replaces standard color-keyed on SE	NC	NC
1SA	**Trans Sport Option Package** — includes model w/standard equipment		
1SB	**Trans Sport Option Package 1** — includes lamp group, tilt steering wheel, cruise control, electronic control air conditioning	1029	1210
1SC	**Trans Sport Option Package 2** — includes Trans Sport Option Package 1 plus power door locks and power windows	818	935
1SA	**Trans Sport SE Option Package** — includes model w/standard equipment		
1SB	**Trans Sport SE Option Package 1** — includes power door locks, power windows, driver 6-way power seat, rear defogger	255	275
R6A	**Trans Sport Value Option Package R6A** — includes 6-way driver power seat, sport LH power and RH power convex mirrors, roof luggage carrier	300	348

6000 LE & SE

Mfgs. Code	Description	Base Cost	Sgstd. List
6000 (4 Cylinder)			
F69	LE Sedan	11218	12999
6000 (6 Cylinder)			
F35	LE Wagon	14411	16699
J69	SE Sedan	15878	18399
Destination Charge:	All models	480	480

STANDARD EQUIPMENT:

6000: Fixed mast black antenna, composite headlamps, fog lamps, front air dam (black on LE, body color on S/E), black front grille with bright periphery (LE Sedan, LE Wagon), body color front grille with black periphery (S/E Sedan), luggage roof rack (LE Wagon), mirrors (sport LH remote control, RH manual (black), aero body color moldings (S/E Sedan), black door frame and window moldings, roof drip and belt reveal (bright on LE, black on S/E), wide body side molding (black with bright insert on LE, body color with bright insert on S/E), soft fascia front and rear bumpers, rear deck spoiler (S/E Sedan), P185/75R14 blackwall steel-belted radial tires (LE Sedan, LE Wagon), P195/70R15 blackwall steel-belted radial Goodyear Eagle GT +4 tires (S/E Sedan), compact spare tire, tri-lace wheel covers (LE Sedan, LE Wagon), specific S/E cast aluminum 15" wheels with wheel locks (S/E Sedan), acoustical insulation, custom air conditioning (LE Wagon, S/E Sedan), cigarette lighter, cloth headliner with foam backing, controlled-cycle windshield wipers (S/E Sedan), resume speed cruise control (S/E Sedan), cut-pile carpeting, day/night rearview mirror, electric rear window defogger (LE Wagon, S/E Sedan), Delco AM/FM stereo radio (LE Sedan, LE Wagon), Delco ETR AM/FM stereo radio with seek and scan, auto-reverse cassette and digital clock (S/E Sedan), front/rear deluxe carpeted floor mats, RH and LH door map pockets (S/E Sedan), dual horns, front and rear door lamp switches, glove compartment with lock, inside hood release, map pocket on front seatback (S/E Sedan), 3-passenger fold-down center armrest (LE Sedan, LE Wagon), power windows (S/E Sedan), rear compartment courtesy lamps (LE Wagon), rear quarter swingout window (LE Wagon), vinyl third seat-rear facing (LE Wagon), automatic color-keyed front, lap/shoulder belts, color-keyed rear lap/shoulder belts, sidewall carpet (LE Wagon), side window defoggers, split-folding second seat (LE Wagon), deluxe, four-spoke steering wheel (LE Sedan, LE Wagon), four-spoke leather-wrapped steering wheel (S/E Sedan), tilt steering wheel (S/E Sedan), tinted glass, trunk lamp, RH and LH covered visor vanity mirrors, 2.5 liter overhead valve 4-cylinder engine with electronic fuel injection (not available with 4-speed automatic) (LE Sedan), 3.1 liter V6 engine with electronic fuel injection (LE Wagon, S/E Sedan), automatic 3-speed transmission (LE Sedan), automatic 4-speed transmission (with 3.1L with V6 only) (LE Wagon, S/E Sedan), Delco Freedom II battery, dual outlet sport exhaust (S/E Sedan), engine coolant recovery system, front-wheel drive, GM computer command control, MacPherson strut front suspension, power front disc/rear drum brake system, power rack-and-pinion steering (increased radio on S/E AWD), trailing arm and beam rear suspension with integral stabilizer bar.

ACCESSORIES

Code	Description	Base Cost	Sgstd. List
—	**Engines**		
LR8	2.5 liter FI 4-cylinder (available 6000 LE Sedan only, available w/MX1 automatic transmission only)	NC	NC
LH0	3.1 liter FI V6 (requires C60 air conditioning) - 6000 LE Sedan	561	660
	- 6000 LE Wagon & SE Sedan	NC	NC
—	**Transmissions**		
MX1	3-speed automatic (available 6000 LE Sedan only)	NC	NC
MX0	4-speed automatic (available w/LH0 V6 engine only) - 6000 LE Sedan (available w/option package 1SC or 1SD only)	170	200
	- 6000 LE Wagon & 6000 SE	NC	NC
C60	**Air Conditioning**	684	805
C41	**Non Air Conditioning** — (available w/option package 1SA on 6000 LE Sedan only)	NC	NC
K34	**Cruise Control, Resume Speed** — 6000 LE Sedan/Wagon	179	210
	- 6000 SE	NC	NC
A90	**Deck Lid Release, Remote Control**	43	50
C49	**Defogger, Electric Rear Window** — 6000 LE Sedan	136	160
	- 6000 LE Wagon & 6000 SE Sedan	NC	NC
NB2	**Emission Requirements for California**	85	100
D86	**Paint, Two Tone** — (NA 6000 SE or LE Wagon w/woodgrain siding)	98	115
AU3	**Power Door Locks**		
	6000 LE Sedan		
	- w/o value option package R6B	196	230
	- t/w value option package R6B	NC	NC
	6000 LE Wagon		
	- w/o value option package R6B	230	270
	- t/w value option package R6B	NC	NC
	6000 SE	NC	NC
A31	**Power Windows** — (includes front door courtesy lamps) - 6000 LE Sedan/Wagon	276	325
	- 6000 SE	NC	NC
B34	**Mats, Carpet Front and Rear Floor** — 6000 LE Sedan	38	45
	- 6000 LE Wagon & 6000 SE	NC	NC
AG1	**Power Seat, Driver 6-Way** — (NA w/notchback bench seat)	247	290
—	**Radio Equipment**		
UM7	AM/FM ETR stereo and clock - consists of Delco AM/FM ETR stereo radio, electronic seek-up/down tuning, integral digital clock, and dual front and rear acoustically matched response speakers	NC	NC
UM6	AM/FM ETR stereo w/cassette and clock - consists of Delco AM/FM ETR stereo radio and cassette w/automatic reverse, electronic seek-up/down tuning, integral digital clock, and dual front and rear acoustically matched response speakers		
	6000 LE Sedan/Wagon		
	- w/o value option package R6A or R6B	119	140
	- t/w value option package R6A or R6B	NC	NC
	6000 SE	NC	NC

Mfgs. Code	Description **PONTIAC**	Base Cost	Sgstd. List
UX1	AM/FM stereo ETR w/cassette, graphic equalizer and clock - consists of Delco AM/FM stereo ETR radio and cassette w/automatic reverse and search and replay, electronic seek-up/down tuning, integral 5-band graphic equalizer, integral digital clock, dual front and rear acoustically matched response speakers, and steering wheel controls (NA 6000 LE Sedan/Wagon - 6000 SE Sedan (includes coaxial speakers)	264	310
U1A	AM stereo/FM stereo ETR w/compact disc player, graphic equalizer and clock - consists of Delco AM/FM stereo ETR radio and compact disc player w/electronic seek-up/down tuning, integral 5-band graphic equalizer, integral digital clock, dual front and rear acoustically matched response speakers, and steering wheel controls (NA 6000 LE Sedan/Wagon) - 6000 SE Sedan (includes coaxial speakers)	456	536
—	**Seats**		
A65	notchback w/center armrest (3-passenger seating) - 'pallex' cloth trim (6000 LE)	NC	NC
AM6	45/55 split w/center armrest (3-passenger seating) 6000 LE only - w/o custom interior trim or value option package R6A or R6B ('Pallex' cloth trim)	156	183
	- t/w custom interior or value option package R6A or R6B	NC	NC
AR9	bucket; includes console - 'metrix' cloth trim (6000 SE)	NC	NC
B20	custom interior trim (6000 LE only) - consists of 45/55 split seat in 'metrix' cloth, power driver and passenger recliners and UB3 gauges - w/o value option package R6A or R6B	453	533
	- t/w value option package R6A or R6B	298	350
—	**Tires**		
QFE	P185/75R14 BW steel belted radial (NA 6000 SE)	NC	NC
QFF	P185/75R14 WW steel belted radial (NA 6000 SE)	58	68
QDP	P195/70R15 BW steel belted radial (NA 6000 LE)	NC	NC
WDV	**Warranty Enhancements for New York** — required on all models sold or registered in New York state	55	65
—	**Wheels**		
N78	14" aluminum sport w/locking package (NA 6000 SE) - w/o value option package R6A	225	265
	- t/w value option package R6A	NC	NC
PH3	15" color-keyed aluminum w/locking package (NA 6000 LE Sedan/Wagon)	NC	NC
BX3	woodgrain siding, simulated (LE Wagon only) includes rocker panel moldings and door edge moldings	251	295
1SA	**6000 LE Sedan Package** — includes model and standard equipment		
1SB	**6000 LE Sedan Package 1** — includes air conditioning, tilt steering wheel, controlled cycle wipers, visor vanity mirror	858	1009
1SC	**6000 LE Sedan Package 2** — includes 6000 LE Sedan Package 1 plus cruise control, power door locks	883	1024
1SD	**6000 LE Sedan Package 3** — includes 6000 LE Sedan Package 2 plus power windows and remote deck lid release	1202	1399
1SA	**6000 LE Wagon Package** — includes model and standard equipment		
1SB	**6000 LE Wagon Package 1** — includes tilt steering wheel and controlled cycle wipers	162	190
1SC	**6000 LE Wagon Package 2** — includes 6000 LE Wagon Package 1 plus cruise control	340	400
1SD	**6000 LE Wagon Package 3** — includes 6000 LE Wagon Package 2 plus power door locks and power windows	497	570
1SA	**6000 SE Sedan Package** — includes model and standard equipment		
1SB	**6000 SE Sedan Package 1** — includes remote deck lid release and mirror w/dual reading lamps	62	73
R6A	**6000 LE Sedan & Wagon Package R6A** — includes 14" aluminum sport wheels, 45/55 split seat, AM/FM stereo with auto reverse cassette	397	463

Mfgs. Code	Description	Base Cost	Sgstd. List
R6B	**6000 LE Sedan Package R6B** — includes power door locks, 45/55 split seat, AM/FM stereo with auto reverse cassette - LE Sedan w/package 1SA or 1SB	409	478
	- LE Sedan w/package 1SC or 1SD	213	248
R6B	**6000 LE Wagon Package R6B** — includes power door locks, 45/55 split seat, AM/FM stereo with auto reverse cassette - LE Wagon w/o Package 1SD	443	518
	- LE Wagon w/package 1SD	213	248

1991 Specifications

MAKE & MODEL	LENGTH	WIDTH	HEIGHT	WHEEL-BASE	CURB WEIGHT	FUEL TANK
BUICK						
Century Custom Cpe	189.1	69.4	53.7	104.8	2832	15.7
Century Custom Sdn	189.1	69.4	54.2	104.8	2869	15.7
Century Limited Sdn	189.1	69.4	54.2	104.8	2870	15.7
Century Custom Wgn	190.9	69.4	54.2	104.8	3071	15.7
Century Limited Wgn	190.9	69.4	54.2	104.8	3072	15.7
Le Sabre Cpe	196.5	72.4	53.8	110.8	3231	18.0
Le Sabre Limited Cpe	196.5	72.4	53.8	110.8	3264	18.0
Le Sabre Custom Sdn	196.5	72.4	54.6	110.8	3269	18.0
Le Sabre Limited Sdn	196.5	72.4	54.6	110.8	3301	18.0
Park Avenue Sdn	205.2	74.9	55.7	110.8	3580	18.0
Park Avenue Ultra Sdn	205.2	74.9	55.7	110.8	3662	18.0
Reatta Cpe	183.7	73.0	51.2	98.5	3392	18.8
Reatta Conv	183.7	73.0	51.2	98.5	3593	18.8
Regal Custom Cpe	193.6	72.5	53.0	107.5	3247	16.5
Regal Limited Cpe	193.6	72.5	53.0	107.5	3251	16.5
Regal Gran Sport Cpe	193.6	72.5	53.0	107.5	3315	16.5
Regal Custom Sdn	194.6	70.9	54.5	107.5	3321	16.5
Regal Limited Sdn	194.6	70.9	54.5	107.5	3324	16.5
Regal Gran Sport Sdn	194.6	70.9	54.5	107.5	3385	16.5
Riviera Cpe	198.3	71.7	53.6	108.0	3496	18.8
Roadmaster Estate Sdn	215.8	78.1	56.9	115.9	4061	23.0
Roadmaster Estate Wgn	217.5	78.9	60.1	115.9	4415	22.0
Skylark Cpe	180.0	66.6	52.1	103.4	2593	13.6
Skylark Custom Cpe	180.0	66.6	52.1	103.4	2628	13.6
Skylark Gran Sport Cpe	180.0	66.6	52.1	103.4	2659	13.6
Skylark Sdn	180.0	66.6	52.1	103.4	2654	13.6
Skylark Custom Sdn	180.0	66.6	52.1	103.4	2692	13.6
Skylark Luxury Edition Sdn	180.0	66.6	52.1	103.4	2716	13.6
CADILLAC						
Allante Cpe/Conv	178.7	73.5	51.2	99.4	3537	22.0
Broughman Sdn	221.0	76.5	57.4	121.5	4282	25.0
Cpe Deville	202.6	73.4	54.9	110.8	3545	18.0
Sdn Deville	205.6	73.4	55.2	113.8	3622	18.0
Eldorado Cpe	191.4	72.4	53.2	108.0	3470	18.8
Fleetwood Cpe	202.6	73.4	54.9	110.8	3593	18.0
Fleetwood Sdn	205.6	73.4	55.2	113.8	3675	18.0
Fleetwood Sixty Special Sdn	205.6	73.4	55.2	113.8	3706	18.0
Seville Sdn	190.8	72.0	53.2	106.0	3512	18.8
Seville STS Sdn	190.8	72.0	53.2	106.0	3584	18.8
CHEVROLET						
Beretta Cpe	183.4	68.2	56.2	103.4	2649	15.6
Beretta GT Cpe	183.4	68.2	56.2	103.4	2797	15.6
Beretta GTZ Cpe	183.4	68.2	56.2	103.4	2795	15.6
Camaro RS Cpe	192.6	72.4	50.4	101.0	3103	15.5
Camaro RS Conv	192.6	72.4	—	101.0	—	15.5
Camaro Z28 Cpe	192.6	72.4	50.4	101.0	3319	15.5
Camaro Z28 Conv	192.6	72.4	—	101.0	3400	15.5
Caprice Sdn	214.1	77.0	56.7	115.9	3907	23.0
Caprice Classic Sdn	214.1	77.0	56.7	115.9	3945	23.0
Caprice Wgn	217.3	79.6	60.9	115.9	4354	22.0
Cavalier Cpe	182.3	66.3	51.3	101.3	2436	13.6
Cavalier Sdn	182.3	66.3	52.9	101.3	2444	13.6

MAKE & MODEL	LENGTH	WIDTH	HEIGHT	WHEEL-BASE	CURB WEIGHT	FUEL TANK
Cavalier Z24 Cpe	181.2	66.3	51.3	101.3	—	13.6
Cavalier Wgn (4 Cyl)	181.1	66.3	52.8	101.3	—	13.6
Cavalier Wgn (6 Cyl)	181.1	66.3	52.8	101.3	—	11.2
Corsica Ntchbk Sdn (4 Cyl)	183.4	68.2	56.2	103.4	2638	15.6
Corsica Ntchbk Sdn (6 Cyl)	183.4	68.2	56.2	103.4	2742	15.6
Corsica Htchbk Sdn (4 Cyl)	183.4	68.2	56.2	103.4	2706	15.6
Corsica Htchbk Sdn (6 Cyl)	183.4	68.2	56.2	103.4	2810	15.6
Corvette Cpe	178.6	71.0	46.7	96.2	3223	20.0
Corvette Conv	178.6	71.0	46.4	96.2	3263	20.0
Corvette ZR-1	178.5	74.0	46.7	96.2	3465	20.0
Lumina Cpe	198.3	71.7	53.3	107.5	3111	17.1
Lumina Sdn	198.3	71.0	53.6	107.5	3192	17.1
Lumina Euro Cpe	198.3	71.7	53.3	107.5	3239	16.5
Lumina Euro Sdn	198.3	71.0	53.6	107.5	3321	16.5
CHRYSLER						
Imperial Sdn	203.0	68.9	55.3	109.3	3554	16.0
Le Baron Conv	184.9	68.5	52.3	100.3	2991	14.0
Le Baron Cpe	184.9	68.5	51.0	100.3	2853	14.0
Le Baron Sdn	182.7	68.1	53.7	103.3	3040	16.0
New Yorker Fifth Avenue Sdn	198.6	68.9	55.1	109.3	3423	16.0
New Yorker Salon Sdn	193.6	68.9	54.8	104.5	3301	16.0
Town & Country Wgn	190.5	69.6	66.4	119.3	3817	20.0
TC by Maserati	175.8	68.5	51.9	93.0	3276	14.0
DODGE						
Caravan FWD Wgn	175.9	72.0	64.6	112.3	3271	20.0
Caravan AWD Wgn	175.9	72.0	64.6	112.3	3271	18.0
Grand Caravan FWD Wgn	190.5	72.0	64.8	119.3	3644	20.0
Grand Caravan AWD Wgn	190.5	72.0	64.8	119.3	3644	18.0
Colt Htchbk	158.7	65.5	51.9	93.9	2205	13.2
Colt Vista Wgn 2WD	176.6	64.8	57.3	103.3	2667	13.2
Colt Vista Wgn 4WD	176.6	64.8	59.4	103.5	2965	14.5
Daytona Htchbk	179.2	69.3	50.1	97.0	2777	14.0
Dynasty Sdn	192.0	68.5	54.8	104.3	2996	16.0
Monaco LE Sdn	192.8	69.3	56.5	106.0	2983	16.0
Monaco ES Sdn	192.8	69.3	56.5	106.0	3060	16.0
Shadow Conv	171.7	67.3	52.6	97.0	2910	14.0
Shadow 3 Dr Htchbk	171.7	67.3	52.6	97.0	2615	14.0
Shadow 5 Dr Htchbk	171.7	67.3	52.6	97.0	2652	14.0
Spirit Sdn	181.2	68.1	53.5	103.3	2801	16.0
Spirit R/T Sdn	181.2	68.1	53.5	103.3	3060	16.0
Stealth Base Spt Cpe	179.1	72.4	49.1	97.2	3076	19.8
Stealth ES Spt Cpe	179.1	72.4	49.1	97.2	3175	19.8
Stealth R/T Spt Cpe	180.5	72.4	49.1	97.2	3352	19.8
Stealth R/T Turbo Spt Cpe	180.5	72.4	49.1	97.2	3793	19.8
EAGLE						
Premier LX Sdn	192.8	69.3	54.7	106.0	2983	16.0
Premier ES Sdn	192.8	69.3	54.7	106.0	3060	16.0
Summit Sdn	170.1	65.7	52.8	96.7	2271	13.2
Talon 2WD Spt Cpe	172.4	66.9	52.0	97.2	2651	15.8
Talon AWD Spt Cpe	172.4	66.9	52.0	97.2	2800	15.8
FORD						
Escort Pony 2 Dr Htchbk	170.0	66.7	52.5	98.4	2287	11.9
Escort LX 2 Dr Htchbk	170.0	66.7	52.5	98.4	2312	11.9
Escort LX 4 Dr Htchbk	170.0	66.7	52.5	98.4	2355	11.9

MAKE & MODEL	LENGTH	WIDTH	HEIGHT	WHEEL-BASE	CURB WEIGHT	FUEL TANK
Escort LX 4 Dr Wgn	171.3	66.7	53.6	98.4	2411	11.9
Escort GT 2 Dr Htchbk	170.0	66.7	52.5	98.4	2364	11.9
Festiva L Htchbk	140.5	63.2	55.3	90.2	1785	10.0
Festiva GL Htchbk	140.5	63.2	55.3	90.2	1785	10.0
LTD Crown Victoria S Sdn	211.0	77.5	55.6	114.3	3822	18.0
LTD Crown Victoria Sdn	211.0	77.5	55.6	114.3	3822	18.0
LTD Crown Victoria Wgn	215.7	79.3	56.5	114.3	4028	18.0
LTD Crown Victoria LX Sdn	211.0	77.5	55.6	114.3	3822	18.0
LTD Crown Victoria LX Wgn	215.7	79.3	56.5	114.3	4028	18.0
LTD Country Squire Wgn	215.7	79.3	56.5	114.3	4028	18.0
LTD Country Squire LX Wgn	215.7	79.3	56.5	114.3	4028	18.0
Mustang LX Sdn	179.6	68.3	52.1	100.5	2759	15.4
Mustang LX Htchbk	179.6	68.3	52.1	100.5	2824	15.4
Mustang LX Conv	179.6	68.3	52.1	100.5	2960	15.4
Mustang LX 5.0L Sdn	179.6	68.3	52.1	100.5	—	15.4
Mustang LX 5.0L Htchbk	179.6	68.3	52.1	100.5	—	15.4
Mustang LX 5.0L Conv	179.6	68.3	52.1	100.5	—	15.4
Mustang GT Htchbk	179.6	68.3	52.1	100.5	—	15.4
Mustang GT Conv	179.6	68.3	52.1	100.5	—	15.4
Probe GL Htchbk	177.0	67.9	51.8	99.0	2730	15.1
Probe LX Htchbk	177.0	67.9	51.9	99.0	—	15.1
Probe GT Htchbk	177.0	68.3	52.0	99.0	—	15.1
Taurus L Sdn	188.4	70.8	54.1	106.0	3049	16.0
Taurus L Wgn	191.9	70.8	55.4	106.0	3276	16.0
Taurus GL Sdn	188.4	70.8	54.1	106.0	—	16.0
Taurus GL Wgn	191.9	70.8	55.4	106.0	—	16.0
Taurus LX Sdn	188.4	70.8	54.1	106.0	—	16.0
Taurus LX Wgn	191.9	70.8	55.4	106.0	—	16.0
Taurus SHO Sdn	191.9	70.8	54.1	106.0	—	16.0
Tempo GL 2 Dr Sdn	176.7	68.3	52.8	99.9	2529	15.9
Tempo GL 4 Dr Sdn	177.0	68.3	52.9	99.9	2587	15.9
Tempo GL 4 Dr Sdn	176.7	68.3	52.8	99.9	—	15.9
Tempo GLS 2 Dr Sdn	176.7	68.3	52.8	99.9	—	15.9
Tempo GLS 4 Dr Sdn	177.0	68.3	52.9	99.9	—	15.9
Tempo LX 4 Dr Sdn	176.7	68.3	52.8	99.9	—	15.9
Tempo 4WD 4 Dr Sdn	177.0	68.3	52.9	99.9	—	15.9
Thunderbird Cpe	198.7	72.7	52.7	113.0	3550	19.0
Thunderbird LX Cpe	198.7	72.7	52.7	113.0	—	19.0
Thunderbird SC Cpe	198.7	72.7	52.7	113.0	—	19.0
GEO						
Metro Htchbk Cpe	146.1	62.0	52.4	89.2	1620	10.6
Metro Htchbk Sdn	150.0	62.0	53.5	93.1	1693	10.6
Prizm Ntchbk Sdn	170.7	65.2	52.4	95.7	2435	13.2
Prizm Htchbk Sdn	170.7	65.2	52.3	95.7	2450	13.2
Storm Sport Cpe	163.4	66.7	51.1	96.5	2282	12.4
Storm Htchbk Cpe	163.4	66.7	51.7	96.5	2371	12.4
Tracker	142.5	64.2	65.6	86.6	2238	11.1
LINCOLN						
Continental Sdn	205.1	72.7	55.6	109.0	3633	18.6
Mark VII Cpe	202.8	70.9	54.2	108.5	3782	21.0
Town Car Sdn	218.8	78.1	56.7	117.4	4035	20.0
MERCURY						
Capri Conv	166.1	64.6	50.2	94.7	2385	11.1
Cougar LS Cpe	199.9	72.7	52.7	113.0	3587	19.0

MAKE & MODEL	LENGTH	WIDTH	HEIGHT	WHEEL-BASE	CURB WEIGHT	FUEL TANK
Cougar XR7 Cpe	199.9	72.7	52.7	113.0	—	19.0
Grand Marquis GS Sdn	213.6	77.5	55.5	114.3	3836	18.0
Grand Marquis LS Sdn	213.6	77.5	55.5	114.3	—	18.0
Grand Marquis Colony Park GS Wgn	218.0	79.3	56.5	114.3	4032	18.0
Grand Marquis Colony Park LS Wgn	218.0	79.3	56.5	114.3	—	18.0
Sable GS Sdn	192.2	70.8	54.4	106.0	3131	16.0
Sable LS Sdn	192.2	70.8	54.4	106.0	—	16.0
Sable GS Wgn	193.2	70.8	55.1	106.0	3260	16.0
Sable LS Wgn	193.2	70.8	55.1	106.0	—	16.0
Topaz GS 2 Dr Sdn	176.7	68.3	52.8	99.9	2546	15.9
Topaz GS 4 Dr Sdn	177.0	68.3	52.9	99.9	2602	15.9
Topaz LS 4 Dr Sdn	177.0	68.3	52.9	99.9	—	15.9
Topaz XR5 2 Dr Sdn	176.7	68.3	52.8	99.9	—	15.9
Topaz LTS 4 Dr Sdn	177.0	68.3	52.9	99.9	—	15.9
Tracer Ntchbk	170.9	66.7	52.7	98.4	2356	11.9
Tracer LTS Ntchbk	170.9	66.7	52.7	98.4	—	11.9
Tracer Wgn	171.3	66.7	53.6	98.4	2468	11.9
OLDSMOBILE						
Bravada	178.9	65.2	65.5	107.0	3939	20.0
Custom Cruiser Wgn	217.5	79.7	60.1	115.9	4435	22.0
Cutlass Calais Cpe	179.3	66.6	52.4	103.4	2518	13.6
Cutlass Calais Sdn	179.3	66.6	52.4	103.4	2585	13.6
Cutlass Calais S Cpe	179.3	66.6	52.4	103.4	2518	13.6
Cutlass Calais S Sdn	179.3	66.6	52.4	103.4	2585	13.6
Cutlass Calais Quad 442 Cpe	179.3	66.6	52.4	103.4	2518	13.6
Cutlass Calais Quad 442 Sdn	179.3	66.6	52.4	103.4	2585	13.6
Cutlass Calais SL Cpe	179.3	66.6	52.4	103.4	2691	13.6
Cutlass Calais SL Sdn	179.3	66.6	52.4	103.4	2754	13.6
Cutlass Calais International Series Cpe	179.3	66.6	52.4	103.4	2823	13.6
Cutlass Calais International Series Sdn	179.3	66.6	52.4	103.4	2896	13.6
Cutlass Ciera Cpe	190.3	69.5	54.1	104.9	2771	15.7
Cutlass Ciera Sdn	190.3	69.5	54.1	104.9	2813	15.7
Cutlass Ciera SL Sdn	190.3	69.5	54.1	104.9	2958	15.7
Cutlass Cruiser Wgn	194.4	69.5	54.5	104.9	2975	15.7
Cutlass Cruiser SL Wgn	194.4	69.5	54.5	104.9	3160	15.7
Cutlass Supreme Cpe	192.3	71.0	53.3	107.5	3187	16.5
Cutlass Supreme Conv	192.3	71.0	54.3	107.5	3602	16.5
Cutlass Supreme Sdn	192.2	71.0	54.8	107.5	3286	16.5
Eighty-Eight Royale Cpe	196.3	72.6	53.9	110.8	3248	18.0
Eighty-Eight Royale Sdn	196.3	72.6	54.6	110.8	3292	18.0
Eighty-Eight Royale Brougham Cpe	196.3	72.6	53.9	110.8	3277	18.0
Eighty-Eight Royale Brougham Sdn	196.3	72.6	54.6	110.8	3303	18.0
Ninety-Eight Regency Elite Sdn	205.8	74.6	55.1	110.8	3606	20.0
Ninety-Eight Touring Sdn	205.8	74.6	55.1	110.8	3689	20.0
Toronado Cpe	200.3	72.8	53.0	108.0	3455	18.8
Toronado Trofeo Cpe	200.3	72.8	53.0	108.0	3525	18.8
PLYMOUTH						
Acclaim Sdn	181.2	68.1	53.5	103.3	2794	16.0
Colt Htchbk	158.7	65.5	51.9	93.9	2205	13.2
Colt Vista Wgn 2WD	176.6	64.8	57.3	103.3	2667	13.2
Colt Vista Wgn 4WD	176.6	64.8	59.4	103.5	2965	14.5
Laser Cpe	170.5	66.5	51.4	97.2	2524	15.9
Sundance 2 Dr Htchbk	171.7	67.3	52.6	97.0	2617	14.0

MAKE & MODEL	LENGTH	WIDTH	HEIGHT	WHEEL-BASE	CURB WEIGHT	FUEL TANK
Sundance 4 Dr Htchbk	171.7	67.3	52.6	97.0	2654	14.0
Voyager FWD Wgn	175.9	72.0	64.8	112.3	3271	20.0
Voyager AWD Wgn	175.9	72.0	64.8	112.3	3271	18.0
Grand Voyager FWD Wgn	190.5	72.0	64.8	119.3	3644	20.0
Grand Voyager AWD Wgn	190.5	72.0	64.8	119.3	3644	18.0
PONTIAC						
Bonneville LE Sdn	197.6	73.0	54.5	110.8	3325	18.0
Bonneville SE Sdn	197.6	73.0	54.5	110.8	3417	18.0
Bonneville SSE Sdn	198.6	73.0	54.6	110.8	3604	18.0
Firebird Cpe	195.1	72.4	49.7	101.0	3121	15.5
Firebird Formula Cpe	195.1	72.4	49.7	101.0	3370	15.5
Firebird Trans Am Cpe	195.2	72.4	49.5	101.0	3343	15.5
Firebird GTA Cpe	195.1	72.4	49.7	101.0	3456	15.5
Grand Am LE Cpe	179.2	66.5	52.6	103.4	2575	13.6
Grand Am LE Sdn	179.2	66.5	52.6	103.4	2630	13.6
Grand Am SE Cpe	179.2	66.5	52.6	103.4	2795	13.6
Grand Am SE Sdn	179.2	66.5	52.6	103.4	2857	13.6
Grand Prix LE Sdn	194.5	71.9	54.8	107.5	—	16.5
Grand Prix SE Cpe	194.5	71.9	53.3	107.5	3214	16.5
Grand Prix SE Sdn	194.5	71.9	54.8	107.5	3282	16.5
Grand Prix GT Cpe	194.5	71.9	53.3	107.5	3357	16.5
Grand Prix STE Sdn	194.5	71.9	54.8	107.5	3434	16.5
Le Mans Aerocoupe	163.7	65.5	53.5	99.2	2105	13.2
Le Mans LE Aerocoupe	163.7	65.5	53.3	99.2	2127	13.2
Le Mans LE Sdn	172.4	65.7	53.7	99.2	2183	13.2
Sunbird LE Cpe	180.7	66.3	52.0	101.3	2484	13.6
Sunbird LE Sdn	180.7	66.3	53.6	101.3	2502	13.6
Sunbird LE Conv	180.7	66.3	52.0	101.3	2661	13.6
Sunbird SE Cpe	180.7	66.3	52.0	101.3	2482	13.6
Sunbird GT Cpe	180.7	66.3	52.0	101.3	2682	13.6
Trans Sport Van	194.5	74.6	65.2	109.8	3515	20.0
6000 LE Sdn	188.9	72.0	53.7	104.9	2815	15.7
6000 LE Wgn	193.2	72.0	54.1	104.9	3145	15.7
6000 SE Sdn	188.9	72.0	53.7	104.9	3021	15.7

Rating the 1991 Cars: The E.P.A. Rates M.P.G.'s

How the fuel economy estimates are obtained: The estimates of the number of miles a vehicle can travel on a gallon of fuel are based on results of the U.S. Environmental Protection Agency (E.P.A) "Emissions Standards Test Procedure."

This procedure is used to certify that cars, vans, and light trucks comply with the Clear Air Act, as amended. Each year, manufacturers submit new vehicle models to the E.P.A.. The procedure for testing simulates everyday driving conditions.

Each vehicle is tested under controlled laboratory conditions by a professional driver. By using a dynamometer to simulate driving conditions, the driver can test each vehicle under identical circumstances in exactly the same way each time. Therefore, the obtained results can be compared accurately.

The test vehicles are broken in, properly maintained, and driven in test conditions which simulate warm weather and dry, level roads. The quality of the fuel used is also very closely controlled.

The test conditions are those the E.P.A. must use to assure accurate emissions measurements. However, no test can cover all possible combinations of actual road conditions, climate, driving and car-care habits of individual drivers. Bear in mind that while E.P.A. tests provide a measure of how much fuel each vehicle uses under precisely controlled laboratory conditions, they *cannot predict exactly what mileage you personally will achieve.*

The following list of ratings for 1991 domestic cars was released by the Environmental Protection Agency in September, 1990. These ratings are estimates; whether you get better or worse mileage depends upon how you drive.

How to read this chart: The first two columns after the model show the E.P.A. city and highway miles-per-gallon estimate. The third column tells you the combined city/highway miles-per-gallon estimate. The fourth column tells you the engine size in cubic inches/liters and the number of cylinders. The letters "T" or "D" may appear at the end of this listing. "T" stands for "turbo" and "D" for "diesel". The fifth column lists the type of transmission, either manual (M), automatic (A), or lockup (L), and the number of gears. The last column tells you if the engine is fuel injected (FI) or the number of barrels in the carburetor. See below for a handy key to aid you in reading the listing.

A = Automatic (see Transmission column)
D = Diesel (see Engine Description column)
FI = Fuel Injection (see Fuel System column)
L = Liter (see Engine Description column)
L = Lockup (see Transmission column)
M = Manual (see Transmission column)
T = Turbo (see Engine Description column)
DOHC = Dual Overhead Cam
SOHC = Single Overhead Cam
MPFI = Multipoint Fuel Injection
SPFI = Single-point Fuel Injection
S-Charge = Supercharge

Make	Estimated MPG City	Hwy	Cmb	Engine Descrip. CID / Cyl. (Type)	Trans.	Fuel Sys.
			TWO SEATERS			
BUICK						
Reatta	18	27	21	231 (3.8L) / 6	L4	FI
CADILLAC						
Allante	15	22	17	273 (4.5L) / 8	L4	FI
CHEVROLET						
Corvette	16	25	19	349 (5.7L) / 8	M6	FI
	16	24	19	350 (5.7L) / 8	L4	FI
	16	26	20	350 (5.7L) / 8	M6	FI
CHRSYLER						
TC by Maserati Convertible	18	24	20	181 (3.0L) / 6	L4	FI
GEO						
Metro LSI Convertible	32	37	34	61 (1.0L) / 3	A3	FI
	41	46	43	61 (1.0L) / 3	M5	FI
			MINICOMPACT CARS			
LINCOLN-MERCURY						
Capri	23	27	24	97 (1.6L) / 4	L4	FI
	25	31	27	97 (1.6L) / 4	M5	FI
	23	28	25	97 (1.6L) / 4T	M5	FI
			SUBCOMPACT CARS			
CHEVROLET						
Camaro	18	27	21	191 (3.1L) / 6	L4	FI
	17	27	20	191 (3.1L) / 6	M5	FI
	17	24	19	305 (5.0L) / 8MPFI	L4	FI
	17	26	20	305 (5.0L) / 8SPFI	L4	FI
	16	26	20	305 (5.0L) / 8MPFI	M5	FI
	17	26	20	305 (5.0L) / 8SPFI	M5	FI
	16	24	19	350 (5.7L) / 8MPFI	L4	FI
Cavalier	23	32	27	134 (2.2L) / 4	L3	FI
	24	35	28	134 (2.2L) / 4	M5	FI
	20	27	22	191 (3.1L) / 6	L3	FI
	19	28	22	191 (3.1L) / 6	M5	FI
CHRYSLER						
LeBaron Convertible	21	26	23	152 (2.5L) / 4	L3	FI
	19	24	21	152 (2.5L) / 4T	L3	FI
	20	27	22	152 (2.5L) / 4T	M5	FI
	20	26	22	181 (3.0L) / 6	L4	FI
	18	27	21	181 (3.0L) / 6	M5	FI
DODGE						
Colt	28	31	30	90 (1.5L) / 4	L3	FI
	31	36	33	90 (1.5L) / 4	M4	FI
	29	35	31	90 (1.5L) / 4	M5	FI
Daytona	23	28	25	152 (2.5L) / 4	L3	FI
	19	24	21	152 (2.5L) / 4T	L3	FI
	24	34	28	152 (2.5L) / 4	M5	FI
	20	27	22	152 (2.5L) / 4T	M5	FI
	20	26	22	181 (3.0L) / 6	L4	FI
	19	27	22	181 (3.0L) / 6	M5	FI
Shadow Convertible	20	28	23	135 (2.2L) / 4T	M5	FI
	23	28	25	152 (2.5L) / 4	L3	FI
	19	23	21	152 (2.5L) / 4T	L3	FI

Make	Estimated MPG City	Hwy	Cmb	Engine Descrip. CID / Cyl. (Type)	Trans.	Fuel Sys.
	24	34	28	152 (2.5L) / 4	M5	FI
	20	26	23	152 (2.5L) / 4T	M5	FI
Stealth	18	24	20	181 (3.0L) / 6	L4	FI
	18	23	20	181 (3.0L) / 6	L4	FI
	19	24	21	181 (3.0L) / 6	M5	FI
	18	24	20	181 (3.0L) / 6T	M5	FI
	18	24	20	181 (3.0L) / 6	M5	FI
EAGLE						
Talon FWD	19	23	21	122 (2.0L) / 4T	A4	FI
Talon 4WD	18	21	19	122 (2.0L) / 4T	A4	FI
Talon FWD	22	27	24	122 (2.0L) / 4	L4	FI
	22	29	24	122 (2.0L) / 4	M5	FI
	21	28	24	122 (2.0L) / 4T	M5	FI
Talon 4WD	20	25	22	122 (2.0L) / 4T	M5	FI
FORD						
Festiva	31	33	32	81 (1.3L) / 4	A3	FI
	35	42	38	81 (1.3L) / 4	M5	FI
Mustang	21	28	24	140 (2.3L) / 4	L4	FI
	22	30	25	140 (2.3L) / 4	M5	FI
	18	25	21	302 (5.0L) / 8	L4	FI
	17	24	19	302 (5.0L) / 8	M5	FI
GEO						
Metro	36	39	37	61 (1.0L) / 3	A3	FI
	45	50	47	61 (1.0L) / 3	M5	FI
Metro LSi	36	39	37	61 (1.0L) / 3	A3	FI
	45	50	47	61 (1.0L) / 3	M5	FI
Metro XFi	53	58	55	97 (1.6l) / 4	M5	FI
Prizm	26	29	27	61 (1.0L) / 4	L3	FI
	23	30	26	97 (1.6L) / 4	L4	FI
	28	34	30	97 (1.6L) / 4	M5	FI
	25	30	27	97 (1.6L) / 4	M5	FI
Storm	24	31	27	97 (1.6L) / 4SOHC	A3	FI
	23	31	26	97 (1.6L) / 4DOHC	L4	FI
	25	33	28	97 (1.6L) / 4DOHC	M5	FI
	30	36	32	97 (1.6L) / 4SOHC	M5	FI
PLYMOUTH						
Colt	28	31	30	90 (1.5L) / 4	L3	FI
	31	36	33	90 (1.5L) / 4	M4	FI
	29	35	31	90 (1.5L) / 4	M5	FI
Laser	23	30	26	107 (1.8L) / 4SOHC	L4	FI
	23	32	27	107 (1.8L) / 4SOHC	M5	FI
	19	23	21	122 (2.0L) / 4DOHCT	A4	FI
	22	27	24	122 (2.0L) / 4DOHC	L4	FI
	22	29	24	122 (2.0L) / 4DOHC	M5	FI
	21	28	24	122 (2.0l) / 4DOHCT	M5	F1
PONTIAC						
Firebird/Trans Am	18	27	21	191 (3.1L) / 6	L4	FI
	17	27	20	191 (3.1L) / 6	M5	FI
	17	24	19	305 (5.0L) / 8MPFI	L4	FI
	17	26	20	305 (5.0L) / 8SPFI	L4	FI
	16	26	20	305 (5.0L) / 8MPFI	M5	FI
	17	26	20	305 (5.0L) / 8SPFI	M5	FI
	16	24	19	350 (5.7L) / 8MPFI	L4	FI

Make	Estimated MPG City	Hwy	Cmb	Engine Descrip. CID / Cyl. (Type)	Trans.	Fuel Sys.
Sunbird	24	32	27	122 (2.0L) / 4	L3	FI
	26	36	30	122 (2.0L) / 4	M5	FI
	20	27	22	191 (3.1L) / 6	L3	FI
	19	28	22	191 (3.1L) / 6	M5	FI
Sunbird Convertible	22	31	26	122 (2.0L) / 4	L3	FI
	24	33	28	122 (2.0L) / 4	M5	FI
	20	27	22	191 (3.1L) / 6	L3	FI
	19	28	22	191 (3.1L) / 6	M5	FI

COMPACT CARS

Make	City	Hwy	Cmb	CID / Cyl. (Type)	Trans.	Fuel Sys.
BUICK						
Skylark	23	33	27	138 (2.3L) / 4	FWD	FI
	22	31	25	151 (2.5L) / 4	FWD	FI
	19	26	22	204 (3.3L) / 6	FWD	FI
CHEVROLET						
Beretta	24	31	26	134 (2.2L) / 4	L3	FI
	24	33	27	134 (2.2L) / 4	M5	FI
	23	33	27	138 (2.3L) / 4	M5	FI
	20	27	22	191 (3.1L) / 6	L3	FI
	19	28	22	191 (3.1L) / 6	M5	FI
CHRYSLER						
LeBaron	23	28	25	152 (2.5L) / 4	L3	FI
	19	24	21	152 (2.5L) / 4T	L3	FI
	20	27	22	152 (2.5L) / 4T	M5	FI
	20	26	22	181 (3.0L) / 6	L4	FI
	19	29	23	181 (3.0L) / 6	M5	FI
DODGE						
Shadow	23	27	25	135 (2.2L) / 4	L3	FI
	23	30	26	135 (2.2L) / 4	M5	FI
	23	28	25	152 (2.5L) / 4	L3	FI
	19	23	20	152 (2.5L) / 4T	L3	FI
	24	34	28	152 (2.5L) / 4	M5	FI
	20	26	23	152 (2.5L) / 4T	M5	FI
EAGLE						
Summit	28	31	30	90 (1.5L) / 4	L3	FI
	26	32	29	90 (1.5L) / 4	L4	FI
	31	36	33	90 (1.5L) / 4	M4	FI
	29	35	31	90 (1.5L) / 4	M5	FI
FORD						
Escort	23	30	26	112 (1.8L) / 4	L4	FI
	26	31	28	112 (1.8L) / 4	M5	FI
	25	33	28	113 (1.9L) / 4	L4	FI
	29	36	32	113 (1.9L) / 4	M5	FI
Escort FS	31	41	35	113 (1.9L) / 4	M5	FI
Probe	21	28	24	133 (2.2L) / 4	L4	FI
	19	25	21	133 (2.2L) / 4T	L4	FI
	24	31	26	133 (2.2L) / 4	M5	FI
	21	27	23	133 (2.2L) / 4T	M5	FI
	19	25	21	182 (3.0L) / 6	L4	FI
	19	26	22	182 (3.0L) / 6	M5	FI
Tempo FWD	22	26	23	140 (2.3L) / 4	A3	FI
	21	29	24	140 (2.3L) / 4	M5	FI
	22	32	26	140 (2.3L) / 4	M5	FI

Make	Estimated MPG City	Hwy	Cmb	Engine Descrip. CID / Cyl. (Type)	Trans.	Fuel Sys.
Tempo AWD	20	24	21	140 (2.3L) / 4	A3	F1
LINCOLN-MERCURY						
Topaz FWD	22	26	23	140 (2.3L) / 4	A3	FI
	21	29	24	140 (2.3L) / 4	M5	FI
	22	32	26	140 (2.3L) / 4	M5	FI
Topaz AWD	20	24	21	140 (2.3L) / 4	A3	FI
Tracer	23	30	26	112 (1.8L) / 4	L4	FI
	26	31	28	112 (1.8L) / 4	M5	FI
	25	33	28	113 (1.9L) / 4	L4	FI
	29	36	32	113 (1.9L) / 4	M5	FI
OLDSMOBILE						
Cutlass Calais	23	33	27	138 (2.3L) / 4	L3	FI
	23	33	27	138 (2.3L) / 4	M5	FI
	22	31	25	151 (2.5L) / 4	L3	FI
	22	34	26	151 (2.5L) / 4	M5	FI
	19	26	22	204 (3.3L) / 6	L3	FI
PLYMOUTH						
Sundance	23	27	25	135 (2.2L) / 4	L3	FI
	23	30	26	135 (2.2L) / 4	M5	FI
	23	28	25	152 (2.5L) / 4	L3	FI
	19	23	20	152 (2.5L) / 4T	L3	FI
	24	34	28	152 (2.5L) / 4	M5	FI
	20	26	23	152 (2.5L) /4T	M5	FI
PONTIAC						
Grand Am	23	33	27	138 (2.3L) / 4	L3	FI
	23	33	27	138 (2.3L) / 4	M5	FI
	22	31	25	151 (2.5L) / 4	L3	FI
	22	33	26	151 (2.5L) / 4	M5	FI
LeMans	27	33	29	98 (1.6L) / 4	L3	FI
	29	38	32	98 (1.6L) / 4	M4	FI
	31	40	35	98 (1.6L) / 4	M5	FI
	23	30	26	122 (2.0L) / 4	L3	FI
	25	31	27	122 (2.0L) / 4	M5	FI
MID-SIZE CARS						
BUICK						
Century	22	31	25	151 (2.5L) / 4	L3	FI
	19	26	22	204 (3.3L) / 6	L3	FI
	19	30	23	204 (3.3L) / 6	L4	FI
Regal	19	30	23	191 (3.1L) / 6	L4	FI
	19	28	22	231 (3.8L) / 6	L4	FI
Riviera	18	27	21	231 (3.8L) / 6	L4	FI
CADILLAC						
Eldorado	16	26	20	299 (4.9L) / 8	L4	FI
Seville	16	26	20	299 (4.9L) / 8	L4	FI
CHEVROLET						
Corsica	24	31	26	134 (2.2L) / 4	L3	FI
	24	33	27	134 (2.2L) / 4	M5	FI
	20	27	22	191 (3.1L) / 6	L3	FI
	19	28	22	191 (3.1L) / 6	M5	FI
Lumina	21	28	24	151 (2.5L) / 4	L3	FI
	19	27	22	191 (3.1L) / 6	L3	FI
	19	30	23	191 (3.1L) / 6	L4	FI

Make	Estimated MPG City	Hwy	Cmb	Engine Descrip. CID / Cyl. (Type)	Trans.	Fuel Sys.
CHRYSLER						
New Yorker	19	26	22	201 (3.3L) / 6	FWD	FI
DODGE						
Dynasty	21	26	23	152 (2.5L) / 4	L3	FI
	20	26	22	181 (3.0L) / 6	L4	FI
	19	26	22	201 (3.3L) / 6	L4	FI
Spirit	19	27	22	135 (2.2L) / 4T	M5	FI
	23	27	25	152 (2.5L) / 4	L3	FI
	19	24	21	152 (2.5L) / 4T	L3	FI
	24	34	28	152 (2.5L) / 4	M5	FI
	20	27	22	152 (2.5L) / 4T	M5	FI
	20	26	22	181 (3.0L) / 6	L4	FI
FORD						
Taurus	20	29	23	183 (3.0L) / 6	L4	FI
	18	26	21	183 (3.0L) / 6	M5	FI
Thunderbird	19	27	22	231 (3.8L) / 6	L4	FI
	17	23	19	231 (3.8L) / 6 S-Charge	L4	FI
	17	24	19	231 (3.8L) / 6 S-Charge	M5	FI
LINCOLN-MERCURY						
Cougar	19	27	22	231 (3.8L) / 6	L4	FI
	18	24	20	302 (5.0L) / 8	L4	FI
Mark VII	17	24	20	302 (5.0L) / 8	L4	FI
Sable	20	29	23	183 (3.0L) / 6	L4	FI
OLDSMOBILE						
Cutlass Ciera	22	31	25	151 (2.5L) / 4	L3	FI
	19	26	22	204 (3.3L) / 6	L3	FI
	19	29	23	204 (3.3L) / 6	L4	FI
Cutlass Supreme	21	29	24	138 (2.3L) / 4	L3	FI
	19	30	23	191 (3.1L) / 6	L4	FI
Trofeo/Toronado	18	27	21	231 (3.8L) / 6	L4	FI
PLYMOUTH						
Acclaim	23	28	25	152 (2.5L) / 4	L3	FI
	24	34	28	152 (2.5L) / 4	M5	FI
	20	26	22	181 (3.0L) / 6	L4	FI
PONTIAC						
Grand Prix	21	29	24	138 (2.3L) / 4	L3	FI
	19	30	23	191 (3.1L) / 6	L4	FI
6000	22	31	25	151 (2.5L) / 4	L3	FI
	20	27	22	191 (3.1L) / 6	L3	FI
	19	30	23	191 (3.1L) / 6	L4	FI

LARGE CARS

Make	City	Hwy	Cmb	CID / Cyl. (Type)	Trans.	Fuel Sys.
BUICK						
LeSabre	19	28	22	231 (3.8L) / 6	L4	FI
Park Avenue	18	27	21	231 (3.8L) / 6	L4	FI
CADILLAC						
Brougham	16	25	19	305 (5.0L) / 8	L4	FI
	15	22	18	350 (5.7L) / 8	L4	FI
Fleetwood/Deville	16	26	20	299 (4.9L) / 8	L4	FI
CHEVROLET						
Caprice	17	26	20	305 (5.0L) / 8	L4	FI

Make	Estimated MPG City	Hwy	Cmb	Engine Descrip. CID / Cyl. (Type)	Trans.	Fuel Sys.
CHRYSLER						
New Yorker Fifth Avenue/I	18	26	21	201 (3.3L) / 6	L4	FI
	17	25	20	232 (3.8L) / 6	L4	FI
DODGE						
Monaco	18	27	21	182 (3.0L) / 6	L4	FI
EAGLE						
Premier	18	27	21	182 (3.0L) / 6	L4	FI
FORD						
LTD Crown Victoria	17	24	20	302 (5.0L) / 8	L4	FI
LINCOLN-MERCURY						
Grand Marquis	17	24	20	302 (5.0L) / 8	L4	FI
Town Car	17	23	19	281 (4.6L) / 8	L4	FI
OLDSMOBILE						
Eighty-Eight	19	28	22	231 (3.8L) / 6	L4	FI
Ninety-Eight/Touring	18	27	21	231 (3.8L) / 6	L4	FI
PONTIAC						
Bonneville	19	28	22	231 (3.8L) / 6	L4	F1
SMALL STATION WAGONS						
CHEVROLET						
Cavalier Wagon	24	31	26	134 (2.2L) / 4	L3	FI
	24	33	27	134 (2.2L) / 4	M5	FI
	20	27	22	191 (3.1L) / 6	L3	FI
DODGE						
Colt Vista	22	23	22	122 (2.0L) / 4	L3	FI
	22	29	25	122 (2.0L) / 4	M5	FI
FORD						
Escort Wagon	25	33	28	113 (1.9L) / 4	L4	FI
	29	36	32	113 (1.9L) / 4	M5	FI
LINCOLN-MERCURY						
Tracer Wagon	25	33	28	113 (1.9L) / 4	L4	FI
	29	36	32	113 (1.9L) / 4	M5	FI
PLYMOUTH						
Colt Vista	22	23	22	122 (2.0L) / 4	L3	FI
	22	29	25	122 (2.0L) / 4	M5	FI
MID-SIZE STATION WAGONS						
BUICK						
Century Wagon	21	28	24	151 (2.5L) / 4	L3	FI
	19	25	21	204 (3.3L) / 6	L3	FI
	19	29	23	204 (3.3L) / 6	L4	FI
FORD						
Taurus Wagon	20	29	33	183 (3.0L) / 6	L4	FI
LINCOLN-MERCURY						
Sable Wagon	20	29	23	183 (3.0L) / 6	L4	FI
OLDSMOBILE						
Cutlass Cruiser	21	28	24	151 (2.5L) / 4	L3	FI
	19	25	21	204 (3.3L) / 6	L3	FI
	19	29	23	204 (3.3L) / 6	L4	FI
PONTIAC						
6000 Wagon	21	28	24	151 (2.5L) / 4	L3	FI
	19	30	23	191 (3.1L) / 6	L4	FI

Make	Estimated MPG City	Hwy	Cmb	Engine Descrip. CID / Cyl. (Type)	Trans.	Fuel Sys.
LARGE STATION WAGONS						
BUICK						
Roadmaster Wagon	16	25	19	305 (5.0L) / 8	L4	FI
CHEVROLET						
Caprice Wagon	16	25	19	305 (5.0L) / 8	L4	FI
FORD						
LTD Crown Victoria Wagon	17	24	20	302 (5.0L) / 8	L4	FI
LINCOLN-MERCURY						
Grand Marquis Wagon	17	24	20	302 (5.0L) / 8	L4	FI
OLDSMOBILE						
Custom Cruiser	16	25	19	305 (5.0L) / 8	L4	FI
VANS PASSENGER						
CHEVROLET						
Astro AWD (Passenger)	16	19	17	262 (4.3L) / 6	L4	FI
Astro 2WD (Passenger)	16	21	18	262 (4.3L) / 6	L4	FI
FORD						
Aerostar Wagon	17	23	19	183 (3.0L) / 6	L4	FI
	18	23	20	183 (3.0L) / 6	M5	FI
	16	21	18	244 (4.0L) / 6	L4	FI
Aerostar Wagon All-Wheel	16	20	17	244 (4.0L) / 6	L4	FI
GMC						
Safari AWD (Passenger)	16	19	17	262 (4.3L) / 6	L4	FI
Safari 2WD (Passenger)	16	21	18	262 (4.3L) / 6	L4	FI
SPECIAL PURPOSE VEHICLES/2WD						
CHEVROLET						
Lumina APV 2WD	18	23	20	191 (3.1L) / 6	L3	FI
CHRYSLER						
Town & Country 2WD	18	23	20	201 (3.3L) / 6	L4	FI
DODGE						
Caravan 2WD	21	25	22	152 (2.5L) / 4	L3	FI
	19	23	20	181 (3.0L) / 6	L3	FI
	19	24	21	181 (3.0L) / 6	L4	FI
	18	23	20	201 (3.3L) / 6	L4	FI
GEO						
Tracker Convertible 2WD	25	27	26	97 (1.6L) / 4	M5	FI
OLDSMOBILE						
Silhouette 2WD	18	23	20	191 (3.1L) / 6	L3	FI
PLYMOUTH						
Voyager 2WD	21	25	22	152 (2.5L) / 4	L3	FI
	19	23	20	181 (3.0L) / 6	L3	FI
	19	24	21	181 (3.0L) / 6	L4	FI
	18	23	20	201 (3.3L) / 6	L4	FI
PONTIAC						
Trans Sport 2WD	18	23	20	191 (3.1L) / 6	L3	FI
SPECIAL PURPOSE VEHICLES/4WD						
DODGE						
Caravan 4WD	17	21	18	201 (3.3L) / 6	L4	FI
Colt Vista 4WD	19	25	21	122 (2.0L) / 4	M5	FI
GEO						
Tracker Convertible 4WD	23	24	23	97 (1.6L) / 4	L3	FI

Make	Estimated MPG City	Hwy	Cmb	Engine Descrip. CID / Cyl. (Type)	Trans.	Fuel Sys.
	25	27	26	97 (1.6L) / 4	M5	FI
Tracker 4WD	23	24	23	97 (1.6L) / 4	L3	FI
	25	27	26	97 (1.6L) / 4	M5	FI
OLDSMOBILE						
Bravada 4WD	17	22	19	262 (4.3L) / 6	L4	FI
PLYMOUTH						
Colt Vista 4WD	19	25	21	122 (2.0L) / 4	M5	FI
Voyager 4WD	17	21	18	201 (3.3L) / 6	L4	FI

Buick Century Custom Sedan

Buick Reatta Convertible

Buick Century Estate Wagon

Buick Reatta Coupe

Buick Lesabre Limited Sedan

Buick Regal Gran Sport Sedan

Buick Park Avenue Sedan

Buick Regal Limited Coupe

Buick Park Avenue Ultra Sedan

Buick Regal Limited Sedan

Buick Riviera

Buick Roadmaster Estate Wagon

Buick Skylark Sedan

Buick Skylark Custom Coupe

Buick Skylark Custom Sedan

Cadillac Allante Convertible

Cadillac Allante Coupe

Cadillac Brougham Sedan

Cadillac Sedan De Ville

Cadillac Eldorado

Cadillac Fleetwood Sixty Special

Chevrolet Cavalier Z24 Coupe

Cadillac Seville Sedan

Chevrolet Cavalier RS Sedan

Chevrolet Beretta Coupe

Chevrolet Cavalier RS Wagon

Chevrolet Camaro RS Convertible

Chevrolet Corsica LT Notchback Sedan

Chevrolet Caprice Wagon

Chevrolet Corvette Convertible

Chevrolet Lumina Z34 Coupe

Chrysler Lebaron LX Coupe

Chevrolet Lumina Euro Sedan

Chrysler Lebaron Sedan

Chevrolet Lumina APV CL

Chrysler New Yorker Fifth Avenue Sedan

Chrysler Imperial Sedan

Chrysler New Yorker Salon Sedan

Chrysler Lebaron GTC Convertible

Chrysler Town & Country

Dodge Caravan SE

Dodge Monaco ES Sedan

Dodge Colt 3 Door

Dodge Shadow Coupe

Dodge Colt Vista Wagon

Dodge Shadow ES Convertible

Dodge Daytona Shelby

Dodge Spirit ES Sedan

Dodge Dynasty Sedan

Dodge Spirit R/T Sedan

Dodge Stealth Coupe

Ford Escort GT Coupe

Eagle Premier ES Limited Sedan

Ford Festiva

Eagle Summit ES Sedan

Ford LTD Crown Victoria Sedan

Eagle Talon TSi AWD

Ford LTD Country Squire Wagon

Ford Aerostar Wagon

Ford Mustang GT Convertible

Ford Probe

Ford Taurus SHO Sedan

Ford Taurus LX Wagon

Ford Tempo GL Sedan

Ford Thunderbird Coupe

Geo Metro LSi 2/4 Doors

Geo Metro LSi Convertible

Geo Prizm Sedan

Geo Storm Hatchback

Geo Storm GSi Hatchback

Geo Tracker Convertible

Mercury Cougar Coupe

Lincoln Continental Signature Series

Mercury Grand Marquis Sedan

Lincoln Mark VII LSC

Mercury Grand Marquis Colony Park

Lincoln Town Car Cartier Designer Series

Mercury Sable Sedan

Mercury Capri XR2 Convertible

Mercury Topaz GS Sedan

Mercury Tracer Sedan

Oldsmobile Cutlass Ciera Sedan

Mercury Tracer Wagon

Oldsmobile Cutlass Supreme Convertible

Oldsmobile Bravada

Oldsmobile Cutlass Supreme Int'l Cpe

Oldsmobile Custom Cruiser

Oldsmobile Cutlass Supreme SL Sedan

Oldsmobile Calais International Series Sedan

Oldsmobile Eighty-Eight Royale Brougham

Oldsmobile Ninety-Eight Regency Elite

Plymouth Acclaim LX Sedan

Oldsmobile Silhouette

Plymouth Colt Vista Wagon

Oldsmobile Toronado Coupe

Plymouth Laser RS Coupe

Oldsmobile Toronado Trofeo Coupe

Plymouth Sundance RS Sedan

Oldsmobile Touring Sedan

Plymouth Voyager SE

Pontiac Bonneville LE Sedan

Pontiac Grand Prix STE

Pontiac Firebird Formula Coupe

Pontiac Lemans LE Coupe

Pontiac Firebird Trans Am Coupe

Pontiac Sunbird GT Coupe

Pontiac Grand Am SE Coupe

Pontiac Trans Sport SE

Pontiac Grand Prix GT Coupe

Pontiac 6000 LE Sedan

How To Save $ $ $ On Gasoline

With gasoline prices at an average of $1.45 per gallon, most motorists need to know effective ways to conserve fuel. There are both obvious and subtle ways to save gasoline in your automobile. Both make the amount of money you spend per mile appreciably less. In fact, most motorists can cut their fuel consumption by as much as 42% by observing some basic rules to avoid gas-guzzling.

This article includes a list of 46 ways to save gasoline, categorized in three sections—"The Obvious," and "Not-So-Obvious,"and "Changing Your Gas Consuming Lifestyle Comfortably." In the third section are outlined some changes that you, a gas-buying consumer, can make in your car-driving habits which will directly affect your M.P.G.—Money Per Gallon.

The Obvious

1. Keep your car properly tuned at all times: Instead of tuning your car every eight or nine months as most manufacturers suggest, get a major tune-up every six months. The extra money spent is a good investment, especially when you fill up your tank. Clean points and plugs and a correctly timed car can cut gas consumption from 3% to 12%. A well tuned engine also enhances the resale value of your automobile.

2. Cut down your highway driving speed to 55 miles per hour: A car that normally gets 20 miles per gallon on the open highway with a tank capacity of 20 gallons going at an average speed of 65 miles per hour could get 23.5 miles to the gallon by decreasing the average highway driving speed to 55 miles per hour. Staying at 55 miles per hour consistently would give the car in the above example an additional tank range of 70 miles. At an average of $1.45 per gallon, that means $5.07 per tankload savings.

3. Keep your tires properly inflated: According to some experts, (Automobile Club of America, Consumer Reports, Road and Track Magazine, among others), 69% of the drivers on the road today are driving with improperly inflated tires. These experts believe that most cars can save an average of two miles per gallon by keeping the tire pressure within the prescribed manufacturer's specifications. Radial tires save 3-7% over bias tires.

4. Learn to start your car properly: The best way to start a cold car efficiently is to depress the accelerator once before turning the ignition, and then slowly depress the pedal while turning the ignition. Release the accelerator when the engine turns over. *Note: starting a car varies from person to person and from car to car; check the owner's manual.*

5. Avoid fast starts: When accelerating from a stop sign, a red light, or a parking spot, gradually depress the accelerator pedal at an even and continual pace. By slowly accelerating to the speed limit, you can cut your starting gas consumption by 35%. Most drivers lose precious miles per gallon by making fast starts from a stopped, idling position.

6. Accelerate to open highway speeds gradually: Most major highways have long acceleration ramps, but most drivers only use about half of the acceleration lane to get up to 55 miles per hour and beyond. By slowly accelerating on the entrance ramp and using most of the acceleration lane to get up to highway speed, you could save up to 8% of the gas normally used in this facet of driving.

7. Coast to save gas: It is the rare driver who coasts on a downgrade, or who coasts into a red light or a stop sign, yet coasting raises gas economy. If your wheel bearings are properly greased and you are on a 15 degree or greater downgrade, if you take your foot off the accelerator, you will only lose up to 5% of your speed and save up to 17% of gas consumption normally used in this aspect of driving. Coast only when traffic conditions are safe to do so.

8. Turn off your engine if you intend to be stopped longer than three minutes: Most traffic lights throughout the country are timed for 30 seconds, a minute, a minute and 15 seconds, 90 seconds, or two minute intervals; therefore, you shouldn't turn off your engine at traffic lights. However, if you anticipate standing for more than three minutes, you should turn off your engine. It will not cool down completely for at least an hour, so when you restart your car you usually don't need to depress the accelerator pedal before turning the ignition key. Check your owner's manual for recommended instructions for your car.

9. Warm your engine before driving: To properly warm up your car, you should let it idle for at least a minute before starting to drive. The automatic choke should be serviced regularly. *Note: Those cars with semi-automatic chokes should start with the choke pulled out all the way. When the engine turns over, the choke should be pushed in about half-way. Cars equipped with semi-automatic chokes should not be driven until the choke pops in or until the temperature gauge moves slightly.*

10. Keep speed consistent on the highway: If you are anticipating driving on a highway for a long distance, you should keep your speed consistent for optimum gas mileage. Any variation in speed of 5 miles per hour or more can decrease fuel efficiency by almost 2 miles per gallon.

11. Never ride the brake: Some motorists are chronic "Brake Riders." A good driver never applies the brake while traveling unless it is necessary to stop. Motorists who drive with two feet, constantly applying the brake while leaving the other foot on the gas, promote drag on the car, and countless miles to the gallon are lost.

12. Check tire balancing and wheel alignment every 6,000 miles: Wheels which have been knocked out of alignment by potholes and rough roads are a detriment to increased gas mileage. Combine that with tires that aren't balanced and your car will shimmy ever so slightly, robbing a car of an estimated 1-1.5 miles per gallon.

13. Start off slower in cold weather: During the cold winter months, it takes longer for your car to heat up to proper operating temperature. The warm-up time of your car should be increased from one to two minutes. Keep your car under 40 miles per hour for the first three miles to insure proper operating temperature. An automobile should never be raced in cold weather to force it to warm up more rapidly. A helpful hint to avoid prolonged warm-ups in winter is to change thermostats during the colder months. Automobile parts manufacturers make thermostats which allow a car to run colder or hotter as the climate dictates. For colder weather a hotter thermostat would be a fuel saver, while in the summer a cooler thermostat should be used.

14. Keep all fluid levels high: All the fluid levels in your car are directly related to the type of gas mileage you will get either on the open road, or just around town. The radiator water should be to the base of the cap stem to keep your car running cool. The oil level should be kept at full capacity to keep the crank case from getting hot and all of the moving parts in your engine from getting sluggish. The most infrequently checked fluids in the car are the transmission and brake fluids; however, both are just as important to good gas mileage as the oil and radiator water. A helpful hint for those cars using regular gasoline: using unleaded gasoline every third fill-up will clean up the spark-plugs keeping them firing hotter longer, enhancing gas mileage. When filling your gas tank on hot days, don't let the gas attendant fill it to the top. Leave some room for expansion so that gas doesn't spill out and ruin your paint job and mileage.

15. Shift into neutral in stop and go traffic: When you're stuck in stop-and-go traffic and there is no way out, the only thing you can do to improve gas mileage is to slip the car into neutral when stopped. This diminishes the flow of fuel into your carburetor, cutting down fuel consumption. Shifting into neutral in stop-and-go traffic also allows the engine to run cooler.

16. Purchase cars with high gas mileage ratings: The Environmental Protection Agency road tests cars at the beginning of each model year. For E.P.A. figures on vans, trucks, and sport vehicles, refer to **Edmund's Vans, Pickups, and Sport Utility Vehicles Buyer's Guide**.

The Not-So-Obvious

1. Keep your car clean: Dirt on the outside of the car creates drag, and harms gas mileage. A clean car gets up to 2 miles per gallon more than a dirty car.

2. Try to keep the windows shut: It's very easy to keep the windows in your car shut during the winter, but it becomes more difficult to keep them closed during the scorching summer months. Open windows create a draft inside the car which tends to "hold" the car back, especially during acceleration. Some experts feel that open windows at speeds of 55 miles per hour or more cut 10% off your miles per gallon.

3. A straight line is the shortest distance between two points: This law of geometry also applies to driving long distances, especially when you're trying to conserve gasoline. Gripping the wheel firmly and keeping your vehicle on a straight line enhances the gas mileage of your car. Change lanes as infrequently as possible to conserve gasoline. Keeping your car on a straight path to your destination can save up to 1 mile per gallon.

4. "The back roads will get me there faster:" But maybe not more economically. Many times motorists will opt for short cuts that cut travel time; however, many short cuts off the main roads are filled with stop and yield signs, railroad crossings and traffic lights. That's a lot of stop and go traffic that is murder on gas mileage. Continuous driving always is better than stop and go, so the next time you think of taking the short cut, think about your money per gallon.

5. Buy cars with a more economical standard transmission: Normally, a standard transmission can get up to 32% better gas mileage than a similarly equipped car with an automatic transmission. However, that savings can be cut in half by driving your standard transmission improperly. To realize the full economy of your standard transmission, shift into high gear as quickly as possible. A car in second gear uses 30% more gas to operate properly than it does in high gear. In first gear, the standard transmission uses almost 50% more gas than in high gear. When slowing down with your standard transmission, it is more economical to go from high gear directly into low gear without any intermediate stops. Shifting to slow down from fourth gear to third, to second is a 20% waste of gas according to the Environmental Protection Agency. You achieve better gas mileage by just applying the brake.

6. Pedularly shift your automatic transmission: It may not seem possible to manually shift an automatic transmission but it is—with your foot. Every car with an automatic transmission slips into the next gear automatically as the R.P.M.'s (Revolutions Per Minute) get faster and faster. You can feel it in your own car. The R.P.M.'s will get to a point, and then the automatic transmission will shift itself into a higher gear. It is tricky, but an automatic transmission can be shifted pedularly if you are aware of the ride and the feel of your car. The key to turning an automatic transmission into a pedular (standard) transmission is to momentarily ease your foot off the gas pedal as the car is about to shift into a higher gear. When you put your foot back on the accelerator, it will have shifted. Even though the gas savings is not as dramatic as with a manual transmission, you can save about 2 miles per gallon by making this a standard practice for your car.

7. Service the air filter regularly: A dirty air filter (which sits on top of the carburetor) can cause a decrease in power output by restricting the flow of air to the engine. Change the air filter at 12,000 or 24,000 mile intervals. More frequent servicing should be done if driving is done in sandy or extremely dusty conditions.

8. When going on a trip, pack evenly: When most people go on a long trip they just throw everything into the trunk. According to the Environmental Protection Agency, you can lose up to 22% of your gas mileage on the open road by doing this. When a trunk is loaded, the front of the car is raised up causing an unnatural wind resistance shield, so your once-sleek automobile becomes a wind plow and a gas guzzler. When going on a long trip, it is "gas-economically" wise to pack evenly throughout your car, sacrificing leg room for better gas economy.

9. Don't use the gas pedal as a brake: When driving a car with an automatic transmission and stopping on an incline, some drivers feed the car just enough gas to stay stationary on the hill without having to brake. This wastes gas at approximately four times the rate of normal idling, and is a certain way to burn up gallons of gas unnecessarily. Some people also do this with a manual transmission by riding the clutch, putting the car in first gear and depressing the accelerator just enough to prevent the car from rolling down the hill. This wastes gas and burns out clutches.

10. On extended trips, stop only to fill up: Gas mileage is improved on a long trip when the car is in continuous motion. You can calculate that each stop will rob you of at least 5% of your M.P.G. rating.

11. Being too slow is as bad as being too fast: Logically it would seem that the slower you travel below 55 miles per hour, the less gas you would use. That holds true to a point. The Environmental Protection Agency and the editors of Road and Track Magazine estimate that in 97% of the cases, optimum fuel burning for a car occurs at 35 miles per hour. Driving at 20 miles per hour with an automatic transmission burns up as much gas as if driving 70 miles per hour. Coincidentally, the E.P.A. ratings for highway driving are gathered by sending a car around a test track at 40 miles per hour. The fuel consumption difference from 40 to 55 miles per hour is about 18%. So, if the E.P.A. says that a car gets 30 M.P.G. on the highway, you can deduct 18% of that to get the total M.P.G. that you get on the highway traveling at 55 miles per hour.

12. Only run the rear defroster when necessary: Rear defrosters burn as much gasoline as a car air conditioner. Never use the rear defroster to thaw ice on the rear windows. Do not run the rear defroster after the fog on the window has disappeared. Running the front and the rear defroster simultaneously drops fuel efficiency by about 13%.

13. Proper turning increases fuel economy: Most turns and exits off highway exit ramps are negotiated improperly. Most drivers only slow down when they're in the turn instead of slowing down before it. By slowing down before the turn and then speeding up while in it, 20% of the gas normally used during this turning procedure is saved.

14. Get a running start up a hill: By increasing your speed 20% before entering the incline, and then easing off the gas pedal, you can actually save gas for the overall run. On inclines of 20 degrees or more, your car's engine works almost three times as hard. By increasing the speed on the flat surface 20%, you are saving a substantial amount of gas going up an incline.

15. Never turn on an air conditioner while idling: If you must use an automobile air conditioner which wastes fuel, you should never turn it on when you first start the car or if you're idling. The first surge of power from the auto air conditioner robs your engine of 25% more gas mileage than normal. An automobile engine can work up to four times as hard when a conventional auto air conditioner is at full blast.

16. Idling your car to save gas: Needless idling deteriorates gas mileage. However, it is recommended that a driver let his car idle for about a minute after the car has been through a long trip. This relieves some of the "hot spots" in an engine. Idling after a long trip also prevents vapor lock which might make it difficult or prohibit you from starting your car the next time you want to use it.

17. Service the manifold heat control valve: Make sure the manifold heat control valve is inspected and serviced at regular intervals. This valve, located in the exhaust system of some cars, allows exhaust gases to heat the intake manifold during cold engine operation. A valve stuck in the open position causes slow engine warm-up and poor cold engine performance. A valve stuck in the closed position will cause a loss of power and hard starting with a hot engine. Sticking in either position makes the engine less fuel efficient.

18. Sub-freezing starting economically: In sub-freezing or sub-zero conditions, a tremendous amount of gasoline is wasted while starting a car because the butterfly valve will stick closed not allowing any air to mix with the gasoline in the carburetor. The best way to start your car under these conditions is to lift the hood, remove the air filter cover from your carburetor, and stick an object through the butterfly valve to keep it wide open. Your car should start instantly, saving gasoline and preventing your car from flooding.

19. Garage your oldest car: Although most owners of more than one car keep their newest car in the garage to keep that new finish, for gas economy this is not best. The oldest car should go into the garage because historically they have more trouble starting than newer ones. A garage will raise the temperature of the overall environment of your engine, and this will help your car get started saving gas and starting time.

20. Using more than one car wisely: Many American families now own two cars—usually a small "around town" car and a larger family-size auto. The economical use of these can be a big gas-saver. For example, on short trips make a habit of using the car with better gas mileage. Also, try to use the car that was used last, as long as it hasn't been sitting for more than an hour or so. Use the larger, less fuel-efficient car sparingly.

21. Plan trips carefully: Combine those short trips and plan the route so that it is the shortest possible. This avoids unnecessary stopping and cuts gas mileage.

22. Be certain the parking brake is off: At times the brake warning light does not come on for a slightly depressed brake. Even if the brake is partially engaged, it can rob you of gas mileage. Besides saving energy, you will be saving wear and tear on your rear brake shoes.

23. Anticipate stop lights: Stopping and starting at every light is not only frustrating, it saps up a lot of gas. Plan ahead and try to time lights to avoid unnecessary stops. Write to your local Traffic Safety Council and encourage them to keep lights synchronized.

24. Lubricate wheel bearings: Unnecessary friction in the wheel bearings from poor lubrication can cause costly repairs and significantly reduce mileage. Rear wheel bearings normally are automatically lubricated; however, front wheel bearings require maintenance every 15-20,000 miles.

25. Replace worn shock absorbers: Worn shock absorbers allow the car to wander back and forth on the road wasting fuel and increasing tire wear.

Changing Your Gas Consuming Lifestyle Comfortably

There are some overall changes in driving habits that can be comfortably incorporated into your daily driving routine which will save a lot of gas and ultimately a lot of money. The editors of **Edmund** have assembled a list of changes that will help the average driver conserve gasoline. Most of the items in the following list are affordable as well as within reach and tolerance of a changing lifestyle. Even though most car drivers will look at these changes as a sacrifice, the alternatives could be even more distasteful. It's just a question of how frequently and how much you are willing to pay at the pumps.

1. All future cars should have a standard transmission: A well-driven standard transmission is one of the best ways to save gasoline. Even station wagons, one of the biggest group of gas-guzzling automobiles, are becoming equipped with standard transmissions. Even though E.P.A. gasoline consumption estimates vary from standard transmission to transmission, and from model to model, the editors of **Edmund** have estimated that two cars similarly equipped will show a difference of up to 32% in gas consumption with a standard transmission. However, to maximize savings, the standard transmission must be driven correctly.

An interesting benefit of the standard transmission is an increase in driver control of the vehicle. Lower gears can slow down a car in an emergency, and a properly down-shifted car in the turns and banks of highway driving decrease the possibility of driving your car off the road. Also, many standard transmission cars come with a fifth gear or "overdrive" which considerably decreases the R.P.M.'s (Revolutions Per Minute) at high speeds saving gasoline and increasing engine economy. Another benefit of the standard transmission is that an automobile can get to highway speeds faster while using less gas.

2. Decrease the overall size of your automobile: Car size has a lot to do with the amount of gasoline used. A wide wheelbase, the overall length, and the total weight play an important part in your car's basic fuel economy. The size of the engine plays the most important role in fuel consumption. A V-8 burns gas more quickly than a 6- or 4-cylinder. The ultimate in fuel economy comes from a 4-cylinder engine. These engines are being made now for peak performance and low gas mileage. Scaling down the size of your car will enhance your gas mileage appreciably.

3. Stay away from electrical convenience items: Many car buyers purchase expensive electrically run options for their automobiles like air conditioners, power windows, power side-view mirrors, power radios and C.B. antennas, power disc brakes, additional lights on the inside of the car, electric gauges and clocks, power seats, electric door locks and electric sun roofs. All of these options in a car rob it of gas mileage. The Environmental Protection Agency estimates that 15-25% of all fuel economy is lost on electric options in an average automobile, and that if there were no air conditioners in automobiles, the savings in oil would average 10 million barrels per day.

4. Never buy exotic carburetors or exhaust systems: There are many cars on the road that use two-barrel carburetors and two exhaust systems that "turbo-charge" the engine by providing it with more power. However, this is a tremendous waste of gas with the gas feeding two sides or "barrels" of the carburetor at the same time. Stay away from dual exhaust systems. If there are two tail pipes, then the engine is too big for one, and guzzles the gas that necessitates both of them.

5. Use alternative means of getting there: The idea of car-pooling arrived when the gasoline shortage of 1974 hit the United States. Car-pooling to work or school was successful during and immediately after the 1974 gasoline shortage, but as the gas lines got shorter, more commuters returned to their cars to drive alone. Car-pooling is an effective way to save gas even if at times it may be inconvenient.

Suburban commuters working in a major metropolis also should start turning to mass transit whenever possible. Many major cities throughout the country are adding express bus and train service to the business districts, and commuters can drive to convenient, free parking lots and take public transportation.

Car Salesmen Give The Impression Of Not Telling Me Everything. Why Would NATIONWIDE Be Any Different?

We have no reason to keep things from you. Our 20 plus year approach has been to be straightforward in working with our clients. The printout you receive clearly reveals our "hand".

I Don't Live In Michigan, How Will I Get My New Vehicle?

You have three options —

1) You may designate a local dealership as your pick up point. (Please provide us with a choice of three.)
2) We will deliver your vehicle to your home via a licensed ICC driveaway service.
3) Your vehicle may be picked up at our headquarters in Southfield, MI.

When I Buy From NATIONWIDE, Is The Vehicle Under Warranty?

All cars and trucks sold by NATIONWIDE Auto Brokers, Inc. are fully factory warranteed and all authorized dealerships throughout the United States and Canada will honor the warranty.

1991 new car prices

Volume 25 Number 2
Library of Congress Catalog Card Number: 71-80100
Standard Book Number: 87759-367-1 • ISSN Number: 1047-0751

CONTENTS

Cover Photo: Dodge Stealth R/T

JOHN BARTLETT
Publisher

WILLIAM BADNOW
Editor

KELLY HULITZKY
Director, Operations & Production

KATHY McMANUS
Production Manager

EDMUND PUBLICATIONS CORP., 200 Baker Avenue, Concord, MA 01742, publishes the Edmund's Car Price Guides nine times a year as follows: Used Car editions four times a year in January, April, July and October; New Car editions three times a year in February, June and December; Import Car editions two times a year in March and July. SUBSCRIPTION RATES: U.S. and its possessions—$43.00.

Edmund books are available at special quantity discounts when purchased in bulk by corporations, credit unions, organizations, and other special interest groups. Custom covers and/or customized copy on certain pages is also available. For further information, write to: Edmund Publications Corp., 200 Baker Avenue, Concord, MA 01742. Business Office: (508) 264-9903; Editorial Office: (516) 292-0044.

IMPORTANT NOTICE

Unless otherwise noted, all prices are effective as of October 1, 1990.

how to use this book

BASE COST: What the dealer pays for the car. A "dealer holdback" and/or "finance charge" is included in the BASE COST of all domestically produced vehicles.

SUGGESTED LIST: The "sticker" price. What the manufacturer recommends as a selling price or "list" price.

BOTH BASE COST and MANUFACTURERS SUGGESTED LIST DO NOT INCLUDE:

1. Destination Charge.

2. State or Local Taxes.

3. Dealer Participatory Advertising.

NOTE: Dealer Preparation and Handling is a factory recommended charge for the dealer's services in performing factory recommended new car preparation for delivery to retail customers. This charge varies depending on make and model.

ABBREVIATIONS: AH - Ampere Hours; AC or AIR COND - Air Conditioning; AMP - Amperes; AWD - All Wheel Drive; B - Belted; BBL - Barrel; BSW or BW - Black Side Wall; CID - Cubic Inch Displacement; CPE - Coupe; CYL - Cylinder; DR - Door; EFI - Electronic Fuel Injection; ENG - Engine; EQUIP - Equipment; ETR - Electronic Transistorized Radio; F (tires) - Fiberglass; FI - Fuel Injection; GRP - Group; HD - Heavy Duty; HP - Horse Power; INC - Includes; L - Liter; LD - Light Duty; LH - Left Hand; MFI - Multi-Port Fuel Injection; MH - Must Have; MSR - Minimum Size Required; NA or n/a - Not Available; NC - No Charge; OPT - Optional; OS - Outside; PKG - Package; RBL - Raised Black Letters; REQ - Required; RH - Right Hand; R or RR - Rear; RWL - Raised White Letters; SBR - Steel Belted Radial; SDN - Sedan; SFI - Sequential Fuel Injection; SP or SPD - Speed; SPT - Sport; ST - Seat; STD - Standard; TBI - Throttle Body Injections; TRANS - Transmission; TW or t/w - Together With; W/ - With, WB - Wheel Base; WGN - Wagon; W/O - Without; WSW or WW - White Side Wall; 2WD - Two Wheel Drive; 4WD - Four Wheel Drive.

NOTE: Occasionally there will appear in the "Base Cost" and "Sgstd. List" columns prices enclosed in brackets - Example: (90). This indicates a credit or refunded amount is involved.